THE HUGUENOT
LEGACY

The HUGUENOT Legacy

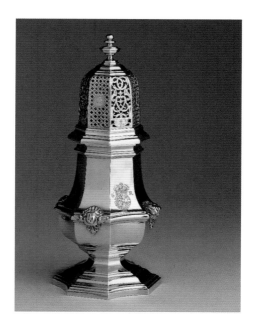

English Silver 1680-1760

from the Alan and Simone
Hartman Collection

Christopher Hartop

THOMAS HENEAGE

London

First published in 1996 by
Thomas Heneage & Co. Ltd
42 Duke Street
St James's
London SW1Y 6DJ
England

*This book accompanies an exhibition of silver from the Simone and Alan Hartman Collection organized
by Exhibitions International, New York. Museums hosting the exhibition include: the Museum of Fine
Arts, Boston; the Wadsworth Atheneum, Hartford; the Indianapolis Museum of Art, Indianapolis;
Cheekwood Museum of Art, Nashville; Cooper-Hewitt, National Design Museum, Smithsonian
Institution, New York; and the Saint Louis Art Museum, St Louis.*

ISBNs
0 946708 28 2 Hard covers
0 946708 29 0 Paperback

British Cataloguing-in-Publication Data
A catalogue record for this book is available from the British Library

Library of Congress Cataloguing-in-Publication Data are available

Editing and production: John Adamson, 90 Hertford Street, Cambridge CB4 3AQ, England
Design: Christine Jones, Design for Art and Science, 4 Camden Terrace, London NW1 9BP, England
Photographs: David Schlegel and Barry Hyman unless otherwise stated

Printed in England by Balding + Mansell, Kettering
Bound in Scotland by Hunter and Foulis, Edinburgh

Cover illustration: Caster, one of a pair, silver-gilt, London, 1727–8, maker's mark of Paul Crespin
overstriking that of Abraham Buteux (no. 10). *Photograph by David Schlegel.*

CONTENTS

ACKNOWLEDGEMENTS

Many are those who have been generous with their help and advice in the preparation of this catalogue, but first I must thank Alan and Simone Hartman for asking me to select the objects for this exhibition and to write the catalogue. In particular I acknowledge my debt to the published researches of James Lomax, Stephen Mennell and Timothy Schroder, on which I have drawn heavily. The biographical details of silversmiths come, for the most part, from Arthur Grimwade's *The London Goldsmiths, their Marks and Lives 1697–1837*. Beth Carver Wees was particularly generous in sharing the results of her, as yet, unpublished researches with me and discussions with Ellenor Alcorn and Ubaldo Vitali provided me with many new perspectives.

Thanks are also due to the following: Robert Barker, David Beasley, H.L. Bradley, A. Methuen-Campbell, Beverly Carter, Stephen Clarke, John D. Davis, Lord Egremont, Michael Gettleson, Gordon Glanville, Philippa Glanville, Alain Gruber, John Hardy, Ian Irving, Peter Gwynn-Jones, Michael Koopman, Rachel Layton, Clare le Corbeiller, Alison McCann, Jessie McNab, Lucy Morton, the Duke of Norfolk, David Oldrey, Lynn Springer Roberts, John Martin Robinson, Janice Rosenthal, Jeffrey Roth, Christopher Rowell, Lord Sackville, Lionel Stopford-Sackville, Gill Sandford, Pippa Shirley, Eric J.G. Smith, Lewis Smith, Kevin Tierney, and Wynyard Wilkinson.

David Hanks, Jan Spak and Eldon Wong of Exhibitions International have worked tirelessly in co-ordinating the exhibition and Thomas Heneage has been a source of inspiration.

Special thanks must go to my colleagues at Christie's, particularly Jeanne Sloane, Julia Halpin and Harry Williams-Bulkeley. Much-needed support was provided by Rachel Kordonowy, Amy Koegel, Vicky O'Mahony, Juliet Nusser, Anthony Phillips, Sarah Stone and Alexis de Tiesenhausen. David Schlegel and Barry Hyman took the photographs and Audrey Goffin, with her usual enthusiasm, pulled it all together.

The biggest thanks, though, are due to Christine Jones and her inspired design, and above all to John Adamson, who brought this book to fruition.

The Alan and Simone Hartman Collection includes 111 extraordinary pieces of English silver ranging in date from 1680 to 1760. All collectors, private and institutional, express their personal taste and their priorities through their acquisitions. It is especially interesting, from the vantage point of a museum whose holdings were largely donated by private collectors, to consider how the Hartmans came to form a personal collection that is related to, yet distinct from, their business interests. Clearly Alan Hartman's vast knowledge of the medium and the market, acquired as a dealer, was an asset. But the Hartmans have also succumbed to the insatiable craving that true collectors share to acquire and to live with beautiful objects. In addition to the thrill of pursuing an unrecognized prize, they have the knowledge that the object will have a particular and permanent voice in a larger chorus. For such passionate collectors there is the additional satisfaction of sharing the whole with specialists and with the public, an aspiration that, in this case, will be fully realized with the publication of this catalogue.

The Hartmans formed their collection with an unerring eye for quality. They were drawn to the visual, often sculptural, aspect of silver that is characteristic of only the most ambitious goldsmiths' work. The condition of these objects is uncompromised. Although they were selected for their aesthetic, rather than their didactic, interest, the collection as a whole also offers an ideal overview of the early eighteenth-century London silver industry. An unusually large proportion of them has a documented history of ownership, a feature that is explored fully in this catalogue. Most importantly, perhaps, the focus of the collection is sufficiently narrow to permit a serious examination of the period, but sufficiently broad to represent the characteristic as well as the exceptional object. The Hartman Collection, unlike many, is truly greater than the sum of its parts, and through this exemplary catalogue, it promises to have a lasting impact on our understanding of the history of English silver.

In 1991 the Hartmans began to make arrangements for an exhibition of their collection. The collection will travel to a distinguished group of museums in North America between 1996 and 1999; following the tour it will be on loan to the Museum of Fine Arts, Boston for a period of three years. Christopher Hartop was invited to finalize the object list and to write the catalogue. Its publication comes at a propitious time. The last decade has witnessed a surge of activity in the study of silver. Borrowing the analytical methods of social and economic historians, decorative arts historians have begun to use new types of evidence to assess the structure and evolution of the silver trade. However, few scholars have successfully pieced the evidence of the objects themselves – style, design, technique, and provenance – into the puzzle represented by these broader issues. Christopher Hartop's meticulous research begins with a thorough investigation of each object's history. Drawing upon a wide range of biographical, political, and economic sources, he places each piece in its appropriate context. These individual studies serve as the foundation for a general reassessment of the history of silver in the first half of the eighteenth century. It is an extremely ambitious undertaking in which he succeeds brilliantly, and his scholarship will set new standards for the field.

The London silver trade flourished in the period 1680–1760, and these pieces embody the full range of the goldsmiths' output. The large group of ambassadorial plate demonstrates the important role of silver not only in international diplomacy but also as a means of displaying the owner's status through all ranks of society. Another important category of objects is domestic plate made for regular use at table. Far from mundane, these pieces were made for some of the most interesting historical figures of the eighteenth century. Through exhaustive scrutiny of inventories and historical sources it is often possible to detect something of the nature of the individual patrons in the silver they commissioned. The innovation of many of these domestic objects, characterized by an almost austere geometry, is manifested not so much in their style as in their function. Understood against the background of social history, these pieces reveal the growing sophistication of England's aristocratic and landed gentry who embraced continental manners and cuisine. This fascination with all things continental paved the way for the great stylistic innovations of the rococo, perhaps the most significant group within this collection. Acquired for their sculptural rather than their social or historical interest, these inventive creations, considered as a whole, shed light on an aspect of London's artistic heritage that is still poorly understood: the evolution of a distinctly English rococo style.

In a sense, silver scholarship has been inhibited by the traditional reputation of the Huguenots as religious refugees and artistic pioneers who introduced the sophisticated French Court Style to the provincial English. This book surveys the whole London landscape in the period under discussion and re-examines many standard assumptions. Not all the foreign goldsmiths working in London were Huguenots; there were other immigrants who had come for purely economic reasons. Furthermore, some of the most radical stylistic innovations seem to be attributable to German-born goldsmiths. The exhibition of this collection offers a rare opportunity to examine side-by-side works marked by little-studied but highly important figures such as Charles Kandler, John White, and James Shruder. These objects can be assessed in the company of over twenty pieces from the prolific workshop of Paul de Lamerie, which, although better known, is still not fully understood.

The achievement of forming such a collection in only fifteen years should not be underestimated. Eighteenth-century English silver has come down to us in relatively large quantity, particularly compared to the survival of objects from the other great centres of Europe, such as Paris. Its literature is also relatively vast. As Christopher Hartop points out, however, the study of hallmarks and the temptation to romanticize the goldsmith as artistic genius has held back both collecting and scholarship. The first collectors of English silver assembled hallmarks, and even today, a perfect set of marks is a prerequisite for many buyers. Useful as they may be in establishing a chronology for the medium, marks are now understood to be not an indication of authorship but of sponsorship. As this book amply illustrates, the silver trade was a sophisticated and specialized industry, where designers and modellers were often far removed from the patron and sponsor.

American collectors in the first half of the twentieth century tended to buy English objects that embodied the plain lines of colonial American silver, as though seeking the aesthetic roots of their own morality. They neglected both monumental silver and silver in the high rococo style, which has often been appreciated more as an aberrant excess than as an integral part of England's artistic and social history. The Hartmans have avoided the conventional and now out-dated criteria of silver collectors, and with this publication of Christopher Hartop's extensive research, they have made a tremendous contribution to the field. When considered in the context of the competitive and rapidly changing London silver trade of the period, the objects in the Hartman Collection, of course, are precisely at the heart of the question – how did the foreign goldsmiths function in and transform the English scene? It is a great credit both to the Hartmans and to Christopher Hartop that so many answers can be found within a single collection.

Ellenor Alcorn
Assistant Curator, European Decorative Arts and Sculpture
Museum of Fine Arts, Boston

Art or Industry?

In recent years a revolution has taken place in the study of English silver. In the same way that social trends are now essential to our understanding of history, so our understanding of material objects such as silver needs to be set against a background of economic and cultural trends. Since silver was first regarded as a "collectible" in the nineteenth century, studies in the subject have been bedevilled by the idealization of the "artist-craftsman", though it is clear now that the production of silverware during the seventeenth and eighteenth centuries was an industrial one and that we must view the silver of the period as manufactured goods, not unique works of art. Nowadays, we do not expect much art, and certainly no symbolism, in our tablewares, and it is easy to forget what educated patrons expected from their household silver three hundred years ago. A high standard of craftsmanship was, of course, to be expected, rigorously enforced by the Goldsmiths' Company, the guild which regulated the trade in London. The guild also enforced a standard of purity for the metal, and the marks it stamped on finished silver were often studied by early authorities to the exclusion of all else. Behind these marks lies a complex, hidden web of interdependent modellers, chasers, casters, engravers, finishers and retailers who all contributed to the finished product. The Victorian ideal of the artist-craftsman, working in splendid isolation at his bench, is really a romanticization of what was, and had been since medieval times, a business of specialists and entrepreneurs.

This confusion is nowhere more apparent than in past assessments of the Huguenots' contribution to the silver of the period. The Huguenot silversmiths, who, it was said, arrived with the latest techniques and styles in the 1680s (and who were often, as their competitors were forced to admit, willing to work for lower prices) have traditionally been said to have revolutionized the silversmithing trade in England, while their low Protestantism has been credited with introducing the fashion for plain silver in what has been described for the last hundred years as the "Queen Anne style". It has become clear in recent years, however, that the reality was much more complex than that, and that we have ignored the influence of other immigrant craftsmen, from Germany and elsewhere, who made their own contribution to the trade. Superior technical skills, as well as innovative decoration like cut-card work, were brought to England by these immigrants some years before the Huguenots. Religion, moreover, had nothing to do with plain silver, the fashion for which was common in the seventeenth century all over Europe. The real significance of the Huguenot influx was that it provided a new sizeable workforce, who were ready to accept low rates and were skilled in the new techniques, at a time when the consumer base for silverware in England was experiencing remarkable growth.

It was really the patron, not the craftsman, who was the driving force behind the adoption of new styles and new types of silverware. The international élite travelled and were exposed to innovations, not only in design, but in food and table decoration. The silver itself started to become the decoration of the dining table, ousting the elaborate medieval displays of food, and new trends in eating and drinking required a host of new types of silver. These new fashions filtered down the social scale, and as the consumer market for silverware broadened during the eighteenth century, they reached a wider section of society. Silver was an essential symbol of one's place in society, not only for public figures like ambassadors but for the middle and upper classes as well. We should consider those who commissioned and owned the silver as much as those who made it – mindful, however, of Sir Ellis Waterhouse's jibe at writers on sporting art when he referred, in *Painting in Britain* (1953), to "those specialist writers who sometimes confuse the history of art with praising famous horses".

Part of Kip's bird's-eye view of London, 1710. London
continued to extend westwards during the period, and
many silversmiths, especially those who catered to the
fashionable, moved their shops away from the vicinity
of Goldsmiths' Hall, their guildhall in the centre of the
old City of London, to the new neighbourhood of St
James's, seen here in the foreground dominated by St
James's Palace. St James's Church, Piccadilly, is to the
left of the centre and beyond that can be seen St
Anne's Church in Soho, in that neighbourhood of
small streets that was to become one of the main
centres of Huguenot activity.
British Library, London

The English Scene 1680–1760

Few Londoners of 1680 would have recognized London as it appeared in 1760, for radical changes, both economic and social, took place during the first half of the eighteenth century. London in the 1680s, still rebuilding after the Great Fire of 1666, remained essentially a medieval city. By contrast, the London of 1760 had spread westwards with great squares of fashionable townhouses. The population of the metropolis had almost doubled and new wealth had spread down the social scale to more and more of those people whom Daniel Defoe had dubbed the "middling sort". Most importantly, though, England had become a superpower; by the end of Queen Anne's reign in 1714, the French threat had been destroyed, Spain was a shadow of its former might, Portugal had been made into a pliant trading partner, the Dutch were long vanquished and England – or Britain, as it is more correct to say after the Union of 1707 – had emerged as the dominant sea power.

At home it was a time of great economic growth and increase in consumer demand. Foreign visitors to London during the late seventeenth century and early eighteenth century were astonished at the enterprise and industry of its inhabitants. Hogarth's moralistic series *Industry and Idleness* well sums up the spirit of the age which seemed to have an uninhibited thirst for money.

England had been reborn at the restoration of King Charles II in 1660. The political upheavals of the middle of the century had tipped the balance of power to the aristocracy, Parliament and gentry. These three groups of landowners, together with a growing number of prosperous urban tradesmen

The Englishman is never satisfied with what he has obtained; his mind gets bored when in rest. The desire to increase always his property by continuous speculations destroys in him the love of tranquillity which inclines all well-to-do men to idleness.

(A French visitor to London in 1679)

Covent Garden by Pieter Angellis (1685–1734), painted c. 1726.
The Yale Center for British Art, Paul Mellon Collection

and merchants, made up the demanding clientele of the silversmiths. For France, in contrast, the outcome of its own upheaval, the Fronde, had been quite different: the Crown had been established as absolute and the aristocracy and gentry made all but impotent, dependent on the monarch for patronage. In England from 1688 onwards William III and his wife Mary ruled at the invitation of Parliament, as George I and his successors did after 1714. No English monarch could create a court like Versailles (although William III tried at Hampton Court) and as a result there was no strong tradition of court patronage of the arts in England. Artistic patronage was left to a small group of aristocratic grandees (the ranks of the peerage remained fairly static during the period, numbering about 160 at the middle of the eighteenth century). This élite, combined with the much more numerous landowning gentry (estimates put this group at between 8,000 and 20,000

A view of Grosvenor Square, London attributed to John Paul 1775–1852). This shows the fashionable square built between 1725 and 1731 as part of the movement westwards of the city. It was in a townhouse here that the Countess of Mountrath, owner of the cake basket (no. 39), lived and died.
Christie's, New York

John, Anne and William Orde by Arthur Devis (1711–87), painted c. 1755. A typically sparse mid-Georgian interior is depicted, with a silver basket on the table. Usually called "cake baskets" it is clear from contemporary portraits that they were also used by ladies for sewing materials, or for flowers or fruit.
Paul Mellon Collection, Upperville, Virginia

during the period) and the nascent middle class, made up the clientele of the silversmith.

England was almost continually at war, with the Dutch and later with the French, during this period and as a result many fortunes were made. War with France was inevitable, for the gentry and middle classes had always been fearful of the Catholic menace, and in the last years of Charles II's reign this became hysteria during what was known as the Popish Plot. The accession of Charles's openly Catholic brother, James, in 1685, made many Englishmen fear that England might become a French satellite state. In constitutional terms, the Glorious Revolution of 1688, which deposed James and set the protestant William of Orange and his wife Mary, James's eldest daughter, on the throne, established the landowning élite as the true rulers of England, but this new regime was under continual threat and the average Englishman, as well as the scores of Huguenot refugees who had flocked to England as a safe haven, must have continued to live in fear of the Catholic menace. The death of Queen Anne, Mary's younger sister, in 1714, again posed a possible crisis and the arrival of George I from Hanover was followed in 1715 by the first Jacobite uprising, which was easily crushed. George I succeeded to the throne by act of Parliament (it was said at the time that there were fifty-seven others with a better claim to the succession)[1] and it was to the landowning class that he owed his throne.

George I did nothing to endear himself to his English subjects, and he and his son made it clear that they preferred their German homeland. They did, however, provide a strong bulwark against the French threat, made possible for much of the 1720s and 1730s by Sir Robert Walpole's regime. Fortunes were made quickly – and lost even more quickly – by many in the South Sea

An English family at tea by Joseph van Aken (?1699–1749).
A maidservant pours hot water from a silver tea kettle for a fashionable family. By the early eighteenth century tea drinking had become a familiar ritual, providing an opportunity to use both elaborate silverware in the latest taste and expensive porcelain from Asia.
The Tate Gallery, London/Art Resource, New York

The Drake-Brockman Family at Beachborough House, Kent by Edward Haytley (*fl.* 1746–61). Typical of the landowning gentry who flourished during Walpole's regime, they are depicted enjoying their newly "improved" park.
The National Gallery of Victoria, Melbourne

Bubble of the early 1720s, but Walpole must be credited with the establishment of a stable regime and true cabinet government in England, with power concentrated in the hands of a small élite. His reluctance to involve England in overseas wars did much to consolidate domestic prosperity, but after his downfall, England once again entered into war with its arch-rival, France, and, in 1745, another Jacobite uprising took England by surprise. A ragged crew of Highlanders and mercenaries managed to strike as far south as Derby before retreating.

Traditionally English silver has been catalogued according to monarchs' reigns, but seldom have political or economic events been considered when analyzing the silver of the period. Consumer confidence, seen for example in the late 1730s and early 1740s and exemplified by the extravagant rococo creations made for the King family (nos. 12 and 80), Lord Mountrath, and others, tapers off after Walpole's fall and the '45 rebellion, only to return in the 1750s.

It was not just economic and social change, however, that Britain experienced between 1680 and 1760. The growing secularization of Britain, as it threw off many of its medieval ideas, must be considered. Personal outlook changed profoundly and this affected the way in which consumers viewed silverware, and the types of silver they used. It was in the eighteenth century that the concept of the pursuit of happiness first took root. Today we are far removed from the hierarchical and narrow mentality that characterized England before the mid-seventeenth century but we can relate easily to the broader bourgeois culture of the late seventeenth and early eighteenth century, epitomized by Samuel Pepys, basking in the reflected glory of his silver on display at a dinner party, "mighty rich and handsome about me".[2] Not only were more and more of the English finding conspicuous consumption, like acquiring silver, within their reach, but they were much more receptive to innovation than ever before. This included not merely science and industry, but also art and design.

Notes
[1] Michael Reed, *The Georgian Triumph 1700–1830*, 1983, p. 15.
[2] Samuel Pepys, *Diary*, November 18, 1666.

Patrons and Consumers

The relationship between silversmith and customer during this period was not one of artist and patron. One must think in terms of consumer demand caused by new fashions, new dining habits and new beverages like tea, coffee and chocolate, rather than a close relationship between craftsman and customer. The complex network of specialists and outworkers meant that the consumer was often far removed from the men and even women involved in the making of the article. This is in contrast to what still prevailed in the American colonies and in some provincial centres in England (although by the eighteenth century the silversmithing trade had become increasingly centralized in London). For example, in the study of American silver of the eighteenth century, one can see clearly the direct relationship between the silversmith and his patron, who were both for the most part middle-class men of business. But in London during the late seventeenth century and throughout the eighteenth, the relationship between makers, suppliers and

Charles Seymour, 6th Duke of Somerset, by John Closterman (1660–1711). Known as the "Proud Duke", his obsession with rank and genealogy was more medieval than Georgian. He rebuilt Petworth, his house in Sussex, in the latest French taste at the end of the seventeenth century and commissioned silver from the Harache workshop, like the dish stand (no. 15) of 1689–90. Perhaps surprisingly, in view of his conservative outlook, at the end of his long life he commissioned silver in the latest French rococo style, like the ladle of 1742 (no. 43).
Petworth House, Sussex: National Trust Photographic Library/Derrick E. Witty

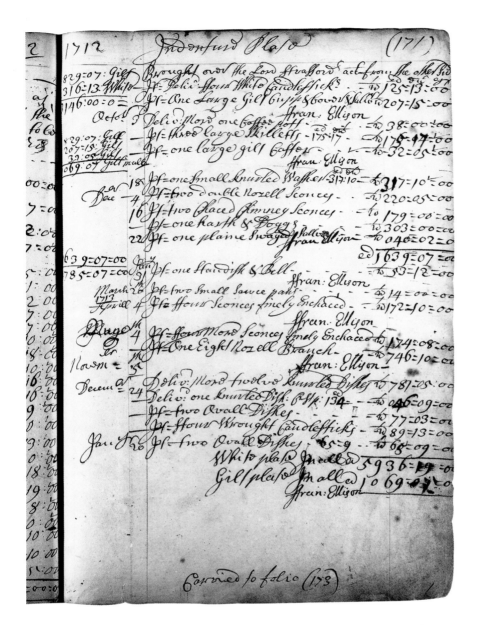

patrons was much more complex. It was the silversmith's clients, whether
they were aristocratic patrons or middle-class consumers, who created the
demand for new styles as well as new types of table silver. The demand for all
things French came from the top of the social scale. As early as 1659
Countess Dysart was buying French silver from Alderman Backwell[1] and
silversmiths' accounts frequently refer to "French plate" or to silver "in the
French fashion". In 1700 John Hervey of Ickworth purchased "a pair of plate
Andirons being French plate" from George Lewis[2] and in 1729 the 3rd Duke
of Beaufort ordered a *surtout*, or centrepiece, from the Paris goldsmith
Thomas Germain.[3] In the same decade both Horace Walpole, brother of Sir
Robert Walpole, the Prime Minister, and Viscount Bateman acquired French
silver, as did the Duke of Kingston and the Earl of Berkeley ten years later.

When the 4th Earl of Chesterfield was issued with a silver dinner service to accompany him on his embassy to the Hague in 1727, he chose an "apargne" (centrepiece), soup tureens and wine coolers, all innovative articles developed in France, to enable him to entertain abroad in the latest French taste (see nos. 8, 9 and 10). Chesterfield is perhaps an extreme case of a francophile aristocrat; he wrote to his son in 1739, "The English are usually boobies; they lack the free and easy, yet polished, manners of the French. Therefore take note of the French and imitate them ..."[4] Chesterfield was part of what might be dubbed the "international cultural network" of men and women who spoke French and looked to the French as the cultural arbiters. They travelled and were exposed to French fashions at foreign courts or in France itself.

The records of the Jewel House, the office of the Royal Household which dealt with the distribution of silver to ambassadors and other officers of state, although somewhat patchy, provide us with an overview of what was thought necessary for public figures at various levels.[5] Ambassadors, as personal representatives of the monarch, were expected to entertain in style and to make a magnificent display of both white and gilt plate, which was often in the latest French fashion, such as that supplied to Lord Chesterfield. Other officers of state, like the Duke of Dorset who, in 1725, was appointed Lord Steward of the Household, received smaller amounts of plate.

The French Court style which had evolved at Versailles was truly international, transcending national boundaries. From 1689 until 1697, and again from 1701 until 1713, England and France were almost continuously at

The Family of Sir John and Lady Cust by Enoch Seeman (c. 1690–1745), c. 1740. The Cust family inherited Belton, the Brownlow's house in Lincolnshire on the death of Viscount Tyrconnel in 1754 (see no. 61). Belton House, Lincolnshire: National Trust Photographic Library/Christopher Hurst

war, yet the international baroque style dominated English fine and decorative arts at the top of the social scale without interruption. Dolls, fully dressed in the latest French fashions, were sent from Paris each year at the start of the London season. Even the hero of the great English victories at Ramillies and Malplaquet, the Duke of Marlborough, had the French painter Louis Laguerre paint the saloon at Blenheim in imitation of Louis XIV's Escalier des Ambassadeurs at Versailles, and he bought silver in the latest French style from the silversmiths of Lille during its occupation.[6]

This ruling élite, both Whig and Tory, bound by intricate ties of marriage and patronage, enjoyed an unprecedented ascendancy, providing an attractive model of lifestyle and attitudes for the gentry and bourgeoisie to emulate. With this prosperity, demand for domestic silverware spread down the social scale. The "consumer base" for the silversmith increased dramatically as did the types of vessel. Interestingly, though, recent studies have shown that while the production of new silverware (measured by weight) increased during the years following the Glorious Revolution, it did not keep pace with the general growth in economic prosperity of the period.[7] The explanation for this is that less was spent on sets of heavy serving platters and dishes, which had hitherto been necessary to serve the elaborate pies and other creations of the old style of dining, freeing up funds for the cruet stands, sauce boats and tureens required for the new mode of dining à la française, as well as for the host of smaller articles associated with serving the new fashionable drinks: tea, coffee and chocolate.

While this consumer demand for art and luxury goods broadened, there was a gap between the patrician élite and the prosperous consumers whether they were of the country gentry or the urban bourgeoisie. Here, further down the social scale, French fashions were often regarded with suspicion and there was a growing anti-French feeling. An eighteenth-century gentlewoman, Mary Berry, observed that French fashions appealed primarily to those Englishmen who had lived abroad a great deal and that "no man standing for his country [i.e., for election to Parliament] or desirous of being popular in it" would be wise to adopt French ideas such as three-pronged forks, or sofas.[8]

The accession of George I in 1714 and the removal of the Tory, or Court party, from power gave a boost to this new patriotism and desire for recognizably English art and culture. Some scholars have attempted to associate the dominant Whig party with the new Palladian style in architecture which emerged in contrast to the French baroque. Yet the reality is not as simple as this and it is always a mistake to view eighteenth-century "parties" as though they were political parties of today. What we today call Whigs or Tories were merely men of influence united by bonds of common interest and family ties in what Sir George Clarke has called "the small world of great affairs". In fact the period of peace between Britain and France beginning in 1714 continuing

until 1744 allowed a tremendous wave of French art, fashions and manners to sweep down the social scale. The truth of the matter is that the patrician élite at the top of the social structure may well have come to regard the baroque as the symbol of absolutism and looked to newer, "purer" forms of decoration. Similarly, attempts to see the rise of the rococo style in England in the 1730s as a movement centred around Frederick, Prince of Wales in opposition to the court style of the king and his Whigs are not successful, for a study of patronage never bears this out. It is clear that the Whig grandees, such as the Earl of Mountrath (no. 39), enjoyed the rococo just as heartily as the Tories. The need to see all artistic expression as politically motivated is very much a twentieth-century tendency.

For the educated patron of the eighteenth century, there was a constant desire for novelty, as well as for things which were "comely" and in the best of taste – the word "taste" signifying more than it does today. In the eighteenth century, good taste was acquired by a thorough grounding in classical literature as well as art. Schoolboys were made to study almost nothing but classical texts in the hope that they would be imbued with the virtues one finds in the works of Horace: moderation, restraint and the love of the countryside.[9] The decoration of an eighteenth-century nobleman's house, his furniture and his silver, was done within this framework. Not only does the goddess of the harvest, Ceres, appear on the Earl of Mountrath's bread basket, thereby alluding to its function, but she appears in conjunction with symbols of Bacchus, the god of wine, to illustrate Terence's often misquoted verse: "Sine Cerere et Tempero friget Venus"; that love withers without the stimulus of wine and feasting. This symbolism, by which an object could be "read" by an educated audience, was a tradition in the decorative arts, and

George Booth, 2nd Earl of Warrington and his daughter by Michael Dahl (1656–1743). Booth managed to salvage his family's fortune, largely destroyed during the political upheavals of the seventeenth century, by an arranged marriage with the daughter of a rich London merchant. In order to build a firm financial foundation for his heirs he greatly improved his estate at Dunham Massey and commissioned a "laying-down" of plate from London silversmiths, a meticulous record of which he kept in his own handwriting. The snuffers and tray (no. 104) were his. Much of his silver came from the workshops of the leading Huguenot craftsmen but in contrast to that commissioned by the Duke of Somerset later in life, it tends to be massive and plain and largely ignores the new rococo style which swept fashionable circles in the 1730s and 1740s.
Dunham Massey, Cheshire: National Trust Photographic Library/John Hammond

especially silver, dating back to the Middle Ages. In the silver of the first half of the eighteenth century it enjoyed a last flowering. As the consumer audience broadened, and took in the less-educated social classes, the importance of imagery declined and ornament was used more and more merely as decoration.

This broadening of the market for silverware had a great impact on the silver trade. The period 1680–1760 can be seen as the age of the middle classes. Actively engaged in trade and industry, they formed an important group of consumers of luxury goods like silver. As the social historian Peter Earle has observed: "In Augustan England, trade did not defile a gentleman as it apparently had done in the past, still did across the Channel, and was again to do in the England of Jane Austen".[10] Much of the hierarchical nature of medieval society had been stripped away and had yet to be replaced with the social rigidity one finds at the end of the eighteenth century. Marriage between the classes, usually for money, was increasingly common, with the financial standing of the parties discussed with all the detachment of the present-day *Financial Times* reporting a corporate merger. The *Gentleman's Magazine* listed the dowry of each bride-to-be, usually with total inaccuracy. The 2nd Viscount Bolingbroke, having lost his fortune, sought to "marry a rich monster and retrieve his affairs",[11] while the 2nd Earl of Warrington (no. 104), having succeeded to a penniless title, publicly launched himself on a search for a heiress. He succeeded in finding the daughter of a rich London merchant whose dowry went a considerable way towards settling his debts. In return, the Oldbury family improved their social standing with an aristocratic alliance.

Social mobility was easier to achieve than it had been. At the top of the scale, a minor scion of a noble house like Thomas Wentworth, Lord Raby, who was later created Earl of Strafford (see nos. 2 and 3), could, through a distinguished military and diplomatic career, vastly enrich himself and become a grandee in his own right, while further down the scale a man "bred to trade" like Henry Fetherstonhaugh, owner of the salvers (no. 4), could accumulate a vast fortune and establish his heir as a landowner.

It was this acquisition of land that was essential to social advancement in eighteenth-century England. John Locke, in his *Essay Concerning the True Original, Extent and End of Civil Government*, published in 1690, had stated unequivocally that the basis of society was property. Acquisition of land was not legally restricted to any social group as in some European countries and it was deemed the most important step in establishing social status. Even middle-class tradesmen like the silversmith Paul de Lamerie bought land outside London for social status as well as financial security, while his fellow Huguenot, David Willaume, having prospered as a goldsmith and banker, bought the manor of Tingrith in Bedfordshire and became a member of the landowning gentry.

After land, silver remained the most common way of investing capital. The Earl of Warrington, having settled his debts, set about improving his estate and accumulating a "laying down" of plate. The earl is exceptional in that he kept a meticulous account of each piece of silver, with its weight, in his own handwriting. Silver was an asset that was readily convertible into cash and often represented a significant proportion of a man's worth.[12] Thomas Wentworth, newly created Earl of Strafford and about to marry an heiress in 1711, drew up a list of his assets which included over £10,000 in jewels and plate, about a quarter of his net worth. By the beginning of the eighteenth century, the amount of plate issued by the Jewel House to ambassadors such as the Lords Strafford and Chesterfield, and to other officers of state like Lord Fitzwalter, who was Treasurer of the Household, had been fixed according to status. For aristocrats, and even members of the gentry and the urban bourgeoisie, a display of silver in keeping with one's social position was essential. As Norbert Elias has commented, "what in retrospect generally appears to us today as a 'luxury' is … anything but superfluous in a society so constricted … In a society where every outward manifestation of a person has special significance, expenditure on prestige and display is for the upper classes a necessity which they cannot avoid".[13] Whether this was a great officer of state like the Duke of Somerset, or Mrs Franks, wife of a prosperous Philadelphia merchant, whose tea table was enriched with silver from Lamerie's workshop in the most extravagant rococo taste (no. 77), the need was the same.

Notes

[1] Philippa Glanville, *Silver in England,* 1987, p. 65.
[2] N.M. Penzer, "The Hervey Silver at Ickworth – I", *Apollo,* February, 1957, p. 39.
[3] A.J.H. Sale, "Records of Plate of the Beaufort Family", *The Silver Society Journal,* 7, Autumn, 1995, p. 385.
[4] *Letters,* October 29, 1739, in French.
[5] Public Record Office, London, LC/9/43–49. The books, which cover the period from the 1680s to the end of the eighteenth century, comprise ledgers recording the delivery of silver to the Jewel House by the Royal Silversmith (usually a retailer rather than a working craftsman), repairs and engraving, and ledgers listing each officer or royal household department and the particulars of the silver issued to them. Coronation years were the busiest, with new ambassadors appointed and numerous gifts, or "claims", given to members of the household who filled various roles in the coronation. The birth of royal children required christening gifts, usually a cup and cover, to be given to members of the household, and regular entries record the distribution of minor things like livery or watermen's badges.
[6] "The Elie Pacot surtout", *The Silver Society Journal,* 6, Winter, 1994, p. 296.
[7] David Mitchell, "Innovation and the transfer of skill in the goldsmiths' trade in Restoration London", in *Goldsmiths, Silversmiths and Bankers,* 1995, p. 12.
[8] Stephen Mennell, *All Manners of Food,* 1985, p. 126.
[9] John Cannon, *Aristocratic Century, the Peerage of Eighteenth century England,* 1984, p. 34.
[10] *The Making of the English Middle Class,* 1989, p. 7.
[11] John Cannon, *op. cit.,* p. 71.
[12] The lion's share of the cost of a piece of silverware was the raw material and it was this part that was convertible back to cash, although as early as the mid-century, one finds reference being made to the secondhand value of workmanship. In a document, "The Weights of The <u>Old</u> Silver of late, as weighed in 1756", in the Stanhope Archives, the anonymous writer (possibly Lord Stanhope himself), speaking of the great cistern and fountain once at Chevening in Kent, comments: "The Workmanship of most of it is almost of equal value to the Bullion", West Kent Archives Office, Maidstone, U1590/E14.
[13] *The Court Society,* 1983, pp. 53, 63.

Dining and Drinking

The period 1680–1760 saw a dramatic change in the way people sat down to eat, in the types of dishes that were served, and in the wines which they drank. It also witnessed the introduction of the new triumvirate of coffee, tea and chocolate. Many of the medieval customs to do with eating and drinking were shaken off at the end of the seventeenth century and replaced, at the top of the social scale at least, with French manners. All of these innovations required new vessels which dramatically increased the types of wares available in silversmiths' shops.

This change in habits is well illustrated by Charles Seymour, 6th Duke of Somerset, whose life spanned almost all of the period in question. In 1689 he ordered a dish stand for his dining table (no. 15) as part of the refurbishment of Petworth, his house in Sussex, where in 1703 he entertained the King and Queen of Spain with great pomp and ceremony. Late seventeenth-century tables were crowded with dishes and platters, often piled high with food extravagantly arranged, making such "stands for the table" necessary. At the end of his long life, in 1740, the Duke bought a magnificent tureen from the workshop of Paul Crespin,[1] elaborately decorated in the latest rococo style, intended for serving French olios and *ragoûts* which had become popular on English tables during the last forty years. Two years later he purchased a ladle also in the latest "French" taste (no. 43). This is paradoxical, as the Duke, who was known as "the Proud Duke", was one of the last great noblemen in the medieval tradition, whose obsession with rank and protocol gave rise to laughter even during his lifetime. Nevertheless, like most grandees of the period, he kept up with the latest fashions in dining table silver.

The medieval custom of a great lord dining in state with all his household was

The true pleasures of a gentleman are, those of the table, but within bounds of moderation; good company, that is to say, people of merit; moderate play, which amuses, without any interested views; and sprightly, gallant conversations, with women of fashion and sense.

Lord Chesterfield to his son, February 24, 1747, written in French

Patterned tart tops, custards, cheesecakes and pies from a plate in Robert May's *The Accomplisht Cook*, 1685 edition. Tarts and pies were baked with plain tops which were replaced with these showpieces before serving. This essentially medieval custom was all but forgotten by the eighteenth century, when the traditional pies and tarts had been replaced with dishes from France like *ragoût* and *oille* which were served in tureens. As a result it was the silverware which replaced the food as the primary table decoration.
British Library, London

replaced in the seventeenth century with private dining, often in a separate room reserved for the purpose. The dining or "eating" room had first appeared in fashionable Paris houses in the early seventeenth century and was quickly adopted in England. Despite this, some old traditions did persist, as at Littlecote in Berkshire, where the Popham family enjoyed the services of a jester as late as 1673.

As dining became more private, so it lost many of its quasi-religious rituals, largely owing to a change in the way people looked at food. This change in attitude is really due to the fact that, by the seventeenth century, food had ceased to be a precious commodity for which one was dependent on the feudal lord. General prosperity and a run of good harvests at the end of the seventeenth century meant that, for the first time, no one in England was in danger of starving. For a brief period during the first half of the eighteenth century, England seemed able to support its population with enough food, and the practice of enclosures, by which landowners claimed ancient common land, was not to affect the food supply until the end of the century. It was a period, therefore, of relative plenty, with a growing bourgeoisie eager to imitate the cosmopolitan manners of those at the top of the social scale. With the decline of ritual, one of the first medieval objects to disappear from the dining table was the ceremonial salt, replaced during the second half of the seventeenth century with sets of small "trencher" salts which could be placed within reach of each diner (nos. 16 and 20).

As late as the 1660s, Robert May, in his book *The Accomplisht Cook,* described elaborate pies made in the form of ships which would perform a naval engagement at the table, complete with gunpowder charges, no doubt much

Elegant people dining by N. Bonnart, early eighteenth century. This shows the custom of dining *à la française*, by which all the dishes for a particular course would be placed on the table at the same time and guests would help themselves, or have a servant help them. Table silver is limited to the dishes and platters used to serve the elaborately decorated dishes.
Musée des arts et traditions populaires, Paris/RMN/ H. Jézéquel

The banquet given for
William and Mary in
Westminster Hall, 1689

to the delight of the surprised guests. Such medieval throwbacks were already
going out of fashion, however, in Restoration London. With the arrival of
new French dishes like *oille*, *ragoût* and soup, the decorative nature of the
food itself could no longer be exploited and the silver tableware itself became
the table decoration.

Yet for affairs of state, something of the ritual remained, as in John Evelyn's
description of the "banquet" or dessert given to the Venetian ambassadors
in 1688:

> The dinner was most magnificent and plentiful, at four tables, with
> music, kettle drums and trumpets, which sounded upon a whistle at
> every health. The banquet was twelve vast chargers piled up so high that
> those who sat one against another could hardly see each other. Of these
> sweetmeats, which doubtless were some days piling up in that exquisite
> manner, the Ambassadors touched not, but leaving them to the spectators
> who came out of curiosity to see the dinner, were exceedingly pleased to
> see in what a moment of time all that curious work was demolished, the
> confitures voided, and the tables cleared.[2]

The engravings of banquet settings in the many editions of Robert May's
books, as well as the depictions of the dinners which followed the
coronations of James II and William and Mary, show long tables cluttered
with these "vast chargers", each holding an elaborately decorated pie or dish.

The pervading influence in all things culinary in this new, prosperous England was France. As early as 1660 Samuel Pepys had described how the Earl of Sandwich was "very high [elated] how he would have a French cook" with the restoration of the king, and it was at the court of Charles II that French cooking was first introduced to the English. It remained, however, at the very top of the social scale for some time. It became *de rigueur* for a man of fashion to have a French cook, a custom which was to last well into the nineteenth century. Arthur Young, writing at the end of the eighteenth century, observed: "every man in Europe that can afford a great table, either keeps a French cook, or one instructed in the same manner".[3] At Woburn, the Duke of Bedford in the early eighteenth century paid his French cook £60 a year, while his English cook got £30. Robert May proudly declared in his book that he had been sent by his employer, Lady Dormer, to France for five years "in the family of a noble Peer and first President of Paris".[4] William Rabisha, in his 1661 cookery book, catered to the contemporary demand for foreign dishes, declaring that his recipes were "according to the best tradition of the English, French, Italian, Dutch, etc …"

Misson, writing at the end of the seventeenth century, remarked that "generally speaking, the English tables are not delicately served. There are some noblemen who have both French and English cooks and these eat after

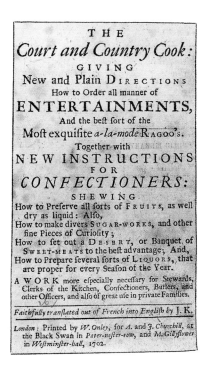

The Court and Country
Cook, 1702, an English
version of Massialot's
*Le Cuisinier Roial et
Bourgeois.*
New York Public Library

Illustration from *The Court
and Country Cook*
depicting a "banquet" or
dessert.
New York Public Library

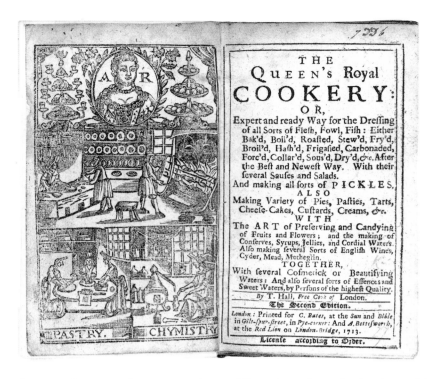

The Queen's Royal Cookery, a 1713 edition of Patrick Lambe's cookery book. The frontispiece shows elaborate desserts in the medieval tradition, but many of the recipes are French.
British Library, London

the French manner but among the Middling Sort of People they have 10 or 12 sorts of common meats which infallibly take their turn at their Tables and two dishes are their Dinners, a Pudding and a fine piece of Roast Beef."[5] The English have always been assiduous carnivores and in the eighteenth century took great pride in the quality of their meat, looking suspiciously upon French food, and thinking the sauces served to cover the bad quality of the meat. Anti-French sentiment in this, as in other spheres, was always present:

> In the days of good Queen Elizabeth, when mighty Roast beef
> was the Englishman's Food; our Cookery was Plain and Simple as our
> Manners; it was not then a Science or Mistery, and required no
> Conjuration to please the Palates of the greatest Men. But we have of late
> Years refined ourselves out of that simple Taste, and conformed our
> Palates to Meats and Drinks dressed after the French fashion.

Thus ranted Robert Campbell in the *London Tradesman*,[6] much as did Addison in the *Tatler*, when he complained of French *kickshaws*. Dr Johnson described a kickshaw as a "dish so changed by the cookery, it can scarcely be known". Charles Carter, in his *Compleat City and Country Cook* declared:

> Some of our Nobility and Gentry have been too much attach'd to French
> customs and French Cookery, so that they have not thought themselves
> capable of being well serv'd, unless they sent for a cook from a Foreign
> Country, who, indeed by the poverty of his Country, (compar'd with our
> own) and the flippant humour of its Inhabitants, whose Gousts are
> continually changing, is constrained to rack his Invention to disguise

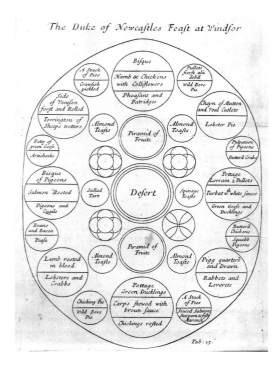

The Duke of Newcastles Feast at Windsor

An engraving from Patrick Lambe's *The Queen's Royal Cookery* depicting "The Duke of Newcastle's Feast at Windsor". The clutter of dishes on the table leaves no room for display silver.
British Library, London

Nature and lose it in Art, rather to puzzle than to please the Palate.

Food at court at the beginning of the eighteenth century was decidedly English,[7] although Queen Anne often had "oleo", a muddling of the French word *oille*, a rich stew served in silver tureens that was typical of the new French cooking. The first two Georges, however, were resolutely un-French in their taste not only for silver but also food, as the surviving menus from meals served to the royal household show. George II even insisted on using German cooks, as, for him "No English, or even French cook could dress a dinner."[8]

Despite this opposition, French dishes and ways of serving food did spread down the social scale, creating demand for new types of silverware. The impetus for this came, not only from the example set by members of the francophile élite like Lord Chesterfield, but also from the growing number of books on the subject. Cookery books were not new, but the innovative feature of most books published on the subject from 1700 onwards is the space devoted to details about setting a table and serving the food. Massialot's *Le Cuisinier roial et bourgeois*, which first appeared in 1691, illustrates new items of tableware like a *surtout*, or centrepiece, set with another innovation, a soup tureen. Many of his ideas were copied by English writers like Patrick Lambe, whose *Queen's Royal Cookery*, first published in 1710, gives recipes for a host of Frenchified dishes including "soups, bisques, olios, terrines, surtouts, puptons and ragoos". Lord Chesterfield's French cook, Vincent la Chapelle, published his own cookery book in English in 1733, which went through a number of editions in both English and French during the following ten years. Not only did he feature table plans, but also items of table silver, like the "Surtout to be left upon the Table till the Dessert is serv'd", which may represent actual pieces of silver belonging to his employer. His was truly an international profession for when la Chapelle left Chesterfield in 1735 he entered the service of the Prince of Orange.

The French practice, copied in England, of placing all the dishes for a course on the table at once, and the guests helping themselves, or instructing their servants to help them, was modified somewhat during the early eighteenth century. The trend towards private dining meant that more items needed to be placed on the table within reach in order to do away with the large number of servants required for public dining. One solution was the *surtout* (later known as an "epergne", presumably from the French *épargner*, to save) in the centre of the table, fitted with oil and vinegar bottles, salt, pepper and other

Saying Grace by Joseph van Aken (?1699–1749). This shows a yeoman's family dining. The table articles would probably have been pewter, but they follow silver forms and show how a table would have appeared during the period.
Ashmolean Museum, Oxford

spice containers, sugar casters and even a "terrine" from which
to serve *oille*. One illustrated in Massialot has a tureen in the
centre fitted with candle branches, necessary as the dinner
hour grew later. *Surtouts* are known from contemporary
accounts and drawings from the beginning of the eighteenth
century in France, but no extant examples are known. In
England, as one would expect, it was the members of the
cosmopolitan élite at the top of the social scale who were the
first to make use of these innovations, and these centrepieces
form part of the plate issued to ambassadors as early as 1714.
The largest item issued to Lord Chesterfield by the Jewel House
in 1727 was an "Aparn with all its appertinencys" weighing a
total of 820 ounces (see p. 98), the "appertinencys" no doubt
including "cruet stands", casters and other condiment holders.
The earliest surviving English *surtouts* in their original form
date from the 1730s,[9] but cruet stands fitted with bottles for oil
and vinegar, such as no. 22, were probably originally part of a
centrepiece. George Treby ordered a "fyne poolished surtout
with cruets" from Paul de Lamerie in 1720, and in 1728 Lamerie supplied a
"Ring with 4 Branches, 4 Buttons, 4 Round Saucers & a Large Bason" to
Lord Fitzwalter.[10] Further down the social scale, bottles for oil and vinegar
and casters for sugar and spices were grouped in a small stand to sit on the
table, like no. 19 of 1718. Such stands can be seen in inventories drawn up
in Germany from the beginning of the seventeenth century and surviving
examples are known from Spain,[11] but the sole English survivor appears to
be a silver pot dating from 1688 surmounted by the initial O, presumably
for oil.[12]

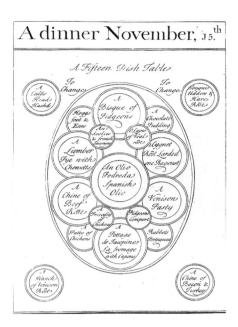

A plate from the 1730
edition of Charles Carter's
*The Complete Practical
Cook* showing a table plan.
Despite Carter's lament
that the English were "too
much attached to French
Customs and French
Cookery", he illustrates a
table setting with such
foreign dishes as an "Olio
Podreda".
British Library, London

Plate 2 from Massialot's
*Le Cuisinier Roial et
Bourgeois*, 1716.
British Library, London

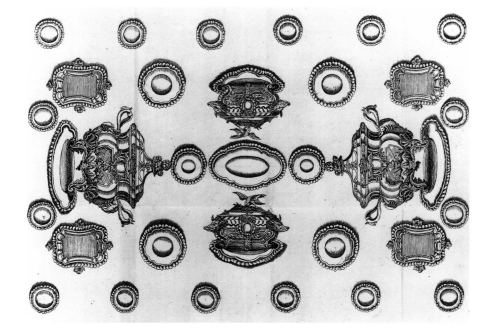

A plate from *Le Cuisinier Moderne*, the 1742 French edition of Vincent la Chapelle's *The Modern Cook*. He shows tables set with what may have been silver belonging to his employer, the Earl of Chesterfield (owner of nos. 8, 9 and 10).
Schlesinger Library, Cambridge, Massachusetts

A "toureene" was issued to Lord Galway on his appointment as ambassador to Portugal in 1708,[13] but the earliest surviving English silver examples date from the 1720s. Those issued to Lord Chesterfield in 1727 (no. 8) are probably the earliest known pair.[14] According to Vincent la Chapelle's table plans, a full setting would include two pairs of tureens, one large and one small, placed around the centrepiece. Other innovations of the period included sauceboats, which, in their double-lipped form, were based on French prototypes (no. 23), and sets of matching flatware (no. 48). The spice box, a small container with two hinged flaps and sometimes a central nutmeg grater, was another purely French object which enjoyed a limited vogue in England (nos. 17, 21, 34) but seems to have competed unsuccessfully with the cruet stand which could contain oil and vinegar bottles in addition to casters for spices.

A plate from *The Modern Cook*, 1733, showing a "Surtout to be left upon the Table till Dessert is serv'd".
Royal Ontario Museum, Toronto

Centrepiece, silver,
London, 1730–1, maker's
mark of Edward Feline,
made for the Williams
family.
Sotheby's, New York

Centrepiece, silver,
London, 1742–3, supplied
by George Wickes to the
Earl of Milltown.
Colonial Williamsburg
Foundation

Men and women seldom intermingled around a table; such "promiscuous" dining was a development of the late eighteenth century. The dining room was essentially a male preserve in which a man's status was expressed, through either the magnificence of the food or the silverware: Sir George Courthoppe (see no. 56) in his will, signed in 1685, gives his wife "ye whole ffurniture of any Chamber that is myne in ye house (except ye dineinge Room wch is noe way suitable for her)".[15] Formal dinner parties were often seated at a number of small tables, as at Knole on the occasion of the visit of one of the royal princesses in 1728, when the company sat at four tables.[16] The medieval custom of a buffet covered with an impressive display of silver and silver-gilt vessels also lingered on through the eighteenth century: the *Tatler* in 1710 observed that "the sumptuous side-board, to the ingenuous eye, has often more the air of an altar than a table".[17]

Books like Massialot's and la Chapelle's were essentially books written by professionals for professionals, but another change which took place in the first half of the eighteenth century was greater involvement in the kitchen by the lady of the house. The job of cook had until then been exclusively a masculine one but the decline of the great open fire and the advent of the kitchen range meant that bourgeois cooking could advance along much the same lines as cuisine in aristocratic households. Charles Carter's two books published in the 1730s enjoyed unprecedented popularity and did much to spread the new ideas of food presentation down the social scale. Perhaps the books that most influenced the middle classes were two written by women: Eliza Smith's *The Compleat Housewife*, published in 1727, and Hannah Glasse's *The Art of Cooking Made Plain and Easy* of 1747 which, despite its anti-French stance, did much to expose the bourgeoisie to French food and

Marriage à la Mode: VI
by William Hogarth
(1697–1764) (detail),
showing a simple meal,
with beer in an old-
fashioned silver two-
handled cup.
National Gallery, London

table manners. The fact that much of these books was taken up with
instructions how to serve meals shows the demand for information from a
new consumer group. These were the assiduous consumers of luxury goods
that made up much of the market for moderately priced silverware like coffee
pots, sauce boats and sets of candlesticks. By the middle of the century,
Massialot's characteristic claim that there is no one who would not be served
"*à la française*" rang true in dining rooms all over England.

Similar changes took place in the way in which drink was served. By the end
of the seventeenth century, the production of glass had improved sufficiently
so that it had replaced silver for the service of wine, although silver remained
popular for beer mugs and tankards and for goblets used for beer or punch.
Wine glasses were seldom placed on the dining table. Instead they were
brought to diners by servants when requested, usually when "toasting" a
companion, and offered on silver salvers with a sturdy central foot (nos. 1
and 2). In the early eighteenth century, however, one development of the new
intimacy in dining was the appearance from France of the single-bottle wine
cooler (no. 60) which could be kept within reach of the imbiber. Wine was
still drunk comparatively young, stored in the cellar in casks and for serving
decanted into jugs or glass bottles which were often bound in raffia to
prevent breakage. The wars with France, and the resulting favourable trading
status afforded Portugal as a result of the Methuen Treaty (see no. 1), saw a
dramatic decline in the consumption of claret and burgundy and their
replacement with Portuguese wines, at first bucellas, calcevella and colares,
but soon port, a red wine from the Douro region fortified with brandy which
enabled it to be kept longer, became "the Englishman's wine". Devoted
Jacobites might secretly drink French wines, but for most it became almost a
patriotic duty to drink port, as Jonathan Swift observed:

> Be sometimes to your country true,
> Have once the public good in view.
> Bravely despise Champagne at Court,
> And choose to dine at home with Port.

The champagne referred to in this verse is unlikely to be the fizzy kind, which did not become popular until the middle of the century, but the still wines of the Champagne region, which rivalled those of Burgundy at the court of Louis XIV.

Punch, another drink with no French connotations, was popular from the middle of the seventeenth century onwards, and ladled out of hemispherical silver bowls which, because of the convivial nature of the drink, were often given as presentation pieces (no. 62). Small versions, like the one of 1736 (no. 64) are much less common and may have been used for serving gin or brandy mixed with hot water and sugar. In Henry Purcell's round written at the end of the seventeenth century, he begins: "Bring the bowl and cool Nantz, and let us be mixing" (Nantz was contemporary slang for brandy, probably from Nantes). The word "punch" is from the Sanskrit *pañca* meaning five, referring to the five customary ingredients, water, sugar, limes or lemons, spices and spirit.

The monteith was also a totally English invention (nos. 57 and 59), its notched rim allowing glasses to be hung to cool in the iced water they contained. Beer, especially the less alcoholic small beer, was still drunk, as it had been for centuries, instead of water and accompanied most meals including breakfast. Drunk by the gentry and bourgeoisie out of silver tankards like nos. 56 and 63, it was often served hot and highly spiced. The

Elegant Merrymaking by Pieter Angellis (1685–1754). Wine glasses were never placed on the table, but brought to diners by servants when requested.
Bridgeman/Art Resource, New York

A family being served with tea, British School, c. 1745.
Yale Center for British Art, Paul Mellon Collection

two-handled cup, which by the beginning of the eighteenth century had acquired a foot (no. 5) was also used for drinking beer and other hot alcoholic drinks and often passed between convivial drinkers. In one of Hogarth's scenes from *Marriage à la Mode*, painted in 1745, a two-handled cup of a type that had been popular for the last fifty years is shown on the table, evidently holding beer, and when Tom Jones and his companion stop at a wayside inn in Fielding's *Tom Jones* they share a "loving cup". It is clear, however, that by the beginning of the century the more expensive vase-shaped two-handled cups like nos. 5 and especially no. 12 were made as display pieces to adorn a sideboard and were not used for drinking.

Beer drinking did decline, however, in fashionable circles, with the arrival of tea, coffee and chocolate during the 1650s. "There were also at this time a Turkish drink to be solde, almost in every street, called coffee, and a nother kind of drink called Tee, and also a drink called Chocolate, which was a very hearty drink," wrote Thomas Rugge in 1659. While the heavily-sugared meats and pastries which were a large part of medieval cooking were edged out by savoury French dishes like fricassees and *ragoûts*, the slight kick to the nervous system that these excess doses of sugar had provided was replaced with caffeine. Tea had first appeared in London by way of the Netherlands, for the Dutch were the first to exploit the tea trade with the Orient. The Portuguese, however, claim that it was Catherine of Braganza, wife of Charles

A lady and gentleman drinking chocolate by N. Bonnart, after R.B. The chocolate pot is typically French. The form was imitated occasionally in England, as in the example of 1722–3 made for Lord Hinchingbrooke (no. 68) but for the most part English tea, coffee and chocolate wares are quite distinct from contemporary French examples.
Bibliothèque nationale, Paris

II, who first introduced the custom of a "dish of tea" to the English. Because of tea's exotic nature, articles associated with it were inspired by Oriental prototypes from the earliest days . By the end of the seventeenth century the Chinese wine pot had become the model for the teapot which, with the occasional addition of decorative motifs, remained the norm until the mid-eighteenth century (no. 76). In one case, a Chinese silver wine pot was retailed in London during the 1680s as a teapot.[18] Chinese ceramics also provided the inspiration for the shape of tea caddies (no. 79) and sugar bowls. When the mania for scenes inspired by the Orient, known as Chinoiserie, was revived in the 1730s, it appears to have been popular for the most part in the drawing room, where the lady of the house would preside over a tea ceremony almost as ritualized as its Japanese equivalent. The custom of adding cream or milk came later, at the beginning of the eighteenth century, and as a result the cream jug has no prototype in Oriental forms. It was, however, the cream jug which was given the most imaginative treatment during the 1730s and 1740s (see nos. 70 and 71), its small sculptural form most adaptable to elaborate rococo decoration, and such extravagant creations in small scale must have produced cries of delight when passed around a fashionable company.

The first coffee house had opened in London in 1652 and by Queen Anne's reign it was estimated that there were 500 coffee houses in London. It was also drunk in fashionable, and later in less fashionable, households. The beans would often be ground by the lady of the house in front of her guests, as Alexander Pope's passage from *The Rape of the Lock* illustrates:

> For lo! the board with cups and spoons is crown'd,
> The berries crackle, and the mill turns around;
> On shining altars of Japan they raise
> The silver lamp; the fiery spirits blaze;
> From silver spouts the grateful liquors glide,
> While China's earth receives the smoking tide;
> At once they gratify their scent and taste,
> And frequent cups prolong the rich repast.

The Earl of Derby bought a "Plaine Coffe pott with a crooked wooden handle" in 1694 from the goldsmith banker, Richard Hoare, who also supplied him with "six pounds of coffe berries" for £1 16s. Like tea, vessels for serving coffee soon became standardized. The tapering form, cylindrical, square or octagonal, (nos. 65 and 66), usually with a rim foot, was most popular, although coffee pots following the French model, raised on three feet, are also known.

In 1657 a Frenchman opened an establishment in London called the Coffee Mill and Tobacco Roll, although its speciality was neither of these things, but a new drink called chocolate. The chocolate trade from the New World had long been a closely-guarded monopoly of the Spanish. The cost of chocolate – some fifteen shillings a pound – hardly rivalled that of tea, which sold for as much as £10 a pound in the 1650s, but it did not go as far. As a morning beverage it was more popular than coffee and was immortalized in Paris by Madame de Sévigné thus: "Day before yesterday I took some chocolate to digest my dinner, in order to sup well, and I took some yesterday to be well fed so I could fast until evening; this is what I find agreeable about it, that it acts as you intend it to do." Pepys also swore by the medicinal properties of chocolate: "Waked in the morning with my head in a sad taking thro' last night's drink, which I am sorry for. So rose and went out [to a chocolate or coffee house] with Mr. Creed to drink our morning draught, which he did give me in chocolate to settle my stomach". Chocolate was boiled in red wine and thickened with egg and sometimes served with additional flavourings such as vanilla, almonds, orange-water or spices like cinnamon, aniseed or cloves.[19]

Silver chocolate pots followed the same model as coffee pots, with the addition of an aperture in the cover for the *molinet*, or "muddler" (no. 68), but today they are much rarer than coffee pots, probably on account of the virtual disappearance of chocolate from fashionable tables by the end of the eighteenth century.

An invitation to dine at
Goldsmiths' Hall, 1707.
The Goldsmiths' Company
closely regulated the trade
and their guildhall also
housed the Assay Office,
which ensured the purity
of the silver used in
manufactured goods.
Worshipful Company of
Goldsmiths, London

Notes
[1] Toledo Museum of Art, Ohio.
[2] Austin Dobson, ed., *The Diary of John Evelyn,* 1906, vol. III, p. 194.
[3] Arthur Young, *Travels in France during the Years 1787, 1788, 1789,* 1889 edn, p. 306.
[4] Colin Clair, *Kitchen and Table*, 1964, p. 253.
[5] Quoted in Sarah Paston-Williams, *The Art of Dining*, 1993, p. 163.
[6] March 21, 1709.
[7] Stephen Mennell has made a study of the court menus in the Public Record Office, see *All Manners of Food*, 1985, pp. 124–5.
[8] Romney Sedgwick, ed., *Lord Hervey's Memoirs*, 1984 edn, p. 98.
[9] One of 1730–1, made for the Williams family, now in the National Museum of Wales; another, supplied to the Earl of Milltown by George Wickes in 1742, is at Colonial Williamsburg.
[10] Mildmay Papers, Essex Record Office, Chelmsford, D/DM/F13.
[11] Edmund Braun, *Die Silberkammer eines Reichsfürsten (Das Lobkowitz'sche Inventar)*, 1923, pl. XXV; Christopher Hartop, "New Light on Spanish Seventeenth-Century Silver", *The Silver Society Journal*, 1, Winter, 1990, pp. 10–12.
[12] Sotheby's, London, March 16, 1961, lot 102.
[13] James Lomax, "Silver for the English Dining Room 1700–1800" in *A King's Feast, the Goldsmith's Art and Royal Banqueting in the Eighteenth Century*, exh. cat. Kensington Palace, London, 1991.
[14] A pair in the Gilbert Collection appear to be of 1723 but were extensively altered in the 1740s.
[15] Courthoppe Papers, West Sussex Record Office, Lewes, SAS/CO/112.
[16] Sackville Papers, West Kent Archive Office, Maidstone, U269/E14.
[17] No. 205, August 1, 1710, quoted in John Gloag, *Georgian Grace*, 1956, p. 145.
[18] Sold from the Wagstaff Collection, Christie's, New York, April 18, 1989, lot 589, now in the Peabody Museum, Salem, Massachusetts.
[19] Sarah Paston-Williams, *op. cit.*, p. 158.

Goldsmiths' Hall
drawn by John Ward,
Surveyor of the
Goldsmiths' Company,
in 1692.
Worshipful Company
of Goldsmiths, London

Craftsmen and Suppliers

One cannot regard English silver of the period 1680–1760 as the work of
individual artists. It was the product of a complex and often long chain
of designers, modellers, raisers, chasers, casters, engravers and planishers.
Smaller objects may bear the mark of the man who made them, but in the
case of important commissions, the so-called "maker's mark" which appears
on a piece is no indication of authorship. Behind the maker's mark there was
an intricate, and hidden, web of specialists.

By law, no finished silver could be offered for sale without being first struck
with the mark of the "maker", and then assayed at Goldsmiths' Hall. If found
to be the required standard of silver alloy, and made without excessive solder,
it was then struck by the Assay Office with "hallmarks", the three official
stamps which signified the standard of the alloy (the "lion passant" or,
between 1697 and 1720, the figure of Britannia), the place of assay (the
"leopard's head" or, between 1697 and 1720, the "lion's head erased",
signifying London), and a date letter changed each year in May.[1] In the case
of successful businessmen like David Willaume I or Paul de Lamerie, it is
clear from the quantity – and quality – of the surviving work struck with
their marks that many artists and workmen must have been employed by
them. Specialization in the craft was nothing new, and can be traced back to
the Middle Ages, and it is clear that not only models and dies but also
components themselves such as cast feet, finials and handles were available
from specialized workshops. We know also from the one surviving set of
account books from a major retailer, George Wickes and his successors, that
many suppliers had a large web of "outworkers" who supplied finished
articles.[2] Some outworkers, especially the larger workshops, would submit
the work for assay themselves, and strike it with their marks, but frequently
work was supplied in finished state to the retailer, who would submit it for
assay himself.

The privilege of registering a "maker's mark" at Goldsmiths' Hall was jealously guarded by the trade, who were particularly concerned by what they saw as inroads being

made into their monopoly by foreign workers. Immigrant goldsmiths were nothing new; they were a common feature in London during the Middle Ages, and England took in thousands of protestant refugees from the Low Countries during the second half of the sixteenth century. This absorption of continental influences was recognized as a constant theme in English art by Sir Nikolaus Pevsner, who gave his conclusions in a celebrated series of Reith Lectures for the BBC in the 1950s.[3]

In the seventeenth century, Christian van Vianen, one of the renowned Flemish family of designers and goldsmiths, visited England at the behest of Charles I and returned again after the Restoration. Despite his royal patronage, he seems to have had to rely on others to submit his work for assay, although his son-in-law, John Coquus, also from Flanders, was successful in registering his own mark with the Company. By the 1660s, others, like Jacob Bodendick from Germany and Wolfgang Howzer from Switzerland, had

arrived in London in search of the opportunities the new prosperity could provide. Opposition from native craftsmen to these industrious workers, whose techniques were far superior to their own, was inevitable. London tradesmen had complained shortly after the Restoration about "the multitude of aliens" who had "taken upon themselves to exercise their several vocations."[4] A petition from 1676 lists twenty-six alien craftsmen including Coquus.[5] Bodendick and Howzer presented a letter from Charles II to the Goldsmiths' Company in 1664, instructing the Wardens to accept their work for assay. In return the king promised that these newcomers would only employ native craftsmen "and not strangers in their manufacture".[6] Work bearing the marks attributed to them is characterized by superior use of casting, particularly handles in the van Vianens' auricular style which was still current in German silver at the time, and in elaborate floral embossing in the newer, French, fashion.

Hallmarks for London, 1689–90, maker's mark of Pierre Harache (from no. 15). The maker's mark, or more accurately, "sponsor's" mark, was struck on the finished article by the workshop owner or retailer before submitting it to the assay office at Goldsmiths' Hall, where, provided the alloy was of legal standard, the wardens would strike "hallmarks" on it: the leopard's head signifying London, the lion passant, denoting sterling (92.5% silver alloy), and a letter which changed in May each year.

Hallmarks for London, 1703–4, maker's mark of Andrew Moore (from no.1). To rectify the shortage of silver coinage caused by silversmiths melting down coins for silver bullion, a new higher standard of alloy, known as Britannia, was introduced by act of Parliament in 1697.

Hallmarks for London, 1748–9, maker's mark of Paul de Lamerie (from no. 46). The sterling standard of alloy was restored once the silver coin shortage was over in 1720.

A French print by Nicolas de Larmessin II (c. 1660–1716) showing the types of silver available from French silversmiths. Royal Ontario Museum, Toronto

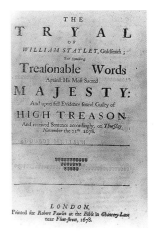

The Tryal of William Stayley, Goldsmith For Speaking Treasonable Words, 1678. England was swept with anti-Catholic hysteria during the Popish Plot.

The picture is clouded, however, by the fact that the new techniques and styles one finds on Howzer's and Bodendick's work also appear on silver struck with the marks of native Englishmen, such as the tankard of 1686, (no. 56), which bears a mark now attributed to William Jennings. The small group of silver struck with Jennings's mark all shows this superior casting and modelling and it is evident that he employed foreigners, or that his workers had been trained by them. It may even be that Jennings, with his shop in the fashionable new street of Pall Mall, close by St. James's Palace, was only a retailer and sold work by foreign craftsmen. This practice of immigrant workers giving their silver to Englishmen to submit for assay was a major concern of the Goldsmiths' Company; in 1715 it was said that Paul de Lamerie "covered Foreigners work and got ye same toucht at ye Hall",[7] so there was evidently a fine line that divided the foreign journeyman craftsman working in an English workshop, and the foreign master with his own workshop.

The problem became acute in the 1680s with the growing numbers of Huguenot workers who arrived in England as a result of Louis XIV's persecution. However much middle-class Englishmen might sympathize with the plight of these co-religionists, victims of the feared regime across the Channel, they were seen even before their arrival as a threat to the silversmith's trade. In 1678 the Lord Mayor had desired:

Het weg vlugten der Gereformeerde uyt Vrankryk.

The Flight of the Huguenots engraved by Jan Luyken in 1696. Louis XIV's revocation of the Edict of Nantes, which had given limited freedom to the French Protestants, or Huguenots, started a flood of refugees in 1685. Many settled in the Low Countries, but after the Glorious Revolution of 1688 and the accession of the Protestant William and Mary, England became the main place of refuge for them, as London offered not only religious freedom but many business opportunities.
Rijksmuseum, Amsterdam

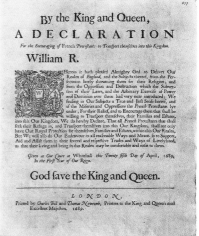

Declaration by William and Mary encouraging Huguenots to settle in England, 1689. William of Orange, conscious that he ruled England by invitation of the Protestant oligarchy, encouraged the Huguenots to settle there.
Museum of London, London

to acquaint the [Goldsmiths'] Company that there was a bill depending in Parliament for the licensing of Protestant strangers to come from parts beyond the seas and here to exercise manual occupations without any let or molestation which if granted would very much tend to the prejudice of the natives of this kingdom and in especial to the artificers of this Company, as he conceived.[8]

The proposed bill became law in 1681, and Charles II declared his intention to grant "Letters of Denization under his Great Seal without any charge whatsoever" to the refugees. One of the first to take advantage of the king's gesture was Pierre Harache, a silversmith thought to be from Rouen (see no. 15), who arrived on October 20 of that year with his stock-in-trade, which was admitted duty-free.[9] Men like Harache, who managed to leave France with much of their liquid assets, were able to set themselves up in business right away; he was evidently a man of influence, for in July of the following year he was admitted a member of the Goldsmiths' Company by an order of the Court of Alderman, described as "lately come from France to avoid persecution".[10] Within a few years the business Harache set up was supplying plate to major patrons like the Duke of Somerset and it is clear he employed a large workforce. Harache, however, was an exception in his success in becoming a member of the Goldsmiths' Company; a similar order from the Court of Aldermen to admit another Huguenot, John Louis, a short time later, was resisted strenuously. As Hugh Tait observes, "again and again, the same pattern seems to occur: the more gifted and influential the alien goldsmith, the more unwelcoming his reception at Goldsmiths' Hall".[11] The easiest way a guild could deny membership to a Huguenot was to insist on the seven-year apprenticeship qualification; this was taken up by the board of the French Church of the Savoy in 1682: "The coming and continuing of Protestants into this Kingdom can so little prejudice, as it must needs be of advantage to it … yet we find so great an aversion in [the people here] from us, as to envy the bread we get by our honest and hard labours …"[12]

Huguenots were a constant reminder of the threat of Catholicism, but the irony was that, in many Englishmen's eyes, all Frenchmen were Catholics and dangerous, and the appearance of the Huguenots in England had coincided

Noon, L'Eglise des Grecs, Hog Lane, Soho by William Hogarth, (1697–1764), engraving c. 1736. The sombrely dressed Huguenots, emerging from church, are in contrast to the elegantly dressed couple in the foreground, who are probably English, aping French fashions. Responding to market demand, the Huguenots were at the forefront of the adoption of new French fashions in art and design, but their own manners and mode of dress were sombre.

with the rise of anti-Catholic hysteria. In the middle class, among the members of the Goldsmiths' Company and the workers in the silver trade, those far removed from the aristocratic court circles that spoke French and demanded French fashions, there was constant fear that Huguenots could in fact be Catholics in disguise. After the Glorious Revolution and flight of James II in 1688, the fear of Catholics did not go away; this is well illustrated by an affidavit given in 1692 by a Mr. Taafe: "That there were 20,000 men in this town [London] ready to take arms for him [James II] most of whom were Frenchmen; that there were several thousands of the French who passed here for Protestants and go duly to the French protestant churches, who are indeed good Catholics and would show themselves to be so upon King James's launching."[13]

It was into this somewhat hysterical atmosphere that men like Pierre Harache arrived and sought to establish themselves in business. David Willaume, who arrived from Metz and was established as a banker and goldsmith by 1686 (see no. 106), was another Huguenot of this first wave of immigration, who, like Harache, evidently arrived with capital to invest. There is no doubt that this infusion of fresh capital helped expand the silversmithing trade in London, just as the influx of so many skilled workers provided much needed manpower for the trade.

In 1685 Louis XIV's persecution of the Huguenots culminated in the revocation of the Edict of Nantes, which had given them a certain amount of freedom for the previous ninety years. The result was a sudden wave of emigration but, unlike those who had already managed to establish themselves abroad, most of these refugees fled with little more than the clothes on their backs. With the accession of Charles II's brother, the Catholic James II, however, most avoided England and went instead to the Low Countries, and it was not until the arrival in England of William of Orange three years later that England appeared to the Protestant refugees as a safe haven. William, as a foreigner himself, could hardly do anything but welcome these immigrants, and lost no time in issuing a proclamation encouraging Huguenot settlement in England. The large numbers of Huguenots who arrived in England during the years that followed have never been accurately assessed, but it seems likely that as many as 50,000 were absorbed into communities in the south of the country. Most congregated in London, where their communities were centred around Spitalfields in the east and Leicester Fields in the west. It was in the west, in Soho, where most Huguenots involved in the "luxury trades" gathered, worshipping at either the Church of the Savoy or "des Grecs", although by 1700 another dozen French protestant churches had sprung up. For the next fifty years this neighbourhood was a totally French community composed of cabinetmakers, gunsmiths, jewellers, clockmakers, perfumers, bootmakers, tailors, wigmakers, fanmakers, furriers, as well as silversmiths. Lord Chesterfield, writing in 1738, suggested that those in search of French fashion would find "a much shorter, less expensive

By the founder of Garrard
An early trade card of George Wickes Circa 1751

Trade card of George Wickes and Samuel Netherton, Panton Street, c. 1755. Wickes was one of the earliest to establish a "high retail" establishment, selling silver to members of the fashionable and court circles.
Garrard & Co., The Crown Jewellers

and more effectual method of travelling and frenchifying themselves ... if they would but travel to Old Soho and stay two or three months in le quartier des Grecs."[14]

How the establishment of this community affected the silversmith's trade in London is a difficult question, made only more confusing by the existing silver and the marks struck on it. Simon Pantin, who did not register a mark of his own until 1701, evidently worked for others (probably the Harache family) before this, or had others take his work to the Hall. Not only did the Huguenots live separately from the English, but their tendency of marrying among themselves meant that they formed tightly-knit groups of inter-married craftsmen who could work for each other if the need arose. While it is not possible to know whether a piece of silver struck with a native English smith's mark was made by an English or Huguenot worker, one can assume that a work bearing a Huguenot's mark was in fact made by Huguenots.

Opposition from the English continued into the eighteenth century; as late as 1711 in a letter to a member of the Goldsmiths' Company reprimanding him for excessive use of solder, it stated that "partly by the general decay of trade and other ways by the intrusion of foreigners ... by the admittance of necessitous strangers whose desperate fortunes obliged them to work at miserable rates, the representing members have been forced to bestow much more time and labour working up their plate than hath been the practice of former times, when prices of workmanship were greater."[15]

The fact that the Huguenots worked at "miserable rates" is perhaps the key to assessing their contribution to the English silver trade during the period 1680–1710. Their poverty and refugee status made them willing to work long hours at low rates, and they provided a significant labour force for the trade at just the moment it was required. Superior techniques of modelling and casting had been introduced with the Restoration, and by the 1680s demand for the new types of silverware in the latest "French" (or "International") style had created a vacuum of talent among the native craftsmen that the Huguenots swiftly filled.

By the time a second generation of Huguenot craftsmen had come of age, the process of integration was much more advanced. It is clear that those English silversmiths like Benjamin Pyne and Anthony Nelme (see nos. 20 and 59), who evidently utilized Huguenot craftsmen, triumphed at the expense of others, like William Gibson, who continued to work in the old ways (see no. 57). In

George Wickes attributed to John Vanderbank (1694–1739). Garrard & Co., The Crown Jewellers

the early eighteenth century, however, it had become clear that a change was taking place in the way in which silver was sold. Traditionally, the trades of silversmithing and banking had been linked: in Sir Walter Scott's *The Fortunes of Nigel*, George Heriot, the goldsmith to James I, says to Nigel, "I am a goldsmith and live by lending money as well as by selling plate". Both trades dealt with ways of investing capital. As tradesmen at that time often waited years before their bills were settled, only a silversmith who was also a banker, holding people's money on deposit, was in a position to fund large orders of plate on extended credit. Prosperous bankers like Edward Backwell, Sir Robert Viner and Richard Hoare, for whom the silverware trade was a sideline, could rely on networks of suppliers of finished wares for their customers, while silversmiths like David Willaume, who kept a "running cash", or in other words took money on deposit and paid interest, evidently did this because it gave them greater liquidity in their business as suppliers of silver.

The fashionable retailer was a development of the eighteenth century, transplanted, like most fashions, from Paris. George Wickes operated one such establishment from the 1720s onwards and numbered among his clients Frederick, Prince of Wales and members of the high aristocracy. The chance survival of most of his business records[16] and those of his successors show us not only the network of suppliers he used, but also the way his shop operated. Many of the transactions were small jobs like "a Black eboney handle for a tea kettle and a Button for a teapot" which he supplied to the Prince in 1735.[17] Such shops, with elegantly interiors, could display a wide range of plate, helping to disseminate new styles and forms; instead of talking to a craftsman, the client would deal with, in Wickes's case, a man of almost gentlemanly status who could advise him on the latest styles.

Paul de Lamerie's account with Benjamin Mildmay, Earl Fitzwalter, of 1728, showing the purchase of an epergne, or centrepiece. Essex Record Office, Chelmsford

One of the most puzzling aspects of silver study is the frequent occurrence of identical objects bearing different makers' marks which poses the question, "who made it?" Moreover, it is sometimes impossible to detect individual styles in pieces bearing the same maker's mark and it is therefore better to examine the output of groups of craftsman. The most important such group in eighteenth-century London is the one centred around Paul de Lamerie, the best-known silversmith of the period, whose mark appears on twenty-one pieces in the Hartman Collection. Unlike Wickes, about whom we know much more than what would have been gleaned just from the work bearing his mark, it is difficult in Lamerie's case to know what sort of establishment he ran. The scant details of his life are well known,[18] but no trade card has come to light, and only two groups of bills are known, none of which is written on a printed bill head. One of these groups, for George Treby in 1721, was published in 1935 but the originals have since been lost.[19] The other group comprises three long bills to Benjamin Mildmay, Earl Fitzwalter, between about 1725 and 1738 (Mildmay was a considerable patron of Lamerie but also patronized others, including Henry Hebert, who supplied the tureen, no. 11, to him).[20] Lamerie had a considerable workshop, and during his career took on thirteen apprentices. We know from the Treby and Fitzwalter bills, and the fact that his "shop" is mentioned in a famous court case of 1722,[21] that he sold silver directly to private clients and he was not merely a manufacturer supplying other silversmiths, but it is clear that his establishment was far more low key than Wickes's. He supplied other silversmiths with finished plate, such as the pair of wine coolers that formed part of the plate issued to the Earl of Chesterfield in 1727 (see p. 100). Paul

Crespin, to whom the order was evidently given, overstruck Lamerie's mark with his own before delivering them to the Jewel House,[22] and several casters are known with Lamerie's mark overstruck by that of Phillips Garden (see below).[23] Additionally, several objects are known which have Crespin's mark overstruck by Lamerie's, so there was obviously considerable exchange of wares between craftsmen. According to Sun Insurance Company policies, between 1723 and 1728 Lamerie was in partnership with Ellis Gamble,[24] the engraver under whom William Hogarth had served his apprenticeship. It seems that Gamble at that time began to operate as a fashionable retailer of silver and jewellery while Lamerie supervised the manufacture or commissioning of the plate. The partnership was not a long-term success, for after 1728, Lamerie and Gamble appear with different insurance policies; finally in 1732, Gamble was made bankrupt with Lamerie as the petitioning creditor. After the partnership ceased, Lamerie may have decided to continue more as a wholesale supplier, although he did go on supplying Lord Fitzwalter directly with plate (see no. 11). The advertisement for the auction of his stock-in-trade and tools after his death lists "Mahogany and other Presses, Counters, Drawers, Shelves, Desks and other Fixtures of the Shop", but this may refer to fittings of his office and workshop rather than retail premises. The distinction between wholesale supplier and retailer can never be clearly defined in the eighteenth century.

Trade card of Ellis Gamble, the engraving by William Hogarth, c. 1725

The wide range of styles represented during Lamerie's forty-year career could not have been made or even designed by one individual, but there are some consistent features in quality, and some "trademarks", like the way in which the bottoms of his coffee pots are constructed, and the fact that his workshop continued to use the higher, Britannia, standard of silver alloy for some twelve years after it ceased to be compulsory[25] that show that Lamerie was obviously a dynamic, and demanding, employer.

Lamerie supplied clients overseas, in Russia and in America (see no. 77), but for the most part his clients at home were not members of the aristocratic élite. He had, in 1716, been appointed Royal Goldsmith, but his mark does not appear on any royal plate, and the covered cup he evidently executed which was sold to the Prince of Wales in 1739 was supplied through Wickes's establishment. Most of his clients were prosperous landowners – members of the Whig ascendancy – like the Earl of Mountrath (see no. 39) and Admiral Anson.[26] His standing in the trade was considerable and it seems that only his declining health during the late 1740s prevented him from serving as Prime Warden of the Goldsmiths' Company. After his death in 1751, the obituary which appeared in the *London Evening Post* spoke of Lamerie as "particularly famous in making fine ornamental Plate, and ... very instrumental in bringing that Branch of the Trade to the Perfection it is now in".

Paul Crespin was obviously closely connected with Lamerie. His mark appears on some of the most cosmopolitan silver of the early eighteenth

Paul Crespin attributed to
Pierre Subleyras
(1699–1749), c. 1726. In
contrast to George Wickes,
Crespin was evidently a
manufacturer, rather than
a retailer, of silverware.
Victoria and Albert
Museum, London

century, made for a host of important clients including the Jewel House (see
nos. 8, 9 and 10), Lord Stanhope (see no. 47) and the Duke of Somerset (see
no. 43). It is tempting, however, to see him as a manufacturing supplier of
finished silver rather than a retailer, although according to newspaper
accounts in 1724 he "showed a fine silver bathing vessel (made for the King
of Portugal) to his Majesty at Kensington who was well pleased with so
curious a piece of workmanship".[27] Crespin's portrait, one of the three
known surviving portraits of a silversmith from the first half of the
eighteenth century, shows him, in his shirtsleeves, holding a large silver urn.
It is difficult to imagine Paul de Lamerie, who was extremely proud of his
rank as Colonel in the Militia and aspired to a coat-of-arms, or indeed George
Wickes, choosing to be painted in such a fashion.

To the Lamerie group can be added another silversmith, John White, who
was not a Huguenot. From White's trade card we know he kept a retail
establishment but work struck with his mark is much rarer than Lamerie's or
Crespin's. Much of the silver acquired by the 1st and 2nd Lords King in the
1720s and 1730s bears White's mark, but most of it is either identical to work
from Lamerie's workshop, such as the candlesticks (no. 101), or has similar
decoration to work bearing either Lamerie's or Crespin's mark, such as the
cup and cover (no. 12). The fact that the King silver was purchased over a
period of some years precludes it from being a rush commission for a "laying
down" of plate which Lamerie had to farm out to colleagues such as White.
It may be that it was White who was the retailer, and that the silver was

Trade card of John White,
1719–24. Evidence suggests
that John White may have
been a retailer who sold
finished silver from
Lamerie's and James
Shruder's workshops during
the 1740s.
British Museum, London

produced in Lamerie's or Crespin's workshop. Intriguingly, in the Fitzwalter Accounts for 1729 (see no. 11), he is described as "Mr. White, silversmith and excise officer".[28]

By the 1740s the composition of the Lamerie group changes, but one can still see the same interchange of components and finished articles. Crespin continued to work closely with Lamerie and a new member appears. He was Nicholas Sprimont, who was not a Huguenot but the son of a silversmith from Liège. He entered his own mark at Goldsmiths' Hall in 1742 but is thought to have been in London several years before that. It has been suggested that Crespin may have "covered his work" during this period,[29] and that the well-known centrepiece made for Frederick, Prince of Wales in the Royal Collection, which bears Crespin's mark, is the work of Sprimont. On the other hand, Sprimont may have been a subcontractor to whom Crespin and other members of the Lamerie group sent components to be assembled and that close co-operation between the two men continued through Crespin's declining years.[30]

In September 1744, however, Sprimont leased workshops in Chelsea where he developed the new Chelsea porcelain factory. A press report six months later remarked: "We hear that the China made at Chelsea is arriv'd to such Perfection, as to equal if not surpass the finest old Japan, allow'd so by the most approv'd Judges here ..."[31] From 1748 onwards Sprimont was totally absorbed by his porcelain factory,[32] and no silver is found after this date bearing his mark. Much of Sprimont's work is identical to Lamerie's like the

Nicholas Sprimont, depicted c. 1759. He appears to have abandoned silversmithing by about 1747 and devoted himself entirely to the direction of the Chelsea porcelain factory. A native of Liège, silver bearing his mark from 1742 onwards shows many similarities to that of other members of the Lamerie group. This recently discovered portrait appears to be the only one to show work in progress at an English porcelain factory. E. & H. Manners Ltd, Kensington Church Street, London

candlesticks (no. 105), or to to Crespin's, like the sauceboats (no. 45). The distinctive stands for these sauceboats are identical to porcelain dishes he was to produce at Chelsea.

James Shruder, whose mark appears on the candelabra (no. 102), the snuffers and tray made for the Earl of Warrington (no. 104), and the tea caddies and sugar bowl (no. 80) was probably a German protestant who was also part of the Lamerie group. The tea caddies and sugar bowl, made in 1748 for the King family, may have been supplied to the family by John White,[33] as were the cup and cover (no. 12) and the candlesticks (no. 101), all of which bear White's own mark. Shruder was declared bankrupt in 1749 but may have continued supplying work to Lamerie and the others after that, for he appears as one of the witnesses to Lamerie's will in 1751. After Lamerie's death, the marks of Henry Hayens and Phillips (or Philip) Garden, both non-Huguenots, appear on many works identical to Lamerie's, like the shell-form basket (no. 51), and it may be that they were buyers of Lamerie's "curious patterns and tools" at Mr. Langford's auction in 1752, or that they were supplied with silver by someone who did. Judging from the magnificence of his trade card, it seems that Garden operated a "high retail" establishment like that started by George Wickes, although his trade card makes the questionable claim: "WORK perform'd in my own House". The candlesticks of 1742–3 (no. 103) bearing his mark are virtually identical to examples from Lamerie's workshop. In 1759 Garden supplied a dinner service to Sir Nathaniel Curzon of Kedleston which bears the maker's mark of William Cripps,[34] who in 1742 had taken over the premises occupied by Christian Hillan (see no. 73) next door to Sprimont in Compton Street, Soho. In 1746 Cripps moved to St James's but he seems to have continued as a member of the Lamerie group, albeit on the periphery.

Whereas the silver of the various members of the Lamerie group has a cohesion of form and design, silver bearing the mark of Charles Kandler has a uniqueness that merits separate study. A German from Saxony, Kandler was the brother of Johann Joachim Kandler, the celebrated modeller of Meissen porcelain.[35] He arrived in London in 1727, no doubt attracted by the opportunities presented by the imminent coronation of the new king, George II, and a court that was wholeheartedly German. Kandler was soon established, at first in partnership with one James Murray, in St Martin's Lane, supplying a number of wealthy patrons with silver which, for the next few years at least, was decidedly German in form and feeling like the spice box (no. 34). The candlesticks (no. 100) show a German handling of a typically London form, as do the candelabra he produced in 1738, adapting a model by Thomas Germain (illus. p. 129). While most Huguenot craftsmen had had to sever all links with their homeland, Kandler kept in close touch with Saxony and consequently some of the work from his workshop directly copies Meissen porcelain forms.[36] He may in fact have returned to Dresden by the end of the 1730s, but the business was carried on by a son or nephew,

Trade card of James Shruder, 1739. Shruder was a German immigrant who was closely connected with the Lamerie group.
British Museum, London

Trade card of Phillips Garden, c. 1755. Garden appears to have operated a retail establishment along the same lines as George Wickes's shop, although his card proudly proclaims, "WORK perform'd in my own House".
British Museum, London

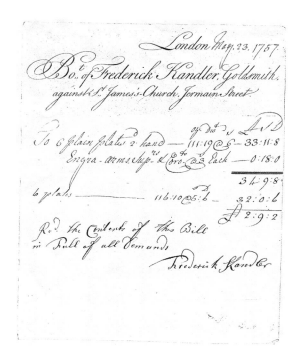

Lady Stanhope's bill for
silver dinner plates from
Frederick Kandler, May
23, 1757.
Stanhope Papers, West
Kent Archive Office,
Maidstone

Entry of Charles Frederick
Kandler's mark in the
Goldsmiths' Company
records, 1727. Kandler was
the brother of Johann
Joachim Kandler, the
celebrated modeller for the
Meissen porcelain factory
and some of the silver
bearing his mark follows
Meissen forms.
Worshipful Company of
Goldsmiths, London

Frederick, into the 1770s. From the Goldsmiths' Company records, we know
that a new mark was registered by a Frederick Kandler in 1739.[37] While some
work bearing this mark still retains many of the Germanic qualities of the
elder Kandler's work (like the sauceboat, no. 42), most of it is in the
mainstream of London-made silver. By the 1750s the majority of the items
from Kandler's workshop such as the "knurled" dishes (no. 50), was identical
to that being produced in other workshops. Kandler supplied silver to
Viscount Fairfax during the 1750s and a letter which has survived, dated
January 14, 1755 from Kandler to Fairfax, shows that he had the usual
problems of a retailer: "May it please your Lordship. I rec'd Mr. Reynoldson's
letter with a draft for £100 by y[r]. Lordship's Order for which I have sent a
receipt and am much obliged. He tells me y[r]. Ldship think the waiter dear,
which I am sorry for, having charged no more than y[r]. Lordship agreed to give
when [we] spoke which is considerably less than what I had for the waiter I
shewed y[r]. Lrsp. Rec'd … £100 in full for a large silver waiter."[38]

By the middle years of the eighteenth century, it is evident that the old
barriers had all but broken down between Huguenot and non-Huguenot
craftsmen. The closely-knit communities in which even the second
generation immigrés lived, and the intricate webs of specialist workers, were
gradually being replaced by new networks comprising Huguenot and non-
Huguenot craftsmen. The lack of distinctive features in work from the
Kandler workshop from the 1750s onwards shows that also for immigrants
other than the Huguenots the process of assimilation was complete.

Entry of Frederick Kandler's
first mark in the
Goldsmiths' Company
records in 1739. This
Frederick was evidently a
son or nephew of the
German immigrant, Charles
Kandler, and work bearing
his mark is more in the
mainstream of mid-
eighteenth-century London
silver than that of his
predecessor.
Worshipful Company of
Goldsmiths, London

Trade card of Thomas Heming, c. 1765. Heming's workshop produced silver in the latest French taste, as the examples illustrated on this trade card show. The same surround was used by Richard Morrison, another fashionable retailer for his trade card in the 1770s. The tureen of 1758 (no. 54) is virtually identical to the one depicted at lower left of the surround.
British Museum, London

Design for a ewer by Pierre Germain, from his *Eléments d'Orfèvrerie* of 1748

Thomas Heming was one of the most successful suppliers of silverware of the mid-century. The son of a Shropshire merchant, he had been apprenticed to the Huguenot Peter Archambo in 1738, and it is clear he learnt his trade in that second-generation Huguenot milieu. Work bearing his mark from the 1750s, like the soup tureen of 1758 (no. 54) is assuredly in the French rococo style and he evidently relied heavily on, among others, the printed designs of Pierre Germain, published in Paris in 1748. He was appointed Principal Goldsmith to the King in 1760, a post which brought him considerable business, not only from official commissions, but from members of the court like John, 3rd Earl of Bute.[39]

Notes

[1] In an unsigned document in the Stanhope Papers, "The Weight of The <u>Old</u> Silver of late, as Weighed in 1756", a note in the margin comments: "Mem^d Plate marked with the stamp of Britannia is reckoned worth a penny a pound more than that marked with a Lyon" (West Kent Record Office, Maidstone, U1590/E14).

[2] See Elaine Barr, *George Wickes, Royal Goldsmith*, 1980 and Helen Clifford, "Paul de Lamerie and the Organization of the London Goldsmiths' Trade in the First Half of the Eighteenth Century", in *Paul de Lamerie: The Work of England's Master Silversmith*, exh. cat. Goldsmiths' Hall, London, 1990, p. 24.

[3] *The Englishness of English Art*, 1956.

[4] Robin Gwynn, *Huguenot Heritage*, 1986, p. 121.

[5] David Mitchell, "Innovation and the Transfer of Skill" in *Goldsmiths, Silversmiths and Bankers*, 1995, p. 19.

[6] Charles Oman, *Caroline Silver 1660–1688*, 1970, p. 33.

[7] Susan Hare, "Paul de Lamerie 1688–1751" in *Paul de Lamerie: the Work of England's Master Silversmith*, exh. cat., Goldsmiths' Hall, London, 1990, p. 9.

[8] John Hayward, *Huguenot Silver 1688–1727*, 1975, p. 15.

[9] Reference from Robin Gwynn, cited in Hugh Tait, "London Huguenot Silver" in *Huguenots in Britain and their French Background 1550–1800*, ed. Irene Scouloudi, 1985, p. 279.

[10] Arthur Grimwade, *The London Goldsmiths 1697–1830*, rev. edn, 1990, p. 533.

[11] Hugh Tait, *op. cit.*, p. 91.

[12] Quoted in Robin Gwynn, *Huguenot Heritage*, 1986, p. 122.

[13] Quoted in Bernard Cottret, *The Huguenots in England*, 1985, p. 107.

[14] Quoted in *The Quiet Conquest: the Huguenots 1685–1985*, exh. cat., Museum of London, 1985, p. ix.

[15] Hayward, *op. cit.*, p. 20.

[16] Rescued from a builder's skip in the 1950s by Arthur Grimwade and Professor N.M. Penzer, the records are now in the Archive of Art and Design, Victoria and Albert Museum, London.

[17] Grimwade, *op. cit.*, p. 700.

[18] The best account is S. Hare, "Paul de Lamerie: a retrospective assessment", *Proceedings of the Huguenot Society*, Vol. XXV, no. 3, 1991; see also P.A.S. Phillips, *Paul de Lamerie, Citizen and Goldsmith of London*, 1935, and *Paul de Lamerie, the Work of England's Master Silversmith*, exh. cat., Goldsmiths' Hall, London, 1990.

[19] A photostatic copy is in the National Art Library, Victoria and Albert Museum, London.

[20] The Fitzwalter accounts include about a dozen account book entries, recording payments made to Lamerie, as well as the three bills (Essex Record Office, Chelmsford, D/DM/F13).

[21] *Armory v. Delamirie* [*sic*].

[22] Also a plain tapering coffee pot of 1730, with Crespin's mark overstriking Lamerie's, is known.

[23] Three casters sold Sotheby's, London, November 26, 1953, lot 163, and a set of three of 1746, fitting into a stand of 1742, in the Israel Museum, Jerusalem.

[24] Robert B. Barker, "De Lamerie, Gamble and Hogarth", privately circulated paper, 1988.

[25] See introduction to *The Dowty Collection*, Christie's, New York, April 22, 1993, and Timothy Schroder, "Paul de Lamerie: Businessman or Craftsman?", *The Silver Society Journal*, 6, Winter, 1994, p. 267.

[26] Christopher Hartop, "Admiral Anson and his Paul de Lamerie Silver", *Antiques*, June, 1994.

[27] Tessa Murdoch, "Harpies and Hunting Scenes: Paul Crespin, Huguenot Goldsmith", *Country Life*, August 29, 1985.

[28] Grimwade, *op. cit.*, p. 737.

[29] Arthur Grimwade, "Crespin or Sprimont? An Unresolved Problem of Rococo Silver", *Apollo*, August, 1969.

[30] Arthur Grimwade, *The London Goldsmiths 1697–1830*, rev. edn, 1990, p. 668.

[31] *Daily Advertiser*, March 5, 1745.

[32] Elizabeth Adams, "The Sites of the Chelsea Porcelain Factory", *Ceramics*, I, 1985, p. 55.

[33] White's date of death or retirement is not known; Grimwade records a John White as late as 1789 but, as he points out, this is unlikely to be the same person (Grimwade, *op. cit.*, p. 699).

[34] Christie's, London, April 19, 1996.

[35] Philippa Glanville, "Silver Torah Scrolls by Kandler" in *National Art Collections Fund Annual Review*, 1992; R Rückert, *Biographische Daten der Meißner Manufakturen*, 1990, pp. 155–6.

[36] For example, silver tureens of fluted oval form from the Kandler workshop, closely following Meissen originals, are known; one is in the Museum of Fine Arts, Houston.

[37] Arthur Grimwade suggests that Charles Frederick and Frederick Kandler were the same person, citing the identical nature of their signatures as evidence, but as the later Kandler was working until the 1770s, this seems unlikely. This Frederick may be the Carl Friedrich, son of Johann Joachim Kaendler and Johanna Salome, baptised at Fishbach, Saxony, in April, 1712 (Mormon Genealogical Index).

[38] Quoted in John Brown, *Pyramids of Pleasure*, exh. cat., Fairfax House, York, 1990, p. 37.

[39] See *Works of Art from the Bute Collection*, sale, Christie's, London, 3 July, 1996, lots 77–83; Grimwade, *op. cit.*, p. 543.

Monteith, silver, London, 1698–9, maker's mark of William Gibson, (no. 57). A typical example of the "English" school with crudely cast heads and scrolls on the rim.

Style and Designs

We have seen in the last chapter how English silver of this period must be examined in terms of styles, rather than makers' marks. Different styles often exist at the same time, making it impossible to see the period as a progression of one style to another. For example, the tradition of unadorned silver, common to most European countries in the seventeenth century, was extremely strong in England and plain silver was produced alongside highly-decorated silver, often in the same workshop, throughout the period. New decorative motifs imported from France, such as "cut-card" work, appear as early as the 1660s on items like tankards. This ornament, by which patterns are cut from sheet silver and soldered on to the flat surface of a vessel, is extremely skilful and the early English attempts are often crude. The demand for French – or what were perceived as French – fashions was insatiable among the aristocratic élite. While a few owned French silver, most had to make do with copies made in London of contemporary French work, like the wine cooler of 1718–9 (no. 60), and the pair of candelabra of 1744–5 (no. 14), or with work

Title page from *Modelles Artificiels* by Christian van Vianen.
Rijksmuseum, Amsterdam

which had French ornament. Often these French motifs are found applied to essentially English forms, like covered porringers or two-handled cups. Yet it is a mistake to see English silver of the period as being an assimilation of only French influences.

There were three quite distinct styles current in English silver during the last quarter of the seventeenth century. The "English" school was a continuation of the tradition of skilfully-chased patterns of scrolls and circles, often on thin-gauge silver, that one finds in small wares such as saucers and dishes of the first half of the century. Handles for small pieces were usually made from drawn wire, but for larger pieces, which required cast handles and borders, the technology was lacking. The monteith of 1698–9 from William Gibson's workshop (no. 57) is a good example of this native school of silversmithing. The skill in raising a hemispherical bowl by hammering, and then chasing it, albeit somewhat naively, with long scrolls, is evident, but the modelling of the heads on the rim is primitive and the casting full of faults and air bubbles. The English school is confined almost exclusively to typically English items which have no parallel in French silver, like the monteith (an invention of the 1680s), the two-handled cup and the tankard. This style declined in importance during the period, so that by the early eighteenth century it was confined to provincial makers.

Tankard, silver, London, 1686–7, maker's mark WI, probably for William Jennings (no. 56). This well illustrates what is best described as the "Germanic" school, introduced by German craftsmen who settled in England after the Restoration. Its characteristics are superior technical skill in casting and the use of continental motifs. Huguenot craftsmen who arrived at the end of the century provided an effective workforce conversant in these new techniques.

Superior technical skills are evident in another, quite distinct, style of silverware available on the London market during the same period. Best described as the "Germanic" school, its characteristics are "auricular" modellings, such as feet and handles, cast with technical brilliance. "Auricular", literally "ear-like", decoration was a development of Mannerist ornament popularized by the Dutch van Vianen family, one of whom, Christian, worked in England during the middle years of the century. Their influence extended, however, far beyond the limited number of commissions Christian carried out for the court circle, for his designs, published under the name of his father, Adam, provided English modellers with ideas for the next hundred years. Shell-like forms were utilized for cream jugs in the 1720s (such as no. 67) and sauceboats in the decade following, but perhaps most striking is the appearance, as late as the 1740s, of plastic auricular-like waves on objects like the plateau of 1749–50 (no. 47). In the 1680s, however, much of this ornament is confined to work bearing the marks of a small group of continental craftsmen working in London like Wolfgang Howzer and Jacob

Wine cooler, silver, London, 1718–9, maker's mark of David Willaume I, (no. 60). Typical of the "French" school, this is a direct copy of a Paris-made article in the monumental classical style of the later years of Louis XIV's reign.

Bodendick, although the tankard of 1686 (no. 56), which is a good example of this Germanic school, in fact bears a mark attributed to an Englishman, William Jennings. Its auricular handle and cast dolphin feet are in the tradition of Hamburg silver of the middle of the century and it is possible that there were many more continental immigrants at work in London during the period than the records show. Their technological influence was far-reaching even though the Germanic style, exemplified by this tankard, was to die out by the end of the century.

It was the "French" school which was the most pervasive influence on English silver during the period, first appearing in court circles with the Restoration. French objects, such as the "caddinet" (a receptacle for the monarch's napkin and flatware), appeared at the court of Charles II, and French ornament, like cut-card work and continuous floral embossing, started to appear in the 1660s and 1670s. The political situation made direct contact with France difficult, however, and most of these motifs appear to have come to London by way of Germany and other continental workers. The Low Countries provided the most convenient conduit for the dissemination of French style in England after the arrival of William and

Mary in 1688. The "William and Mary style" is in fact almost purely French, brought to England through the published and actual work of men like Daniel Marot. Marot, a Huguenot who had trained under Jean Berain, left France in 1685 and worked in both the Netherlands and England, producing thousands of designs in the French neo-classical court style, described as "a la manniere de France". With its intricate Berain-like patterns, contained in well-defined borders, the work of Marot is well shown by the wine cooler of 1718–9. This object is an exact copy of a French original, but for the most part English silver in the French taste assimilates French ornament rather than copying actual examples. Purely French forms, like the three-legged chocolate pot (no. 68) and the spice boxes (nos. 17 and 21) are unusual. The dearth of surviving French silver from the period, brought about by wars, revolutions and successive meltings by the monarchy, makes it difficult to form an accurate picture for comparison, but surviving work, and objects depicted in prints like the fantastical silversmith (illus. p. 42), are quite different from the silver produced in London for the gentry and upper bourgeoisie. These sections of the consumer audience continued to order tankards (a northern European form in use throughout the period), two-handled cups for display or for drinking, and monteiths and punch bowls. In addition, the new demand for wares for serving coffee, chocolate and tea was met with a host of new vessels, most of which have no stylistic parallel in contemporary French silver. These clients, who were far removed from the cosmopolitan aristocratic élite, were

Spice box, silver, London, 1721–2, maker's mark of Paul de Lamerie, (no. 21). The tradition of unadorned silver, common to most of Europe at the time, was especially popular in England and silver in this style is found with the makers' marks of Huguenot and non-Huguenot alike.

nevertheless behind the increasing demand for objects in the "new" or "French" style.

The fashion for plain silver, which existed parallel to the "schools" discussed above, continued well into the 1740s. By the first decade of the eighteenth century, geometric shapes like the square, octagon and hexagon were applied with architectural mouldings and used for functional objects like coffee pots (nos. 65 and 66) and the cruet stand (no. 19). For aristocratic patrons like the Duke of Buccleuch, these wares could be made of the highest quality with heavy cast mouldings, like the complete service for tea he ordered from Louis Mettayer and now at Boughton House, but most of the silver in this style is made of comparatively thin sheet and was therefore within the reach of clients much further down the social scale.

With virtually no ornamentation, the cost per ounce of "fashioning" this silver was less than the elaborate French-style pieces, the only additional cost being perhaps an engraved coat-of-arms. Forms taken from Oriental porcelain, like the ginger jar with its flaring shoulder, were used as models for silver objects like casters and chocolate pots but in time the "baluster" shape – essentially an inversion of the ginger jar form – was recognized as infinitely more practical.[1]

The rococo, with its asymmetry and restless movement, starts to appear in English silver in the 1730s, largely as a result of books of designs from France and Germany but also from the presence of French-made silver purchased by the international élite. At first, this new style was confined to the chased or engraved borders of salvers (no. 86), or on the rims of punch bowls (no. 64), but by 1735 there is a fluidity of outline in objects like the cake basket from John Pero's workshop (no. 29). Yet this basket, and even the one made for the Earl of Mountrath four years later in 1739–40 (no. 39), despite their sinuous curves, remain symmetrical objects and their decoration, a mixture of classical elements and auricular waves with a smattering of *rocaille*, is still basically baroque. Asymmetrical cartouches formed of shell-like scale,

Cup and cover, silver-gilt, London, 1737–8, maker's mark of John White, (no. 12). This cup is applied with rococo decoration, but the form remains baroque.

known as *rocaille*, proved to be extremely popular, either as cast ornament, or engraved onto the surface of the object.[2] The other element of rococo, naturalism, is evident in the carefully delineated lion faces, and the dolphins and other creatures, which figure so often on the silver of the late 1730s. Yet so much of the silver we regard as "rococo" is really baroque and it is not until the end of the decade that one finds a small number of objects made in London that are wholeheartedly rococo. The sauce boats (no. 38) have the lightness and movement of the true rococo, but more commonly one finds rococo motifs applied or incorporated into old symmetrical forms like two-handled cups or coffee pots.

Chinoiserie, that whimsical evocation of the Orient, had been in vogue as decoration of silver during the 1680s, when it appeared almost exclusively as flat-chased decoration on traditional forms like tankards, porringers and toilet services. It was revived in European court circles in the 1730s and was adopted enthusiastically by the English:

Pair of sauceboats, silver, London, 1739–40, maker's mark of David Willaume II, (no. 38). These are excellent examples of the true rococo style in English silver.

> Of late, 'tis true, quite sick of Rome and Greece
> We fetch our models from the wise Chinese;
> European artists are too cool and chaste,
> For Mand'rin is the only man of taste …
> On ev'ry shelf a Joss divinely stares,
> Nymphs laid on chintzes sprawl upon our chairs;
> While o'er our cabinets Confucius nods,
> Midst porcelain elephants and China gods.
>
> James Cawthorn
> *Of Taste*, 1756

Title page from Pierre Germain's *Eléments d'Orfèvrerie*, Paris, 1748. Germain's designs required less ambitious casting than Meissonnier's. His forms were used by Thomas Heming's workshop and others.

Title page from Juste-Aurèle Meissonnier's *Livre d'Ornemens*, Paris, 1744. Meissonnier's published works did much to spread rococo motifs during the period.

Detail of engraving on
tankard, London, 1686–7,
(no. 56)

Detail of engraving on
salver, London, 1702–3,
(no. 2)

Detail of engraving on casket,
London, 1704–5,
(no. 107)

Detail of engraving on
charger, London, 1713–14,
(no. 3)

Detail of engraving on
salver, London, 1723–4,
(no. 84)

Detail of engraving on
salver, London, 1724–5,
(no. 6)

By the 1740s Chinoiserie had spread down the social scale and become a
popular theme for smaller wares, usually those associated with tea and coffee,
like the tea caddies, (nos. 78, 79 and 81). Oriental scenes based on
engravings by Bernard Picart and designs by Pillement were enclosed by
auricular waves and foliate scrolls.

The decorative possibilities of engraving were exploited for the first time and
the art of heraldic engraving underwent a revolution during this period.
Hitherto heraldic engraving had been purely functional, its intention to
identify the owner or donor of an object, and it usually appears as an
afterthought wherever the decoration would allow. Larger scale objects with
plain surfaces, introduced at the end of the seventeenth century, were perfect
for elaborate engraving. We can see how the engraver moved away from the
traditional vertical emphasis, as on the tankard of 1686 (no. 56) to a much
more expansive horizontal one in which shields and supporters were often
encased in architectural cartouches, or supported on elaborate brackets.

Detail of engraving on
waiter, London, 1725–6,
(no. 85)

Detail of engraving on
salver, London, 1727–8,
(no. 86)

Detail of engraving on
basket, London, 1750–1,
(no. 49)

While we know the names of many engravers on silver during the period, very
few works can be ascribed to a particular artist; engravers on silver were part
of the complex, hidden network of outworkers who supplied the retailers. It is
a mistake, therefore, to view engraving of the time in terms of individuals, and
to try and attribute engraving to specific artists, for there are too few surviving
signed works. Initial drawings, which would be pricked onto the surface of
the object to be engraved, could be saved and re-used, as could "pulls", which
were (reversed) impressions made by rubbing ink into the design. This meant
that the same cartouches could be produced repeatedly, even by different
engravers. This, combined with the widespread use of printed pattern sheets,
means that engraving of the period must be studied in terms of schools, or
workshops, rather than individuals.

The engraving on a group of items in the Hartman Collection provides us with
a comprehensive survey of the craft during the period. The influence of
Huguenot immigrants such as the Gribelins, father and son (see p. 59), and
Blaise Gentot (see no. 107), can be seen in the rich nature of much of the
heraldic work at the end of the century. At the same time, native-born
engravers like Benjamin Rhodes, whose work is known from his order book
for Sir Richard Hoare, and Joseph Sympson, whose signature appears on a
number of engravings on silver of varying styles and quality, were becoming
bolder and more expansive in their compositions, doubtless as a result of this
Huguenot influence. An "S. Sympson" (probably a relation to Joseph)
published an undistinguished work of cyphers in 1726 which is interesting to
us today as it includes a list of engravers. It features no Huguenot names,
showing that some forty years after the initial Huguenot influx, the two
artistic communities remained quite distinct.

Engravers are seldom mentioned in contemporary records; the Jewel House
accounts record the engraving of a "parcell of plate" with no mention of who
carried out what must have been lucrative steady work of a perfunctory nature

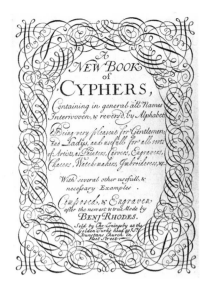

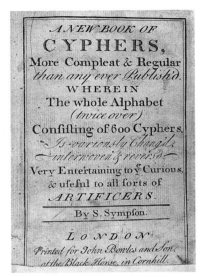

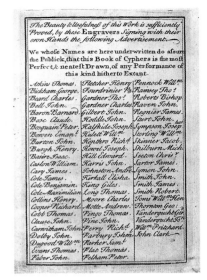

Title page from Benjamin Rhodes's *New Book of Cyphers*, early eighteenth century.

Title page from S. Sympson's *New Book of Cyphers*, published in 1726

List of subscribers to Sympson's *New Book of Cyphers*

(see no. 6). Moreover, what little evidence survives in documents and as signatures on surviving plate is often contradictory. The craft was regarded as lowly; William Hogarth wrote disparagingly of his apprenticeship to the engraver and retailer, Ellis Gamble, who must have operated a prolific workshop. Workmanlike engraving from Gamble's workshop has often been attributed to Hogarth (see no. 85) without foundation. There were many different craftsmen engraving in the same styles, and subsequent wear on silver makes it impossible to detect individual hands. Equally, there were a number of different styles in circulation at the same time and a silversmith was free to choose his engravers from the large pool available. Nonetheless, the Huguenot influence in this area is perhaps the most innovative, and enduring.

How revolutionary was the Huguenots' impact on English silver? Since Joan Evans remarked in the 1930s that "any history of the craft in England from 1680 to 1775 must chiefly concern itself with Huguenot smiths", it has usually been assumed that the Huguenots "revolutionized" the trade with their introduction of new forms and styles, as well as their technological innovations. Successive writers on English silver, in their zeal to attribute all that was new during this period of rapid growth to the Huguenots, have ignored other influences with the result that the Huguenot contribution to the silver trade has been misunderstood. It was in reality the cosmopolitan élite at the top of the social scale and not the silversmiths who set the fashions for new types of silver to meet the needs of the new "cuisine".

French forms, like the helmet-shaped ewer, and ornament like cut-card work, were already in use in England by the 1670s,[3] and the technological revolution is perhaps really due to the continental immigrants who came to London throughout the second half of the century as a result of the economic opportunities the city afforded. The vase-shaped two-handled cup, traditionally seen as a Huguenot innovation (although without a parallel in French silver) has been shown by Hugh Tait to have been an English development of the Restoration years.[4] But it is in the matter of style that the Huguenots have been perhaps most misunderstood. Severely plain silver, which dates back to the early seventeenth century and has been erroneously equated with puritanism, has often been seen as a continuing tradition in the Huguenot workshops. In reality, the dour puritans of legend may well have inveighed against luxuries and extravagant festivities, but such extremism was in reality limited to a small minority of sects which sprang up at the end of the seventeenth century. The Protestant religion had nothing to do with the fashion, which was common to most of Europe, for plain silver, and Huguenots were just as adroit at producing elaborately decorated wares. The true importance of the Huguenot "revolution" lay in its timing, for they provided a large, skilled workforce, at just the right moment, to fill new consumer demands, while their refugee status made them all the more eager to work harder and for less money than their English counterparts.

Notes
[1] Casters with flared shoulders were supplied to Paul Methuen (1672–1757) as part of his ambassadorial plate in 1714 (see Yvonne Hackenbroch, *English and other Silver in the Irwin-Untermyer Collection*, 1969, no. 132) but this form is rare compared with the more practical bellied form; similarly, ginger-jar shaped chocolate pots are known (one c. 1685 sold Christie's, New York, April 19, 1990, lot 344, another, maker's mark of John Edwards of Boston is in the Worcester Art Museum, Massachusetts). These were soon superseded by the bellied coffee, chocolate and tea pots of the early eighteenth century.
[2] Jacques de la Joue's *Second Livre de Cartouches* was published in Paris about 1735, followed by Pierre-Edme Babel's *Cartouches décorés d'une fontaine en pyramide* and, in London, Augustin Heckel's *A New Book of Sheilds*. Heckel was a German immigrant who was renowned as a gold chaser.
[3] For example a bowl and cover, given to Queen's College, Oxford, in 1670; another, of 1672, at Merton, College, Oxford; a helmet-shaped ewer of 1671–2 with cut-card work in the Ashmolean Museum, Oxford.
[4] "The Advent of the Two-Handled Cup: the Croft Cups", *Proceedings of the Silver Society*, vol. II, 1982, nos. 11–13, pp. 202–10.

A note about the arrangement of the catalogue

The objects in the Hartman Collection have been grouped according to function. The catalogue begins with a section devoted to silver intended for display and official silver issued to ambassadors and other officers of state. Even though many of these pieces are obviously functional, they are all united by the common theme of display, and even small objects in this category, like the pair of casters (no. 10), cannot be described as personal silver.

The Franks salver (no. 77), is now known to have been the stand for a kettle, and therefore it has been included in the section devoted to tea, coffee and chocolate wares.

Weights are given in troy ounces and pennyweights, the traditional way of weighing silverware. There are 20 pennyweights (*dwt*), in a troy ounce (*oz*), (and there are 24 grains in a pennyweight). The gram equivalents are given in parentheses. Weights are not given for objects in which silver is not the primary medium, but in cases where, for example, there is a wooden handle, a "gross" weight is given.

References frequently cited for makers' marks

GRIMWADE: Arthur Grimwade, *The London Goldsmiths 1697–1837*, rev. 3rd edn, 1990

HARE: Susan Hare, ed., *Paul de Lamerie: the Work of England's Master Silversmith*, exh. cat., Goldsmiths' Hall, London, 1990

JACKSON: Ian Pickford, ed., *Jackson's Silver and Gold Marks of England, Scotland and Ireland*, rev. edn, 1989

*Time, which antiquates
antiquities, and hath an art
to make dust of all things,
hath yet spared these minor
monuments.*

Sir Thomas Browne, *Urne-Burial*
Norwich, 1658

DISPLAY and
OFFICIAL PLATE

Buffet with silver vessels by François Desportes (1661–1743).
Metropolitan Museum of Art, New York, Bequest of Mary Wetmore Shively in memory of her husband, Henry L. Shively, MD, 1964 (64.315)

PAIR OF SALVERS

1

Silver (Britannia standard), gilt
Maker's mark of Andrew Moore (Grimwade, no. 2047)
Hallmarks: London, 1703–4

*Of circular form on spreading domed octagonal
bases cast and chased with a band of gadrooning
below a knop, the sockets enclosed by a calyx of
radiating alternating pointed and keyhole cut-card
straps, the rims applied with a band of gadrooning,
the centres engraved with an oval coat-of-arms
within a circular cartouche of scrolls and foliage*

Heraldry
The arms are those of Methuen, as borne by Sir
John Methuen (?1650–1706).

As personal representatives of the sovereign,
ambassadors were expected to maintain great
state while abroad. The custom of granting a
silver dinner service – or part of one – to
ambassadors and other officials sent abroad, paid
for from the sovereign's personal treasury, dates
from the sixteenth century. By the end of the
seventeenth century the size of the allowance had
been standardized when ambassadors usually
received about 5,000 ounces worth about £2,900.
These salvers form part of the service issued by
the Jewel House to John Methuen on his
appointment as Ambassador Extraordinary to
Portugal in 1703. Methuen, who had been in
Portugal as British envoy off and on since 1692,[1]
had been directed to negotiate a treaty with the
Portuguese to secure them as allies against France
in the War of Spanish Succession. This treaty was
followed – almost as an afterthought – by a
commercial one, the impact of which was to be far
greater than the military one. Signed on
December 27, 1703, it allowed the import of
English woollen goods and dried fish into
Portugal in exchange for which Portuguese

Height: 2½ in (6.5 cm)
Diameter: 10¼ in (26 cm)
Weight: 62 oz 4 dwt (1935 g)

Sir John Methuen in the robes of Lord Chancellor of Ireland by Adriaen Carpentiers (*fl.* 1739– 1778).
Methuen Collection, Corsham Court, Wiltshire

wines entered England at a favourable rate of duty equivalent to two-thirds that charged on French wines.[2]

John Methuen spent much of his life abroad. Trained as a lawyer, he had become a Master in Chancery in 1685. He interrupted his first posting to Portugal to return as Lord Chancellor of Ireland in 1697 but he seems to have spent little time there. As a loyal Whig he was the obvious candidate to settle the much-needed treaty with Pedro II. "In his complexion and manners [he was] much of a Spaniard," wrote John Macky some years after his death, "a man of intrigue, but very muddy in his conceptions and not greatly understood in anything".[3] The Tory Dean Swift was even more vituperative: "a profligate rogue without religion or morals, but cunning enough; yet without abilities of any kind".[4]

Methuen was issued with an unusually large allowance of nearly 7,000 ounces of plate to accompany him on his mission. These salvers are two of twelve "gilt knurled sallvers" weighing a total of 483 ounces delivered to him on October 25, 1703 by the Jewel House.[5] They were part of a gilt dessert service which included cutlery, plates and casters, all of which was sold by a descendant in the 1920 auction.[6] All of it is engraved, not with the royal arms, as one would expect with ambassadorial plate, but with Methuen's own. It is unlikely that Methuen would have had the royal arms removed and his own substituted and one can only assume that in view of the urgency of Methuen's mission, there was no time for the service to be engraved by the Jewel House before it was delivered to him.

The salvers bear the mark of Andrew Moore, who supplied most of the service to Samuel Swithin, the Royal Goldsmith at the time, whose duty it was to fulfil the orders on behalf of the Jewel House. Moore, the son of Samuel Moore, also a goldsmith, was admitted to the Goldsmiths' Company in June 1664. He carried out important commissions such as the celebrated silver table

presented by the City of London to William III, now in the Royal Collection,[7] and a pair of andirons made for the king in 1696.

The reverse of each salver has four small "blow" holes behind the gadrooning, to allow the hot air to escape when each salver's rim was soldered on.

Marks
Struck on reverses with hallmarks (lion's head erased, Britannia, date letter) and with maker's mark; the feet with lion's head erased and maker's mark

Provenance
Sir John Methuen (?1650–1706)
By descent to Field Marshall the Rt Hon. Lord Methuen, sale, Christie's, London, February 25, 1920, part of lot 63
William Randolph Hearst
Sold privately by his estate, c. 1965
Spink & Son Ltd, London (set of eight)
S.J. Phillips Ltd, London

Bibliography
Octagon, vol. XXIV, no. 3, October, 1987, illus. pp. 12–13

Notes
[1] There is some confusion as to the date of his first appointment; see D.B. Horn, ed., *British Diplomatic Representatives 1689–1789*, Camden Third Series, vol. XLVI, 1932, p. 95.
[2] Sarah Bradford, *The Story of Port*, 1983 edn, p. 32.
[3] John Macky, *Memoirs of the Secret Service*, 1733, p. 123.
[4] Rose Macaulay, *They Went to Portugal*, 1946, p. 217.
[5] Public Record Office, London, LC/9/44 f. 95; I am grateful to Professor Gordon Glanville for making this available to me.
[6] A pair of larger salvers from the same set is in the Untermyer Collection, Metropolitan Museum of Art, New York, no. 99.
[7] John Hayward, *Huguenot Silver, 1688–1727*, 1959, p. 59.

THE WENTWORTH PLATE

Plan for alterations at Wentworth Castle by Johann von Bodt, 1708, showing the proposed dining chamber with a display of plate.
Victoria and Albert Museum, London

Thomas Wentworth had a distinguished career as both soldier and diplomatist. Born in 1672, he entered military service at an early age and served with distinction in the campaigns in Flanders during the 1690s. In 1695 he succeeded his cousin as Baron Raby. In 1702 he was present at the battle at Helchteren, where his horse was shot from under him. Later, in 1706 at the siege of Menin, he narrowly escaped capture by the French. From 1701 until 1711 he also served on occasion as envoy to the Prussian court at Berlin and 1711 was created Earl of Strafford and sent to the United Provinces as Ambassador Extraordinary and Plenipotentiary at the Hague, where he served for three years. Strafford received a number of allowances of plate for his various diplomatic postings, and to this he added a considerable quantity of silver he purchased himself from other silversmiths, such as the salver

One of a pair of salvers, silver-gilt, London, 1705, maker's mark of Philip Rollos.
Al-Tajir Collection

Ewer, silver, London, 1702–3, maker's mark of David Willaume I.
Sotheby's, London

Ewer and dish, silver-gilt, London, 1705–6, maker's mark of Philip Rollos.
Sotheby's, London

*Thomas Wentworth, Earl of
Strafford and his family*
by Gawen Hamilton
(?1697–1737), c. 1732.
National Gallery of
Canada, Ottawa

Pair of wine coolers, silver,
London, c. 1710, maker's
mark of David Willaume I,
and ewer and basin, silver,
London, 1705, both
maker's mark of David
Willaume I.
Christie's, London

Three casters, silver-gilt,
London, c. 1705,
attributed to Philip Rollos.
Christie's, London

of 1702–3 (no. 2), and the dish of 1713–4 (no. 3),
both of which are engraved with his, rather than
the royal, arms.[1]

Strafford maintained great state while in Berlin; a
description of his household there in 1705 lists some
64 persons including a "French valet",
housekeepers, confectioner, *sommillier* [*sic*], butler,
garçon de cave, master cook, second cook, six pages,
three running footmen including a "Black a moor",
and 20 footmen among them Dutch John, French
John and Simon the Dane.[2]

Strafford was a strong Tory and fell from favour after
the accession of George I in 1714. In 1715 an
attempt was made to impeach him for his
involvement in the Treaty of Utrecht, after which he
never again held public office. During his retirement
he was an active Jacobite and in 1722 was appointed
by the Pretender, James III, as Commander-in-Chief
of all his forces north of the river Humber and
created Duke of Strafford. A few months later he was

Cup and cover, silver-gilt,
London, 1712, maker's mark
of Philip Rollos.
Sotheby's, London

Salver, silver, London,
1712, maker's mark of
Thomas Farren.
Partridge Fine Arts PLC,
London

made one of the nine Lords Regent who were charged to look after the Pretender's affairs in England until the hoped-for Jacobite invasion.[3] No Jacobite uprising occurred in the 1720s, however, and Strafford did not live to see the Young Pretender's invasion in 1745.

In 1711, Strafford married Anne Johnson, a rich heiress who, it was said, brought him a fortune of £60,000. In a paper drawn up by him at the time of his marriage, he estimated his income to be £4,000, and listed £36,000 in ready money and investments including plate and jewels worth £12,000.[4]

While ambassador to Prussia, Strafford purchased a house at Stainborough in Yorkshire and commissioned Johann von Bodt, who had been Frederick of Brandenburg's chief architect, to draw up plans for an ambitious new house to be called Wentworth Castle, which was never built. One of von Bodt's drawings shows a grandiose buffet of plate in the dining room on the ground floor.

Notes
[1] The surviving Wentworth plate includes: salver, 1702–3, maker's mark of David Willaume I, Wentworth arms as Baron Raby (no. 2); ewer, 1702–3, same maker's mark, same arms, Property of a Gentleman, Sotheby's, London, June 27, 1963, lot 52; pair of salvers, gilt, 1705–6, maker's mark of Philip Rollos, royal arms, same sale, lot 50, now Al-Tajir Collection; ewer and dish, 1705–6, maker's mark of David Willaume I, same arms, Property of a Lady, Christie's, London, May 23, 1990, lot 231; ewer and dish, gilt, 1705–6, maker's mark of Philip Rollos, same arms, Property of a Gentleman, Sotheby's, London, June 27, 1963, lot 49; set of three casters, gilt, unmarked but issued in 1705, attributed to Philip Rollos, cypher of Queen Anne, Executors of the late Mrs. A.C. Vernon-Wentworth, Christie's, London, December 8, 1994, lot 58; pair of wine coolers, arms of Wentworth impaling those of Johnson, as Earl of Strafford, c. 1711, maker's mark of David Willaume I, Property of a Lady, Christie's, London, May 23, 1990, lot 231; cup and cover, gilt, 1712–13, maker's mark of Philip Rollos, arms of Wentworth as Earl of Strafford, Property of a Gentleman, Sotheby's, London, June 27, 1963, lot 53; salver, 1712–13, maker's mark of Thomas Farren, royal arms and initials of Queen Anne, Executors of the late Mrs. A.C. Vernon-Wentworth, Phillips, London, May 24, 1994, lot 198; dish, 1712–13, maker's mark of John Bache (no. 3).
[2] J.J. Cartwright, ed., The Wentworth Papers 1689–1739, 1883, p. 17.
[3] Ruvigny, The Jacobite Peerage, 1974 edn, p. 170.
[4] The Wentworth Papers, op. cit., p. 29.

SALVER

2

Silver (Britannia standard)
Maker's mark of David Willaume I (Grimwade, no. 3192)
Hallmarks: London, 1702–3

Of circular form, on unscrewable domed circular spreading foot cast and chased with a band of gadrooning below a knopped stem, the centre of the reverse applied with a calyx of radiating cut-card foliage, the rim applied with a band of gadrooning, the centre engraved with an oval coat-of-arms within a cartouche of scrolls, foliage and fish-scale with a leopard mask below, surmounted by a baron's coronet and flanked by gryphon and lion supporters standing on a ledge hung with foliate strapwork from which is suspended a ribbon motto

The reverse with scratch weight 38 on.=10 p.

Heraldry
The arms are those of Wentworth, as borne by Thomas Wentworth, Baron Raby (1672–1739), who in 1711 was created Earl of Strafford.

A salver was defined in a 1661 dictionary as "a new peece of wrought plate, broad and flat, with a foot underneath, and is used in giving Beer or other liquid to save the Carpit or Cloathes from drops". Sir George Courthoppe, in his will of 1685 leaves "the silver servour & silver candlesticks to be my youngest daughter's by guift".[1] It is most likely that salvers like this, however, with its extravagant armorials, and the set made for Sir John Methuen (no. 1), were intended for display or to be arranged as part of a "banquet" or dessert.

Marks
The reverse struck with hallmarks (lion's head erased, Britannia, date letter) and with maker's mark

Provenance
Thomas Wentworth, Lord Raby, later Earl of Strafford (1672–1739)
Subsequent provenance unknown until anonymous sale, Phillips, London, June 2, 1989, lot 179

Note
[1] Courthoppe Papers, East Sussex Record Office, Lewes, SAS/CO/106.

Height: 2½ in (6.5 cm)
Diameter: 11½ in (29.3 cm)
Weight: 38 oz 4 dwt (1189 g)

CHARGER

3

Silver (Britannia standard), gilt
Maker's mark of John Bache (Grimwade, no. 118)
Hallmarks: London, 1713–14

Of circular form with applied gadrooned rim and broad plain border, the centre engraved with a coat-of-arms enclosed by the Order of the Garter, within a cartouche of scrolls, foliage and fish-scale with berried laurel above, surmounted by an earl's coronet and flanked by gryphon and lion supporters standing on a ledge hung with foliate scrolls and a ribbon motto

Heraldry

The arms are those of Wentworth, as borne by Thomas Wentworth, Baron Raby (1672–1739), who in 1711 was created Earl of Strafford. He was made a Knight of the Garter on October 25, 1712.

Some of the Wentworth Plate, including this dish, lay in the vaults of the London bankers Glyn, Mills & Co for over 100 years. It was first deposited at the bank in 1831 by a descendant of the earl and over the next twenty years it was withdrawn on a few occasions for the season. It returned finally to the bank in 1859 and, after the death of the owner shortly afterwards, remained in storage, unclaimed, until 1963. As a result, the condition of these pieces is remarkable. Not only is the gilding on this dish in pristine condition, but the original scribe marks made by the engraver can be seen enclosing and bisecting the armorials. The gilding has been burnished to a high polish on the plain surfaces of the dish around the circle but the arms themselves are set against a frosted background. Usually such subtle features have been lost through wear and polishing, so the exceptional state of preservation of this piece is almost unique.

John Bache was one of the signatories of the petition protesting the work of "aliens and foreigners" submitted on August 11, 1697. From his surviving work he was obviously a silversmith

Diameter: 24 in (61 cm)
Weight: 180 oz (5603 g)

of some substance and a major supplier to Samuel Swithin, the Royal Goldsmith. His maker's mark appears on a large gilt dish issued to the Earl of Lindsey in 1702,[1] as well as on a quantity of gilt plates of the same date[2] and on two jugs of 1705–6,[3] all engraved with the Lindsey arms. Bache served as Warden of the Goldsmiths' Company in 1718 and again 1722–3, and as Prime Warden in 1726.

Marks
Struck on reverse with hallmarks (lion's head erased, Britannia, date letter) and with maker's mark

Provenance
Thomas Wentworth, Earl of Strafford (1672–1739)
By descent until anonymous sale, Sotheby's, London, June 27, 1963, lot 51
The International Publishing Corporation, sale, Christie's, London, June 25, 1969, lot 114
Hilmar Reksten, Bergen, Norway
The Reksten Collection, sale, Christie's, London, May 22, 1991, lot 127

Bibliography
Sidsel Helliesen, *Hilmar Rekstens Samlinger*, 1972, illus. p. 123
Christie's Review of the Season, 1968/69, illus. p. 170
Christie's Review of the Season, 1991, illus. p. 186

Notes
[1] Public Record Office, London, LC/9/44; sold Christie's, New York, October 15/16, 1985, lot 328; Anthony Phillips, "A Royal Puzzle" in *Christie's Review of the Season*, 1986.
[2] Yvonne Hackenbroch, *English and other Silver in the Irwin Untermyer Collection*, 1969, no. 109.
[3] Sotheby's, London, November 19, 1987, lot 47.

PAIR OF SALVERS

4

Silver (Britannia standard), gilt
Maker's mark of Simon Pantin I (Grimwade, no. 2124)
Hallmarks: London, 1713–14

Of shaped circular form, each raised on three bifurcated scroll and openwork bellflower feet, the rims applied with gadrooning and strapwork moulding with stylized shells at intervals and enclosing a circular border of applied dot and dash and alternating shells and double foliate scrolls, the centres engraved with an oval coat-of-arms within a cartouche of foliate scrolls, and scalework headed by a wild mask and flanked by two serpents, with a fruit and foliate festoon below

The reverses numbered 1 and 2 and with scratch weights 74=7=0 and 74=12=0 respectively

Heraldry
The arms are those of Fetherstonhaugh of Blackesware with a baronet's badge, probably as borne by Sir Henry Fetherstonhaugh, 2nd Bt (1654–1746).

Sir Henry Fetherstonhaugh was "bred to trade"[1] and lived some years in Spain as a merchant before succeeding to the baronetcy on October 23, 1711. He was appointed Sheriff of Essex in 1713, a post which entailed expense to the holder, who was expected to entertain the county in some style. These salvers were presumably part of the plate he ordered at the time of his appointment. His arms also appear on a silver-gilt ewer of 1715 and a basin of 1714, both with the maker's mark of Paul de Lamerie.[2] He had married Anna-Maria, daughter and heiress of James Williamson, a merchant of London, although she had died at the age of twenty in 1689. He never re-married and lived until 1746 when, having outlived his two brothers and six sisters, all of whom died without issue, the baronetcy became extinct and his estates, said to be worth £400,000, passed to Matthew Fetherstonhaugh, his kinsman. Two conditions in Sir Henry's will were that his kinsman should purchase a baronetcy (which he did a few months after inheriting) and should settle in the south of England. As a result, Matthew Fetherstonhaugh purchased the estate of Uppark in Sussex from

Height: 1¾ in (4.5 cm)
Diameter: 15 in (38 cm)
Weight: 149 oz 8 dwt (4648 g)

Sir Henry Fetherstonhaugh,
2nd Bt, c. 1700.
Uppark: National Trust
Photographic Library/John
Hammond

quarrelled with the Prince of Wales and to have
retreated to Uppark, where he lived until the age
of ninety-two in 1846. He had shocked society
some years earlier by marrying one of his dairy
maids, who after his death continued to maintain
Uppark as it had been in the eighteenth century.
On her death in 1895, the house and contents
passed to the Hon. Keith Turnour, who assumed
the name and coat-of-arms of Fetherstonhaugh.
The house is now owned by the National Trust.

These salvers were intended as display pieces
rather than for use as serving trays and their
engraved arms are important elements of the
decoration. The baroque cartouches have features
taken from the printed designs of Jean Tijou, first
published in London in 1693. Tijou's ironwork at
Hampton Court and elsewhere is characterized by
its tightly scrolling acanthus leaves and its
grotesque masks, and both of these motifs figure
prominently in the cartouches.

Following contemporary taste, Sir Harry
Fetherstonhaugh purchased in 1819 a pair of
more elaborate dishes and a pair of flasks in late
seventeenth-century style.[3] All are engraved with
the Fetherstonhaugh arms in decorative
cartouches based on the printed designs of the
sixteenth-century Italian artist Stefano della Bella.
This raises the question whether the engraving on
the Pantin salvers was also added at that time.
Neither Sir Henry in 1713 nor Sir Harry in 1819
was married, so the lack of any impaled arms on
the shield does not provide a clue to the dating of
the engraving. Yet there is an immediacy to the
engraving not found on the 1819 examples and it
seems reasonable to suppose that the 1713–4
salvers provided the model from which the
engraving in 1819 was copied.

The salvers are listed in an inventory of Uppark
prepared by Gillows in 1910; they appear to have
been sold, along with other silver and furniture,
shortly afterwards.[4]

It is thought that Simon Pantin was apprenticed

Lord Tankerville in 1747 for £19,000.
Fetherstonhaugh was MP for Morpeth 1755–61,
and for Portsmouth from 1762 until his death in
1774. He married on December 24, 1726, Sarah,
only daughter of Christopher Lethieullier, a rich
Huguenot merchant, and a week later he was
created a baronet.

Matthew Fetherstonhaugh was succeeded by his
son Harry, born in 1758, who enjoyed a racy
youth and the friendship of the Prince of Wales,
later George IV. He installed Emma Hart (later to
be Emma Hamilton and best known as the
mistress of Admiral Nelson) at Uppark in the
1780s but later in his life appears to have

Detail of engraved
cartouche

Detail of an iron screen at
Hampton Court, from
Tijou's *New Booke of
Drawings*, 1693

Title page from Jean Tijou's *A New Booke of Drawings*, published in London in 1693.
Redwood Library and Athenaeum, Newport, Rhode Island, Cary Collection

to Pierre Harache the elder. By contrast to his master, though, he appears to have arrived in England destitute, for in 1682–3 he received charity for himself and family from the church in Threadneedle Street. Nevertheless, at the height of his career, he seems to have been extremely prosperous and undertook a number of major commissions. He was one of the group of Huguenot silversmiths who sent a consignment of wares to Russia in 1726.[5]

Marks

The fields struck with hallmarks (lion's head erased, Britannia, date letter) and with maker's mark

Provenance

Sir Henry Fetherstonhaugh, Bt (1654–1746)
By descent at Uppark, Sussex, until after 1910

Subsequent provenance unknown until the Hochschild Collection, sale, Sotheby's, London, November 30, 1978, lot 86
The British Rail Pension Fund, sale, Sotheby's, London, November 19, 1987, lot 48
Spink & Son Ltd, London

Bibliography

Art at Auction, 1978–9, illus. p. 385
Michael Clayton, *The Collector's Dictionary of the Silver and Gold of Great Britain and North America*, rev. edn, 1985, illus. no. 460
Vanessa Brett, *The Sotheby's Directory of Silver*, 1986, illus. no. 682
Octagon, vol. XXV, no. 1, May, 1988, illus. p. 4
Timothy Schroder, *The National Trust Book of English Domestic Silver 1500–1900*, 1988, illus. p. 299

Exhibited

Doncaster Museum and Art Gallery, 1983–7

Notes
[1] Margaret Meade-Fetherstonhaugh and Oliver Warner, *Uppark and its People*, 1964, p. 28.
[2] Offered Christie's New York, April 28, 1992, lot 263.
[3] Christie's, London, April 26, 1972, lot 20.
[4] Uppark Papers, West Sussex Record Office, Chichester, 224; I am grateful to Christopher Rowell, Historic Buildings Representative of the National Trust, for making this available to me.
[5] A tureen by him is in the Hermitage, illus. p. 104.

CUP AND COVER

5

Silver (Britannia standard)
Maker's mark of Anthony Nelme (Grimwade, no. 69)
Hallmarks: London, 1720–1

The bell-shaped body on domed spreading foot, the lower part applied with alternating vertical straps formed of foliate scrolls and bellflowers against a matted ground, with applied moulded mid-rib and two leaf-capped tubular scroll handles; the domed cover chased with an outer band of rocaille enclosing eight applied radiating straps of foliate scrolls and bellflowers against similar matting, with multi-baluster finial chased with similar rocaille; one side engraved with a baroque cartouche of scrolls and foliage flanked by birds and enclosing a crest

Heraldry

The crest, which was probably added during the nineteenth century to replace earlier engraving, appears to be that of Shuttleworth.

The Huguenot silversmiths were at one time said to have introduced the two-handled cup and cover to England, but Hugh Tait has successfully shown that it is an English development of the mid-seventeenth century and has no precedent in contemporary French silver.[1] Such cups were intended primarily for display although more modest examples were for drinking, often passed back and forth between drinkers. The form lends itself well to applied strapwork which on this cup has been enhanced by a background of matting.

Mark

Struck under base and on cover flange with hallmarks (lion's head erased, Britannia, date letter) and with maker's mark

Provenance

Anonymous sale, Christie's, London, May 23, 1990, lot 205

Note
[1] "The Advent of the Two-Handled Cup: the Croft Cups", *Proceedings of the Silver Society*, vol. II, 1982, pp. 202–10.

Height: 12¼ in (31 cm)
Width: 12½ in (31.8 cm)
Depth: 7 in (17.8 cm)

SALVER

6

Silver (sterling standard), gilt
Maker's mark of Fleurant David (Grimwade, no. 675)
Hallmarks: London, 1724–5

Of circular form with gadrooned border, the foot, which unscrews, of spreading circular form with a band of similar gadrooning, the stem with ribbed knop; the centre engraved with the royal arms

Heraldry
The royal arms are those borne by George I.

The presence of the royal arms on this salver suggests that it was issued through the Jewel House either for use in one of the royal households, or for presentation to an ambassador or other official for use during his term of office. The Jewel House accounts for the year this salver was made list few allowances of plate as no ambassadors were appointed, and it was not a coronation year. Under the heading "Christening Plate", a number of gilt cups and covers are listed, however, as gifts commemorating the birth of a royal child. One such also lists a stand which may be the present salver, now separated from its cup and cover:

1723	£	s	d
May 8			
Delv'd unto Count de Lippe as a gift for his Majtie. at the Crist. of his Child Imp: One large gilt cupp & cover & salver			
	131 - 0 - 0[1]		

By the end of the seventeenth century the word "salver" usually referred to a circular tray on a

Height: 3⅜ in (8.5 cm)
Diameter: 13 in (33 cm)
Weight: 54 oz 2 dwt (1682 g)

Detail, side view

Seal box, silver, London,
1715–6, maker's mark of
George Garthorne.
Christie's, London

central foot (see no. 2). On their own they were used for serving glasses of drink at table, but often they are found in company with a cup and cover, like the example in the Jewel House records, or as a stand for a covered porringer. In the Sackville Papers, several inventories from the Restoration period refer to a "round state dish with Cup & Cover to it", which is presumably a salver on central foot like this example.[2]

The small scale and cramped composition of the royal arms on this salver are typical of much of the plate issued by the Jewel House during the 1720s. It is in striking contrast to the much larger scale compositions of a few years before, such as that found on a seal box of 1715, with the maker's mark of George Garthorne.[3]

Fleurant David, a Huguenot, appears in the Denization Patent Roll for September 12, 1723, but it is evident he was in England by 1720. He probably worked as journeyman in the workshop of one of his fellow Huguenots until he entered

two marks, for sterling and Britannia standard, after June, 1724.

Marks

The field struck with hallmarks (leopard's head, lion passant, date letter) and with maker's mark; the foot with date letter and traces of two further defaced marks

Provenance

A Gentleman, sale, Christie's, London, February 15, 1967
Spink & Son Ltd, London

Notes
[1] Public Record Office, London, LC/9/44, f. 253.
[2] West Kent Archive Office, Maidstone, U269/E79.
[3] The Bute Collection, Christie's, London, July 3, 1996, lot 76.

BASKET

~

7

Silver (sterling standard)
Maker's mark of Thomas Farren (Grimwade, no. 2749)
Hallmarks: London, 1725–6

Of circular form on spreading foot chased with a band of radiating acanthus leaves on a matted ground, the deep everted sides pierced with diaperwork formed of scrolls and rosettes above a chased band of strapwork and stylized bellflowers on a matted ground, all between moulded borders; the fixed overhead handle, held in place by two nuts at each end, headed by twin scrolls with a knop between, applied with leaves and chased with bellflowers on a matted ground; the centre engraved with the royal arms within the Order of the Garter and surmounted by a crown

Engraved under base with scratch weight 95=15

Heraldry

The royal arms are those borne by George III after the union with Ireland in 1801, when the arms of France were removed from the 3rd quarter, but before 1816 when the electoral bonnet surmounting the arms of Hanover was changed to a crown.

Lionel Cranfield Sackville, who succeeded his father as Earl of Dorset in 1706, was a Whig grandee who held a number of posts, both political and ceremonial, during his long life. Described by his descendant, Vita Sackville-West, as "amiable rather than brilliant",[1] he appears to have made few enemies and may have owed his success to the fact that, as Lord Shelburne described him, he was "in all respects a perfect English courtier and nothing else: he never had an opinion about public affairs".[2] He was created Duke of Dorset in 1720 and in 1725 was appointed both Vice-Admiral of Kent and Lord Steward of the Household. In this last capacity he

Detail of the royal arms engraved on the centre of the basket. These were evidently added by Lord Whitworth, who used the basket, and other Sackville silver, on his diplomatic mission at the beginning of the nineteenth century.

Height: 12 in (30.5 cm)
Diameter: 12⅞ in (32.7 cm)
Weight: 94 oz 10 dwt (2941 g)

Lionel Sackville, 1st Duke of Dorset by John Wootton (?1678–1764), c. 1727. The Duke was appointed Lord Steward of the Household in 1725 and received this basket as part of his "allowance of plate" from the Jewel House.
Private collection

Detail of page from the Jewel House Delivery Book, showing the two baskets delivered to the Duke, December 14, 1725.
Public Record Office, London

received a modest allowance of plate which included this basket, one of a pair listed under the heading "Indenture Plate" in the Lord Chamberlain's accounts of the Jewel House:

1725
Dec.r. 14

Delivered to his Grace the Duke of Dorsett Lord Steward of his Majestys Household, the following Particulars
of Plate to be returned upon demand, viz.
Two Bread Basketts......w.t.   188 - 1 - 0
Four sauce boats   64 - 0 - 0[3]

The Duke served as Lord Lieutenant of Ireland from 1730 to1737 and as Lord President of the

Basket, silver, London,
1733–4, maker's mark
of Louis Laroche.
Christie's, London

1696[7] and a circular basket of about 1700, some 12¼ inches in diameter and weighing 97 ounces, is in the Portland Collection at Welbeck Abbey.[8] Only one other example of the same form as the Farren basket is known to survive from this period. It is hallmarked 1733–4 and bears the maker's mark of Louis Laroche.[9] Although they are usually referred to in contemporary accounts as "bread baskets", it is clear from contemporary pictures that they were also utilized for other things. Large-scale examples may have been used as centrepieces, dressed with a dessert, for *The Court and Country Cook*, a pirated printing in English of Massialot's great culinary work, which appeared in 1703, speaks of "a banquet of Fruits, as well Raw, as Preserved, with all its Appurtenencies, may be dress'd either upon a Level or in a Basket". The scale of this example suggests that its use was for display.

Provenance
Lionel Sackville, 1st Duke of Dorset
(1687/8–1765)
By descent to the Trustees of the Knole Settled Estates, sale, Christie's, London, May 20, 1987, lot 172

Bibliography
Octagon, vol. XXV, no. 2, Autumn, 1988, illus. p. 17

Council from 1744 to 1751. In contrast to his elevated career, Horace Walpole remarked that he "with the greatest dignity of his appearance, was in private the greatest lover of low humour and buffoonery".[4] His Duchess, whom he had married in 1708/9, owned the toilet service (no. 111).

The basket remained in the Sackville family at Knole, the family's house in Kent, after the 1st Duke's death[5] and descended to Arabella, wife of the 3rd Duke, who, after his death in 1799, married Lord Whitworth, a successful diplomatist. Whitworth served with distinction as Minister to France during the difficult time 1802–3 and he seems to have used much of the Sackville silver on his mission, having it engraved with the royal arms of George III.[6]

Silver baskets are extremely rare before the 1730s, although the 1st Earl of Bristol bought a "great silver chased baskett weighing 128 oz 4 dwt" in

Notes
[1] *Knole and the Sackvilles*, rev. edn, 1991.
[2] G.E.Cokayne, ed., *The Complete Peerage*.
[3] Public Record Office, London, LC/9/44 f. 271.
[4] *Annals of the Reign of George II*, vol. I, p. 98.
[5] The two baskets are mentioned in two eighteenth-century inventories: "An Account of the Plate June 1749" and "A List of His Grace the Duke of Dorset's Plate taken the 9th of August 1776". Sackville Papers, West Kent Archive Office, Maidstone, U269/E79.
[6] The other basket, its whereabouts unknown, seems to have left the collection some time before 1830, as an undated inventory of silver at Knole which appears to date from that time lists only one "round bread basket" weighing 89 ounces. Sackville Papers, U269/E79/9.
[7] N.M. Penzer, "The Hervey Plate at Ickworth – I, *Apollo*, February, 1957, p. 42.
[8] E. Alfred Jones, *Catalogue of the Plate belonging to the Duke of Portland*, 1935, p. 51.
[9] Christie's, London, November 11, 1992, lot 91.

THE CHESTERFIELD PLATE

A considerable quantity of plate was issued to Philip Dormer Stanhope, 4th Earl of Chesterfield, on his appointment as ambassador to the Hague in 1727. The warrant, given to the Jewel House on September 12 of that year, specified 5,893 ounces of white silver as well as a gilt dessert service weighing 1,066 ounces. The allowance was delivered on February 15 of the following year:

> Del'd to the Rᵗ. Honᵇˡᵉ. the Earl of Chesterfield Ambassador Extraordinary and Plenipotentiary from his Majesty to the States Genˡ. the underwritten Particulars of Plate to be return'd into the Jewell office upon demand ...[1]

Much of the surviving silver is in the advanced French taste of the time and, as James Lomax has observed, Chesterfield took full advantage of the fact that the Jewel House placed no limit on the amount spent on "fashioning".[2] No single workshop could have produced so much silver in so short a space of time and, moreover, John Tysoe, the King's Principal Goldsmith to whom the order was given, was not, as was customary at the time, a working silversmith, so the order was farmed out to a number of workshops. Many of the plates were produced by the Willaume workshop, while the flatware was supplied by Charles Jackson. A surviving coffee pot bears the maker's mark of Charles Kandler. The lion's share of the order, though, appears to have been given to Paul Crespin who in turn called upon the Lamerie workshop to supply the "two ice pails" weighing 388 ounces, striking his mark over Lamerie's before delivering them.[3] Unfortunately the "Aparn with all its appertinencys" weighing a total of 820 ounces does not seem to have

survived, although in 1778 the silversmiths Wakelin and Tayler charged Chesterfield's successor, the 5th Earl, for "repairing a large epergne in a great many places: boiling and burnishing".[4]

A unifying theme of the decoration of much of the Chesterfield plate is the use of gadrooned borders with cherub heads at intervals. They appear on the rims of the tureens supplied by Crespin (no. 8) and on the rim of the salvers, dishes and plates supplied by the Willaume and Le Sage workshops. Less artistic co-ordination seems to have occurred between Crespin and the Lamerie workshop since the wine coolers are considerably more elaborate, as one would expect of sideboard, rather than table, plate. The candlesticks (no. 9), like the tureens, are exact copies of contemporary French examples, and the casters that were part of the gilt "dessert service" are in the monumental classical style, with minimal ornamentation, popular in England during the first quarter of the eighteenth century.

The 4th Earl of Chesterfield is best known today as the author of the celebrated *Letters to his Son*, about which Samuel Johnson said that they "inculcated the morals of a strumpet and the manners of a dancing master". From them he appears as a fastidious francophile. His longstanding quarrels with Sir Robert Walpole and George II ultimately damaged his public career and reputation and we are therefore likely to forget that he was one of the most skilled diplomatists of the time. Chesterfield had wanted the Paris posting but he was considered too young and was sent instead to the Hague where he deftly negotiated the proposed marriage between the Prince of Orange and George II's daughter as well as the inclusion of the Dutch in the Treaty of

Phillip Dormer Stanhope, 4th Earl of Chesterfield,
unknown artist, c. 1742.
National Portrait Gallery, London

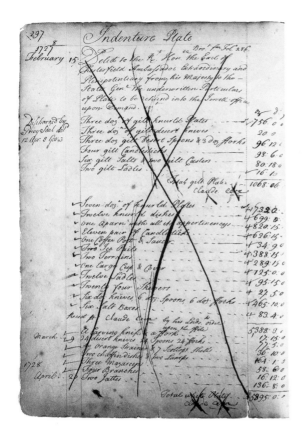

Seville.[5] While posted there Chesterfield soon acquired a reputation for splendid entertaining. In October he wrote to the Duke of Richmond, then in Paris, asking for help in acquiring a French "maître cuisinier d'un génie supérieur" who could invent "des morceaux friands et parfaits".[6] Chesterfield, like others of the cosmopolitan élite, dined *à la française* all his life. Some years after his return from the Hague, a French visitor wrote: "You know what high favour Voltaire and Montesquieu are in with the English; yesterday we drank their healths at the Earl of Chesterfield's; after a meal which was by no means philosophical, that is to say frugal; this learned Nobleman has the misfortune of having a French cook".[7] It is not surprising, therefore, that Chesterfield's table silver was copied from French prototypes.

As a *bon vivant*, Chesterfield continued to be an active patron of silversmiths after his return to England in 1730. Two rococo tureens, which are

Page from the Delivery Book of the Jewel House accounts, listing the silver delivered to Lord Chesterfield at the time of his appointment as ambassador to the Hague. The list has been crossed out, and an entry in the margin records that it was "discharged" (in other words, returned) in 1768, but as the silver evidently remained in Chesterfield's possession, it is assumed that he paid back the cash equivalent (some forty years later!).
Public Record Office, London

Pair of wine coolers, silver, London, 1727–8, maker's mark of Paul de Lamerie overstruck by that of Paul Crespin. Sotheby's, London

Part of a table service, silver, some pieces, Paris, 1740–1, maker's mark of Nicolas Touraillon, the rest, London, 1742–3 and 1749–50, maker's mark of Paul Crespin. The earl had these French spoons and forks copied in London by Crespin.
Sotheby's, New York

quite different in style from the pair issued to him in 1727, appear as part of a table setting in a plate illustrating *The Modern Cook*, a book published by his cook, Vincent la Chapelle, in 1742, and are probably depictions of examples supplied by Paul de Lamerie to the earl.[8] In 1740 Chesterfield acquired flatware from the Paris workshop of Nicolas Touraillon which he had copied by Crespin in 1742–3 and again in 1749–50.

Much of the Chesterfield plate was evidently dispersed among descendants during the nineteenth century and items have appeared frequently at auction during the twentieth century. The most significant groups were offered by Christie's, London, in 1927 and Sotheby's, London, in 1988, but the tureens and casters discussed here passed out of the family by private sale.

Notes
[1] Public Record Office, London, LC/5 and LC/9/44 f. 297.
[2] "Silver for the English Dining Room 1700–1820" in *A King's Feast*, exh. cat., London, 1991, p. 124.
[3] Much of the Chesterfield plate (but none of the items in the Hartman Collection) was sold by Sotheby's, London, February 4, 1988, lots 100–2, 104, 108, 109, 117. The wine coolers, lot 112, were purchased by Alan and Simone Hartman; an export licence was denied and the coolers were purchased for the British nation, where they are now divided between the Victoria and Albert Museum and the Royal Scottish Museum.
[4] Timothy Schroder, "The Chesterfield Knife Trays", *Partridge: Recent Acquisitions*, 1993, p. 7; the Chesterfield Plate was augmented by Wakelin & Tayler and again by Garrard's in 1826 for the 6th Earl's coming of age. For example, twenty-four dinner plates sold Christie's, New York, April 28, 1992, lot 163, and other silver sold by Sotheby's in 1988 including a pair of wine coolers made to match the pair of 1726–7.
[5] Chesterfield's most enduring legacy has proved to be his steering through Parliament of the legislation to alter the calendar which brought the British calendar in line with the rest of Europe's and moved the first day of the calendar year from March to January 1.
[6] Letter to the Duke of Richmond, October 10, 1728.
[7] Letter of Madame de Boccage, quoted in Roger Coxon, *Chesterfield and his Critics*, 1925, p. 57.
[8] Having passed out of the family in the eighteenth century, they were separated and re-engraved with new arms; one was offered by the Drury-Lowe family, Sotheby's, London, June 2, 1992, lot 186; the other is in the Metropolitan Museum of Art, New York.

PAIR OF SOUP TUREENS

8

Silver (sterling standard)
Maker's mark of Paul Crespin (Grimwade, no. 2143a)
Hallmarks: London, 1726–7

Each of oval form raised on four scroll feet terminating in stylized shells, with two double-scroll hinged handles applied with leaves, the sides applied with vertical fluted straps formed on shells and bellflowers alternating with long and short lobes, all on a matted ground; the domed covers applied with a band of conforming decoration within a dentilated border with applied winged heads at intervals, with unscrewing double-scroll handles headed by leaves; the covers engraved on one side with the royal arms within the Order of the Garter and surmounted by a crown, flanked by the initials GR

The first engraved under base No. 1 and with scratch weight 83 oz 7 dwt, also scratched R. Jones, the cover flange with scratch weight 60=11½; the second engraved under base No. 2 and with scratch weight 85 oz=3 dwt, the cover flange with scratch weight 60=18

Heraldry
The royal arms are those borne by George II.

These tureens, listed as "two terrains" weighing 289 ounces in the Jewel House warrant, are part of a handful of English examples made during the late 1720s and 1730s that seem to follow the shape of contemporary French examples, although virtually none of the latter have survived. A similar tureen, however, appears in an engraving of a centrepiece in the 1716 edition of Massialot's *Cuisinier Roial et Bourgeois*. An almost identical London-made tureen, but without the decorative borders, struck with the maker's mark of Simon Pantin (a "duty dodger") is in the Hermitage. Pantin's example has traditionally been dated about 1715 but it is clear, based on the date of the Chesterfield tureens, that it dates from the late 1720s, and was probably part of the 568 ounces of silver supplied by him as part of a large consignment of silver sent to the Russian court by a group of London silversmiths in August 1726.

Height: 10½ in (26.6 cm)
Width: 14 in (35.6 cm)
Depth: 10 in (25.5 cm)
Weight: no. 1: 137 oz 4 dwt (4269 g)
no. 2: 138 oz 14 dwt (4314 g)

Design for a centrepiece, from Massialot's *Cuisinier Roial et Bourgeois*, 1716 edition. This tureen, with candle sockets added to each end, forms part of a *surtout*.

Marks

No. 1 Struck under base and on interior of cover with hallmarks (leopard's head, lion passant, date letter) and with maker's mark

No. 2 Struck under base and on cover flange with hallmarks (leopard's head, lion passant, date letter) and with maker's mark under base

Provenance

Philip Dormer Stanhope, 4th Earl of Chesterfield (1694–1773)

Subsequent provenance unknown until E. & C.T. Koopman Ltd, London, 1989

Soup tureen, silver, c. 1726, maker's mark of Simon Pantin.
Hermitage, St Petersburg

FOUR CANDLESTICKS

9

Silver (sterling standard)
Maker's mark of Paul Crespin (Grimwade, no. 2143a)
Hallmarks: London, 1727–8

On circular spreading bases cast and chased with a band of shells and foliage on a matted ground, with circular wells, rising to knops chased with ovolo and flowerheads and octagonal vase-shaped sections chased with classical profile busts with panels of strapwork and bellflowers below, with square flanges with canted corners chased with diaperwork and with bellflowers at the corners, and campana-shaped sockets

With later removable circular nozzles with ovolo borders, struck with hallmarks for London, one 1825–6, two 1826–7, one with unclear date letter, all with maker's mark of Robert Garrard II (Grimwade, no. 2322)

Engraved under the bases with scratch weights 25=1, 24=15=2, 25=8 and 25=2=½; the nozzles stamped with numbers 11, 13, 15, and ?12

Heraldry
The royal arms are those borne by George II.

These candlesticks are copies of French originals and well illustrate the dignified classicism of the end of Louis XIV's reign. Surviving French candlesticks with vase-shaped stems decorated with profile busts date from as early as 1690–1, while candlesticks identical to the present examples appear in the printed designs of Daniel Marot dating from the beginning of the eighteenth century. The form appears in English silver by 1701, when a set of twelve was supplied by the Jewel House to Robert Harley on his appointment as Speaker of the House of Commons.[1] The English diplomatist William Bateman ordered a set from the Paris court goldsmith Nicolas Besnier in the early 1720s and commissioned copies from David Willaume on his return to England.[2] Willaume made further copies for other English clients like Lord Brudenell.[3] The form was also sold by Paul de Lamerie.[4]

These examples are part of a set of 22 furnished to Lord Chesterfield by the Jewel House in 1727/8.[5]

Height: 9 in (23 cm)
Diameter of bases: 5⅛ in (13 cm)
Weight: 104 oz 15 dwt (3263 g)

Candlestick, one of a pair,
silver, Paris, 1690–1,
maker's mark of Charles
François Croze.
Metropolitan Museum of
Art, New York, Bequest of
Catherine D. Wentworth,
1948 (48.187.249, 250)

Daniel Marot, Designs for
Silver, c. 1712.
Ecole Nationale Supérieure
des Beaux-Arts, Paris

Marks

Struck under bases with hallmarks (leopard's
head, lion passant, date letter) and with maker's
mark; the nozzles struck on flanges with lion
passant, duty mark, date letter and maker's mark

Provenance

Philip Dormer Stanhope, 4th Earl of Chesterfield
(1694–1773)
Subsequent provenance unknown until
anonymous sale, Sotheby's, London, July 26,
1945, lot 72
Asprey, London

Bibliography

Vanessa Brett, *The Sotheby's Directory of Silver*,
1986, p. 187, illus. fig. 777

Notes
[1] E.A. Jones, *Catalogue of Plate belonging to the Duke of Portland at Welbeck Abbey*, 1935, p. 60.
[2] A pair by Besnier with his arms sold Christie's, New York, October 15, 1985, lot 51; six copies by Willaume sold Parke-Bernet, New York, October 18, 1956, lot 100.
[3] A pair of 1730 sold Sotheby's, New York, February 5, 1987, lot 98.
[4] A set of four of 1733 sold Sotheby's, London, December 4, 1969, lot 246.
[5] Fourteen sold by a descendant, Christie's, London, May 11, 1927; another pair, Christie's, Geneva, April 27, 1976; another pair, sold by a descendant, Sotheby's, February 4, 1988, lot 99.

PAIR OF CASTERS

10

Silver (sterling standard), gilt
Maker's mark of Paul Crespin (Grimwade, no. 2143a), the mark on one
overstriking that of Abraham Buteaux (Grimwade, no. 8)
Hallmarks: London, 1727–8

Of octagonal form with alternating straight and incurved sides, on spreading bases of conforming outline, the lower part of the bodies applied with a bold mid-rib with winged female masks with shells above and bellflowers below, applied at the rim with moulding; the high domed covers of conforming outline, pierced and engraved with alternating panels of diaperwork enclosing oval scroll cartouches containing female profile busts, and interfaced scrolls and shells, surmounted by double-baluster finials; the sides engraved with the royal arms within the Order of the Garter surmounted by a crown and flanked by the intitials G R

Engraved under the bases with scratch weights 25=8 and 25=12

Heraldry
The royal arms are those borne by George II.

Marks
Struck under bases with hallmarks (leopard's head, lion passant, date letter) and with maker's mark

The simplicity of the octagonal shape of these casters is embellished with female masks. The reflections of their dynamic surfaces, combining flat and incurved sides, give them a baroque rhythm. They were part of the gilt "banquet" or dessert service issued to the Earl of Chesterfield in 1727/8 and would have been used for sugar, or a spice such as nutmeg which was a popular flavouring for puddings. "Six salts & 2 Casters" weighing just over 80 ounces were delivered on February 15, 1727/8. The discrepancy between the scratch weights and the actual weights of these casters may perhaps be explained by the horizontal seam which runs around the unusually long flanges to the covers, suggesting that the original flanges were damaged and replaced, thus adding to the total weight.

Provenance
Philip Dormer Stanhope, 4th Earl of Chesterfield (1694–1773)
Subsequent provenance unknown until Spink & Son Ltd, London, c. 1985
Kerry Packer

Bibliography
Octagon, vol. XXIII, no. 1, March, 1986, illus. p. 9

Height: 8⅝ in (22 cm)
Width: 2½ in (6.5 cm)
Depth: 2½ in (6.5 cm)
Weight: no. 1: 25 oz 15 dwt (803 g)
no. 2: 26 oz 2 dwt (813 g)

SOUP TUREEN

11

Silver (sterling standard)
Maker's mark of Henry Hebert (Grimwade, no. 1000)
Hallmarks: London, 1739–40

Of circular form, raised on four scroll feet applied with palmettes and terminating in stylized shells, the bowed sides applied with alternating plain lobes headed by balls and shaped straps chased with shells and bellflowers on a matted ground, with two hinged double-scroll handles capped by leaves, the everted gadrooned rim with acanthus at intervals, the domed cover with conforming applied decoration and with detachable threaded double-scroll handle capped with leaves, the rim of the cover and side engraved with the royal arms enclosed by the Order of the Garter and surmounted by a crown

Engraved under the base with scratch weight 105=12 and on cover 51

Heraldry
The royal arms are those borne by George II.

Benjamin Mildmay, Earl Fitzwalter, was a minor political figure of the time and a member of a small group of anti-Walpolean Whigs which included Lord Chancellor Hardwicke, Admiral Anson (whose will he witnessed)[1] and the Earl of Mountrath (see no. 39). He married, in 1724, Frederica, eldest daughter and co-heiress of Meinhardt, 3rd Duke of Schomberg, the famous military adventurer, and widow of the Earl of Holdernesse. Of the impending marriage, Lady Mary Wortley Montagu wrote: "My only refuge is the sincere hope that she is out of her senses, and taking herself for the Queen of Sheba and Mr. Mildmay for King Solomon" and, a few months later, "Could anyone believe that Lady Holdernesse is a beauty and in love? … [She] is tenderly attached to the polite Mr. Mildmay and sunk in all the joys of happy love, notwithstanding she wants the use of her two hands by a rheumatism, and he has an arm he cannot move. I wish I could send you particulars of the amour which seems to me as curious as that between two oysters and as well worth the serious enquiry of the naturalists".[2] As a Whig, Fitzwalter was the subject of some of

Height; 11½ in (29 cm)
Width: 13½ in (34.3 cm)
Depth: 11¾ in (30 cm)
Weight: 150 oz 10 dwt (4691 g)

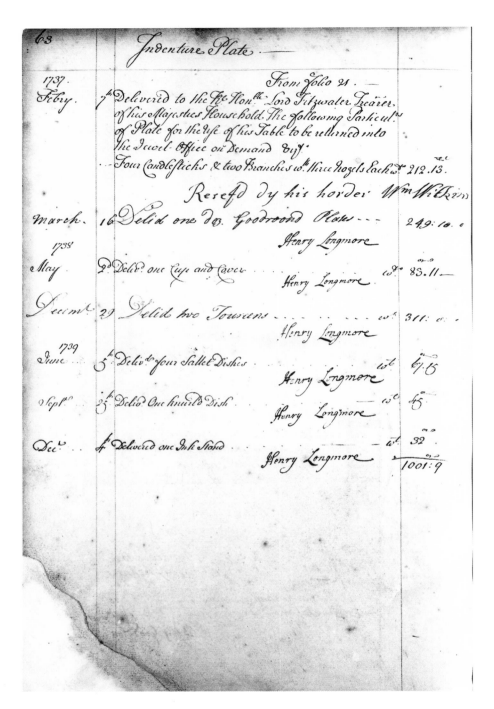

Page from the Delivery Book
of the Jewel House accounts
for February 7, 1737,
recording the delivery of
just over 1,000 ounces of
silver to Lord Fitzwalter,
Treasurer of the Royal
Household, "for the Use of
his Table".
Public Record Office, London

Dean Swift's most bitter jibes: "so avarice [sic] a wretch that he would let his own father be buried without a coffin to save charges".

Fitzwalter was not, though, parsimonious in his purchases of plate. He had bought from Paul de Lamerie a quantity of plain dishes and plates in the late 1720s[3] as well as an epergne and candlesticks. The earl's personal account books provide a wealth of information about his way of life. Time was divided between his estates in Essex and his townhouse, Schomberg House in Pall Mall, which still stands today although in somewhat altered form. There was still something medieval in the way in which eighteenth-century noblemen travelled between their estates and to and from London, for they were accompanied by numerous servants as well as most of their personal silverware. The Mildmay Accounts contain frequent references to packing and carting. A sturdy travelling case was invariably supplied with items of silver like epergnes by George Wickes and other retailers.

In 1739, Fitzwalter was appointed Treasurer of the Household and given an allowance of plate from the Jewel House which he augmented with purchases of his own. This tureen is one of the pair issued to him[4] and, like the rest of the allowance, was supplied by Henry Hebert, who was one of the seven Subordinate Goldsmiths to the Crown:

1737
Feb^{ry} 7th

    Deliver'd to the R^t. Honble. Lord Fitzwalter Treasurer of his Majesties Household The following Particulars of Plate for the Use of his Table to be returned into the Jewel-Office on Demand, viz …

The list includes four candlesticks (two with candelabra branches), a cup and cover, an inkstand, one "knurled" (i.e., with a gadrooned, or ropetwist, border) and four "sallet" dishes[5] and a dozen "gadroon'd" plates. Each item was signed

Soup tureen, silver, London 1726, maker's mark of Thomas Farren. This tureen, like Lord Fitzwalter's, follows contemporary French forms. The scroll feet cannot have provided a sturdy base like the rim foot of no. 11.
S. J. Phillips Ltd, London

as it was received by Henry Longmore, the earl's butler.[6]

Fitzwalter was somewhat dilatory in settling the incidental bills connected with his allowance of plate, for it is not until September 26, 1739 that he recorded in his personal account book:[7]

    Paid Mr. Sidwick his and the housekeeper's fees at the Jewel House for the 1000 ounces of silver plate allowed me by the King as Treasurer of his Household   £4 - 9 - 0

An inventory of the earl's silver was taken that year, entitled, "An Account of the Right Honble. the Earl of Fitzwalter's Plate taken this 22nd day of June 1739". This lists, in addition to the dishes

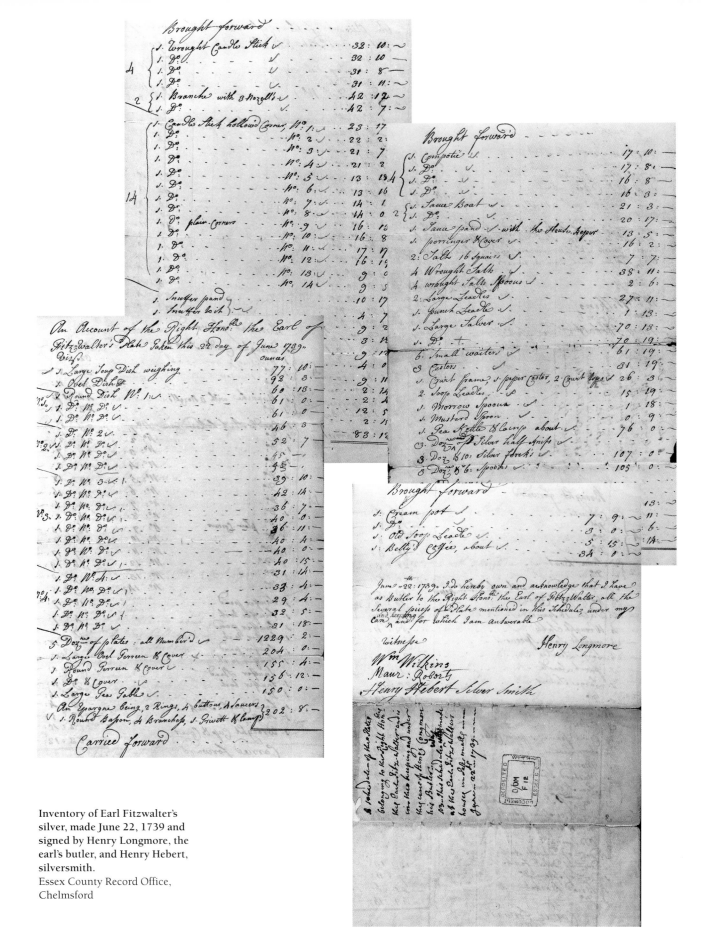

Inventory of Earl Fitzwalter's silver, made June 22, 1739 and signed by Henry Longmore, the earl's butler, and Henry Hebert, silversmith.
Essex County Record Office, Chelmsford

and plates supplied by Lamerie:

1 Large oval Terreen & Cover..	204 :	0
1 Round Terreen & Cover.......	155 :	4
1 Do. & Cover.........................	156 :	12

The present tureen is the third in the list. The inventory, which was prepared by Henry Longmore, was witnessed by William Wilkins, Maurice Roberts and Henry Hebert, "Silver Smith".[8]

On October 6, 1739 Fitzwalter went back to Hebert for "two silver ladles for the tureens, &[ca], and [paid] in full £9 19s 6d" and shortly after, on December 11, he paid Hebert for "… a silver standish weight about 50 ounces at 2s 6d per ounce fashion of which allowed at the Jewel Office 32 ounce and for what is over and above I now pay said Hebert £8 8s".

Henry Hebert, or Herbert, first entered a mark as a largeworker on January 18, 1734. His address was The Three Crowns, Corner of Hedge Lane, Leicester Fields and the three crowns appear as part of his maker's mark. Later marks registered in 1748 record a new address in Soho at The Golden Hart, St Ann's Court, Dean Street.[9] Hebert was probably a retailer, rather than manufacturer, of silver. There is no record of his apprenticeship or freedom of the Goldsmiths' Company and it has been suggested by Elaine Barr that he may be the Henry Arthur Herbert who served as treasurer to Frederick, Prince of Wales until May, 1738.[10] Henry Hebert served as Subordinate Goldsmith to the King between 1736 and 1740, a position often held by retailers or bankers rather than manufacturing smiths.[11] Although listed by Joan Evans as a Huguenot, his name is not a Huguenot one.[12] It may be that he was related in some way to Thomas-Joachim Hebert, the leading retailer of luxury goods in Paris at the time,[13] or to the Amsterdam family of silversmiths of the same name.

Marks

Struck under base and on interior of cover with hallmarks (leopard's head, lion passant, date letter) and with maker's mark

Provenance

Benjamin Mildmay, 19th Baron Fitzwalter and 1st Earl Fitzwalter (1672–1756)
Subsequent history unknown until James Robinson Inc., New York, before 1963 (a pair)
Charles E. Dunlap, sale, Parke-Bernet, New York, April 13, 1963, lot 71 or 72
Sir Michael Sobell, sale, Sotheby's, London, June 9, 1994, lot 301

Notes
[1] Christopher Hartop, "Admiral Anson and his Paul de Lamerie Silver", *Antiques*, June, 1994.
[2] To the Honourable Miss Calthorpe, December 7, 1723, and to the Countess of Mar, February, 1724.
[3] A number are in the Sterling and Francine Clark Art Institute, Williamstown, Massachusetts, others have been sold Sotheby's, New York, October 26/7, 1976, lots 404–6A; Christie's, London May 13, 1992, lot 177.
[4] The pair remained together until separated in the 1963 auction. The other is now in the Campbell Collection, Wintherthur Museum, Wilmington, Delaware and illustrated in K. Buhler, *The Campbell Collection*, no. 4.
[5] The four "sallet" dishes were sold Sotheby's, New York, October 28, 1992, lot 327.
[6] Public Record Office, London, LC/9/45 f. 63.
[7] Mildmay Accounts, Essex Record Office, Chelmsford, D/DM/A6.
[8] Mildmay Accounts, D/DM/F12; I am grateful to Beth Carver Wees for kindly giving me a copy of this inventory.
[9] Arthur Grimwade, *The London Goldsmiths 1697–1830*, rev. edn 1990, p. 542.
[10] Elaine Barr, *George Wickes, Royal Goldsmith*, 1980, pp. 140, 145; footnote to lot 301, Sotheby's, London, June 9, 1994.
[11] Major General H.W.D. Sitwell, "The Jewel House and the Royal Goldsmiths", *Archaeological Journal*, CXVII, p. 155.
[12] "Huguenot Goldsmiths in England and Ireland", *Huguenot Society Proceedings*, XIV (1929–33).
[13] Carolyn Sargentson, *Merchants and Luxury Markets: the Marchands Merciers of Eighteenth-Century Paris*, 1996, p. 20 and *passim*.

CUP AND COVER

12

Silver (sterling standard), gilt
Maker's mark of John White (Grimwade no. 1735)
Hallmarks: London, 1737–8

*Vase-shaped on shaped spreading foot elaborately
cast and chased with* rocaille *and lion masks under
a band of leaf-tied reed, the body applied with heavy
floral swags and mermaids driving chariots of sea
horses, and mermen below, with two leaf-capped
scroll handles chased with panels of foliage; the
domed cover with an outer border of leaf-tied reed,
chased and applied with foliate scrolls and* rocaille
*and swags of sea shells and surmounted by a foliate
bud finial; applied front and back with a baron's cast
armorials, the cover applied with a cast crest*

Heraldry
The arms are those of King, as borne by John, 2nd
Lord King and Baron of Ockham (1704–40).

The cup and cover are part of a large group of
plate supplied to the King family by John
White between 1728 and 1737 and sold at auction
by the family in 1993 and 1995.[1] Much of it, like
the candlesticks (no. 101), is virtually
indistinguishable from items from Paul de
Lamerie's workshop and it is possible that White,
who, judging from the relative scarcity of his
surviving work, cannot have had a large
workshop, bought much of it in finished state
from Lamerie. It may even be that White was not
a manufacturing silversmith at all but was a
retailer who obtained much of his silver from
Lamerie. That the King silver from White dates
from over a ten-year period supports that
hypothesis. It is therefore very unlikely that this
was a single major order which White had farmed
out to others, having found that he could not
complete it in his own workshop.

The decoration of this cup has many affinities
with silver from the Lamerie group (discussed in
the introduction, pp. 48–52): the floral swags,
bold *rocaille* ornament and distinctive handles are
all hallmarks of Lamerie's workshop, although the

Height: 14 in (35.5 cm)
Width: 14 in (35.5 cm)
Depth: 6½ in (16.5 cm)
Weight: 110 oz (3421 g)

rocaille on the foot is also comparable to work from Lewis Pantin's workshop (see no. 90). The plastic nature of the applied ornament is similar to silver bearing the mark of James Shruder, such as a set of tea caddies and sugar bowl supplied to the King family in 1748 (no. 80). Perhaps most importantly, the contrast between this applied decoration and the flat surfaces of the body of the cup is shared with that on the pair of wine coolers bearing the mark of Paul Crespin, supplied to the Duke of Marlborough in 1733–4 and now at Blenheim Palace.[2]

John, 2nd Lord King, was the eldest son of Peter, 1st Baron King, who had founded the family's fortunes through a brilliant legal career which had culminated, in 1725, with his appointment as Lord Chancellor. In May 1726, John King married Elizabeth, daughter of John Fry, who brought with her a large dowry. Lord Egmont spoke thus of the marriage: "My Lord [Lord Chancellor King] married her at twelve years old to his eldest son, because she was a great fortune; but she being so young, the children were only put between the bedclothes, since which, though grown up, they never consummated … My Lady King is charged by the world with influencing her husband to act in this scandalous manner. She says to everybody that her daughter-in-law is ugly, and a fool, to which the young woman replies, that they knew she was ugly before they made the marriage, and as much a fool as she is, she never showed it more than marrying Mr. King".[3] She died in 1734 and her husband, having succeeded his father in that year, died in 1740 on board HMS Ruby, off Lisbon, whither he was travelling,

Details of front and of reverse

Detail of cover

presumably because of failing health.

Marks
Struck under base with hallmarks (leopard's head, lion passant, date letter) and with maker's mark

Provenance
John, 2nd Lord King (1704–40)
Then by descent to the Earl and Countess of Lovelace, sale, Sotheby's, London, June 8, 1995, lot 113

Notes
[1] The 1995 sale cited above, and also Christie's, London, May 12, 1993.
[2] These wine coolers show signs of the marks being inserted, suggesting that they may be "duty dodgers", so the precise dating of them is impossible.
[3] *Hist. MSS Commission*, vol. I, p. 121.

PAIR OF SOUP TUREENS AND STANDS

13

Silver (sterling standard)
Total weight: 331 oz (10,295 g)

Tureens and covers:
Maker's mark of John Edwards II (Grimwade, no. 1277)
Hallmarks: London, 1740–1
Height: 8 in (20.3 cm)
Width: 14 ¾ in (37.5 cm)
Depth: 9 ⅛ in (23.2 cm)

Stands:
Maker's mark of John Parker I and Edward Wakelin
(Grimwade, no. 1602)
Hallmarks: London, 1768–9
Length: 15 in (41 cm)

Liners:
Maker's mark of John Wakelin and William Tayler
(Grimwade, no. 1764)
Hallmarks: London, 1777–8

Of oval form, raised on four scroll feet applied with leafage and headed by shells, with tied-reed rim and two double-scroll handles at each end, the domed covers chased with a band of lobes within a tied-reed band, one with cast lobster, the other with artichoke finial; the shaped oval stands with conforming decoration and tied-reed rims, engraved on one side and cover with a viscount's armorials, on the other sides with the royal arms, the stands engraved in the centre with a coat-of-arms

Heraldry

The arms on the tureens and covers are those of Harcourt, with those of Le Bas quarterly with those of Moyer on an escutcheon of pretence, as borne by Simon, 2nd Viscount Harcourt, later 1st Earl Harcourt of Stanton Harcourt (1714–77); and the royal arms as borne by George III.

The arms on the stands are those of Harcourt, as borne by Simon Harcourt as Earl Harcourt (so created in 1749).

In 1727, at the age of thirteen, Simon Harcourt, nicknamed "Precious", succeeded his grandfather, the 1st Viscount Harcourt. His early education was completed with a four-year Grand Tour of Europe and on his return in 1735 he was made a Lord of the Bedchamber, starting a close association with the royal family which lasted until his death. He married, in the same year, Rebecca, daughter and heiress of Charles le Bas, who brought him a dowry of £60,000. Harcourt was created Earl Harcourt in 1749 and was sent as ambassador to Mecklenberg-Strelitz in 1761 on the occasion of the marriage of George III to the Princess Charlotte. He held a number of court appointments and Horace Walpole spoke of him in these harsh terms: "an empty man, devoted to the Court, but diffident and complaisant".[1] After the death of his wife in 1765, he was apppointed ambassador to the French court and was given an allowance of plate to take with him. He chose,

Detail of finial

Plate from *Livre de Légumes Inventées et Dessinées Par J. Mer.* [Juste-Aurèle Meissonnier], published in Paris in 1744

Simon, 1st Earl Harcourt
by Robert Hunter
(*fl.* 1752–1803)
Private Collection

however, to use much of his own silver, such as these two tureens, sending them to George Wickes's successors, Parker and Wakelin, in early 1769 to have an additional two made to match, as well as stands for all of them. The firm in turn farmed the order out to their "outworkers", Ansill & Gilbert.[2] Harcourt also paid for the royal arms to be engraved on them: "to Eng. ... 4 King's Coats on 2 Old Terrines 1/6 ea[ch]".[3] The total cost of the refurbishment and the additional plate he commissioned came to £3,862 11s 2d, much of which was no doubt refunded to him by the Jewel House (unfortunately the relevant Jewel House accounts are not clear). In the Parker and Wakelin ledgers, we learn that the silver was sent to the Jewel House probably for weighing: "Cartage to ye Jewel Office D[itt]o back & D[itt]o to ye Inn [15s]".[4]

It is interesting to compare these tureens, which incorporate rococo elements, with the tureen made for Earl Fitzwalter just a year before (no. 11), which is firmly in the baroque classicism of French silver of some thirty years before. The Harcourt tureens follow the form of contemporary French examples, but unlike most French *soupières* or *pots-à-oilles*, they were originally supplied without stands as was

Soup tureen, silver, London,
1737–8, maker's mark of
John Edwards.
Christie's, London

customary in England, and it was not until
Harcourt's departure to France in 1769 that stands
were added. The removable liners for the tureens
were added by Harcourt in 1777: the ledgers of
Wakelin and Tayler, the successors to Parker and
Wakelin, record "4 Linings to old Terrines"
weighing 95 oz 8 dwt, at a cost of £34 19s 8d.[5]
Foliate handles were added to the stands by Hunt
and Roskell in 1863, which were removed after
the 1993 sale, restoring them to their original
condition.

Work bearing John Edwards's mark is usually
large scale and often features large cast marine
ornament such as the lobster on the cover of one
of these tureens, based on plates from Juste-
Aurèle Meissonnier's *Livre de Légumes*, which
were engraved by Huquier and published in Paris
in 1734. A similar lobster adorns a tureen from
Edwards's workshop of 1746–7 in the Campbell
Collection, Winterthur Museum, but the most
extravagant tureen from his workshop is one of
1737–8, applied with a crab, dolphins and swags
of seashells.[6]

Marks
Struck under bases, and on covers of tureens, on
reverses of stands and on rims of liners with
hallmarks (leopard's head, lion passant, date
letter) and with makers' marks

Provenance
Simon, 1st Earl Harcourt (1714–77)
By descent to the Harcourt Collection, sale,
Sotheby's, London, June 10, 1993, lots 110
and 113

Bibliography
Art at Auction, 1992–3, p. 220 (one of the pair
illustrated)

Notes
[1] G.E.Cokayne, ed., *The Complete Peerage*.
[2] Harcourt's account with Parker and Wakelin is extensively
quoted in the Sotheby's 1993 sale catalogue, which also
chronicles the earl's life in great detail.
[3] Victoria and Albert Museum, London, Gentlemen's Ledger
1765–75, GL No. 1, f. 293; I am grateful to Philippa Glanville,
Curator of Metalwork, and to Garrard's, the Crown Jewellers, for
their permission to quote from these ledgers.
[4] *ibid.*
[5] Gentlemen's Ledger 1776–82, GL No. 1, f. 278.
[6] Christie's, London, March 31, 1976.

PAIR OF CANDELABRA

14

Silver (sterling standard)
Maker's mark of John Hugh Le Sage (Grimwade, no. 1680)
Hallmarks: London, 1744–5

On spreading circular bases each raised on four splayed scroll and shell feet, cast and chased with a band of pearled ribbon-guilloches, the circular broad wells chased with panels of basketweave with anthemion on a matted ground between, rising to fluted knops supporting waisted pedestals chased with pastoral trophies and each supporting a male and female satyr holding aloft a campana-shaped socket applied with garlands of oak leaves, each with three swirling sunflower branches supporting everted foliate sockets, four with removable serrated nozzles, the pedestals and the branch flanges engraved with the royal arms within the Order of the Garter and surmounted by a crown

Numbered on sockets and branch flanges with three and four nicks respectively

Heraldry
The royal arms are those borne by George II or George III.

These candelabra are copies of examples made in the workshop of the French royal goldsmith, Thomas Germain. The model was evidently a popular one for Germain and a source of pride to him, for he chose to be depicted pointing to the model in the celebrated portrait Nicolas de Largillière painted of him and his wife in 1736.[1] Following the revolutions and upheavals in France, only a handful of examples with Germain's mark are known to have survived, all of them outside France. Two pairs were supplied by him to the Portuguese court and another pair, with Paris hallmarks for 1732–3, is now in the Detroit Institute of Arts. The latter pair was commissioned by an English patron, Sir Lionel Tollemache, for his house at Richmond.[2] Two pairs bearing the mark of Germain's son, François-Thomas, are also known.[3]

In England, Germain's model was adapted in the workshop of Charles Kandler in 1738–9.[4] Here the fauns have been replaced with Hercules and the nymph Iole. The stems are supported on heavier, shaped square bases and so lack the movement of Germain's original. In addition to the present pair, another pair of exact copies of

Height: 16¼ in (42.5 cm)
Width: 11 in (28 cm)
Depth: 11 in (28 cm)
Weight: 277 oz 4 dwt (8621 g)

Thomas Germain and his wife
by Nicolas de Largillière
(1656–1746), 1736.
Museu Calouste Gulbenkian,
Lisbon

Germain's originals is known, supplied by George Wickes to the Earl of Kildare. Wickes's ledgers record "2 fine chas'd candlesticks & branches & false nozzles" weighing 308 ounces 10 pennyweight, delivered to the earl on May 27, 1745 for a total cost of £154. The unusually high charge made for "making", at 10s per ounce, accounts for a significant portion of this cost, and is explained by the skilled work required in casting – presumably from one of Germain's originals – and finishing the figures. We can assume that John Le Sage charged a similar amount for the present pair.

Germain's model proved to be a popular one in England, for a further pair of copies was supplied by Parker and Wakelin in 1770–1[5] and the present examples provided the model for a pair of copies supplied to the 6th Duke of Leeds by Paul Storr in 1816–17[6] and a similar centrepiece of 1825, maker's mark of John Bridge.[7] Robert Garrard's firm used the same base for several candelabra during the 1820s[8] but replaced the fauns with male and female figures closely based on figural candlesticks made by the Parisian court goldsmith Etienne de Launay for Louis XIV at Versailles. A pair of late eighteenth-century bronze

Design for a caryatid stand by Jean le Pautre, perhaps from his *Nouveau Livre de Termes*, c. 1680.
Victoria and Albert Museum, London/Art Resource, New York

Corneille van Cleve (1646–1732), who is known to have designed or made models for silver furnishings at the court of Louis XIV.[9]

Figural stems used for candlesticks are common in the printed designs of Jean le Pautre (1618–82). He was influenced by Italian designers like Orazio Scoppa (c. 1607–47), who popularized groups of twisted figures incorporated into candlesticks. The present candelabra have a movement together, and lightness, which were to become the overriding themes of the rococo in the 1730s. They are typical of the tantalizingly small group of surviving silver from the workshop of the elder Germain, of whom Léonor d'Orey has commented, "He was able to marry fantasy and

One of a pair of candelabra, silver, London, 1738–9, maker's mark of Charles Frederick Kandler.
Partridge Fine Arts PLC, London

candlesticks cast from the models for de Launay's originals is in the Wallace Collection, London. These, like another pair recently on the market, have been identified by Christiane Perrin as being cast from models of "Le Grand Ballin" (the great French court goldsmith of the turn of the century), which were owned by the Germains and sold after François-Thomas's bankruptcy in the 1760s. It is tempting to attribute the fauns adorning the stems of these silver candelabra to de Launay's models of the beginning of the eighteenth century. These in turn appear to be based on designs by de Launay's brother-in-law,

Pair of candlesticks,
bronze, after de Launay
originals of 1702, late
eighteenth century.
Christie's, London

Orazio Scoppa's design
for a candlestick, 1642,
engraving.
Victoria and Albert
Museum, London

equilibrium, extravagance and solidity,
restraining the most unbridled excesses of the
rococo with a strict internal logic of a powerfully
architectural nature."[10]

It was fitting that the branches of these
candelabra, formed of sunflowers emblematic of
the sun god, Apollo, should support candles. The
sunflower was the symbol of Chlyte, who,
according to Ovid's *Metamorphoses*, was loved by
Apollo and transformed into a sunflower, forever
turning her head to follow the path of her lover,
represented here by the light shed by the
candles.[11] The male and female satyrs hold aloft
garlands of oak leaves, emblematic of hospitality,
but the true theme of these candelabra is
Arcadian love. Thomas Germain, pointing to the
model of one candelabrum in his portrait, is also
pointing to his love for his wife, shown seated at
his elbow.[12]

The presence of the royal arms on these
candelabra is a mystery. The 4th Duke of Leeds
held no ambassadorial or other official post
which would have qualified him for an allowance

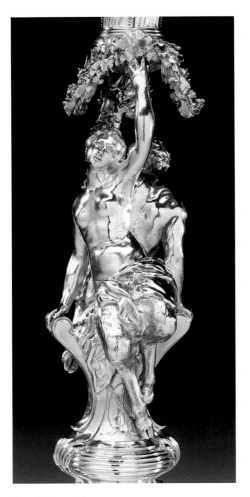

Detail of no. 14

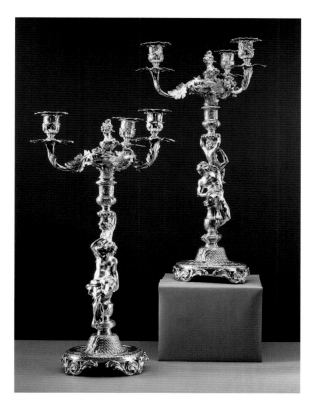

Pair of candlelabra, silver,
London, 1819–20 (bases)
and 1826–7 (branches),
maker's mark of Robert
Garrard.
Christie's, New York

was one of the Subordinate Goldsmiths to the
King at the time this plate was made[14] perhaps
makes the first hypothesis more likely, but
unfortunately the relevant Jewel House accounts
have not survived.

Marks
Struck under the bases with hallmarks (leopard's
head, lion passant, date letter) and maker's mark
(struck three times on no. 4)

Provenance
Either Thomas Osborne, 4th Duke of Leeds
(1713–89) or Francis Osborne, 5th Duke of Leeds
(1750–99)
By descent to the 10th Duke of Leeds Will Trust,
sale, Christie's, London, October 24, 1990, lot 247
E. & C.T. Koopman & Son Ltd, London

of official plate from the Jewel House. On the
other hand, his son, the 5th Duke, was appointed
ambassador to Paris in 1783 and it is possible that
these candelabra were part of a group of
secondhand official plate re-issued to the duke at
that time. Other Leeds family silver dispersed in
1983 included plates and dishes from Le Sage's
workshop, also of 1744–5 and engraved with the
royal arms, and further dishes, similarly
engraved, dating from 1783–4.[13] Another
possibility is that these candelabra and the dishes
were part of a "laying down" of plate furnished to
the 4th Duke by Le Sage in the 1740s and utilized
by his son for his embassy, much as Lord Harcourt
used his existing plate (enlarged with additions
from the Jewel House) for his Paris embassy in
the 1760s (see p. 123). The fact that John Le Sage

Notes
[1] Now in the Museu Calouste Gulbenkian, Lisbon.
[2] The first two pairs are in the Ortiz-Patiño Collection; the other
pair was sold by Tollemache's descendants in 1955, the pair is
now in the Firestone Collection, Detroit Institute of Arts.
[3] One pair is in a private South American collection. They are part
of the "Penthièvre-Orléans Service", and were all probably
supplied by Germain, along with other silver, to Louis-Alexandre
de Bourbon, comte de Toulouse (1678–1737), and described in a
1797 inventory as "avec des faunes". They were applied with the
Bourbon arms in the early nineteenth century. All four were
recorded in a Belgian collection in 1937 according to Stéphane
Boiron (see *The Lopez-Willshaw Collection*, Sotheby's, Monaco,
June 20, 1992, note preceding lot 23).
[4] Sotheby's, New York, November 3, 1989, lot 363.
[5] Now at Anglesey Abbey, Cambridgeshire.
[6] Christie's, London, March 19, 1986, lot 131, now in the Al-Tajir
Collection.
[7] Sold by the 6th Duke's descendants, Henry Spencer & Sons,
Retford, November 17, 1983, lot 364.
[8] A pair with bases of 1819–20 and branches of 1826–7, Christie's,
New York, April 18, 1991, lot 365; a pair of 1825–6 in the Gans
Collection, Richmond Museum of Art, Virginia.
[9] Peter Hughes, *The Wallace Collection, Catalogue of Furniture*,
1996, p. 1200.
[10] *The Silver Service of the Portuguese Crown*, 1990, p. 21.
[11] I am grateful to John Hardy for this interpretation.
[12] I am grateful to Ubaldo Vitali for this suggestion.
[13] Henry Spencer & Sons, Retford, November 13, 1983.
[14] Major General H.W.D. Sitwell, "The Jewel House and the Royal
Goldsmiths", *Archaeological Journal*, CXVII, p. 155.

Elegant Merrymaking by
Pieter Angellis (1685–1754).
Bridgeman/Art Resource,
New York

SILVER for the
DINING TABLE

STAND

15

Silver (sterling standard)
Maker's mark of Pierre Harache I or II (Jackson, p. 140, line 4)
Hallmarks: London, 1689–90

The base of octagonal form, cast and chased with a bold band of gadrooning, rising to a central stem, the lower part of which is applied with a calyx of cut-card stylized foliage, with rounded flange, the top of flat circular form, the underside double-walled and chased with a band of gadrooning under the edge, the centre of the top engraved with a circular coat-of-arms within laurel, fruit and scrolls and surmounted by a ducal coronet

Engraved under the base with scratch weight 58 on and with Hilmar Reksten's inventory number 101

Heraldry
The arms are, quarterly, 2 and 3, those of Seymour and, 1 and 4, the special coat of augmentation awarded to the Seymour family by Henry VIII on his marriage to Jane Seymour, daughter of Sir John Seymour, with those of the Dukedom of Brabant and Louvain quarterly with those of Percy and Lucy on an escutcheon of pretence, as borne by Charles, 6th Duke of Somerset (1662–1748).

The function of this intriguing object has been a source of speculation during the twentieth century. Michael Clayton first suggested that, because of the Duke of Somerset's role as bearer of the queen's crown at the coronation of William and Mary (which took place the year this stand was hallmarked), it may have been intended as a crown stand. While it is true that certain hereditary officers of state were allowed to claim a piece of plate for their services at the coronation and ensuing banquet, it is unlikely that Somerset would have felt he needed to keep a crown stand.[1] The diameter of the top is not wide enough to support an ermine-lined crown comfortably, which also precludes its use as a stand for the duke's own coronet, a use which was also suggested at the time.

A clue to its function is, however, to be found in the Petworth Archives.[2] Silver appears infrequently in the household accounts of Petworth, the duke's house in Sussex, as most of the entries deal with building and household expenses. (Silver would most likely have been a capital expenditure handled by the duke's bankers

Height: 3 in (7.6 cm)
Diameter: 7 in (17.6 cm)
Weight: 56 oz 10 dwt (1757 g)

and as such was unlikely to be entered in household accounts.) The present stand does not appear in the accounts, but an entry in the miscellaneous expenditure book of the duke's comptroller, John Bowen, for 1689–90 records: "… to Mr. Rogers for a stand for the Middle of a Table, weighing 68 ounces 16 d.weights at 6s-6d the ounce £221-6s-0d".[3]

In the late seventeenth century, the huge spread of food served at each course was laid out on the table on oval and circular silver dishes. Each diner then helped himself or was helped by his servant. Silver table ornaments were rare, as the elaborately decorated food itself provided the decoration. Pies and terrines were often moulded to look like their contents, adorned, for example, with feathers or even real stuffed birds' heads. Space on a dinner table was therefore at a premium, making such stands necessary to fit as many dishes as possible before the diners. Randle Holme in his *Academy of Armory* published in 1688 describes "a stand or stand for a dish … This is to set on a table full of dishes, to set another dish upon, which kind of stands, being so sett, make the feast looke full and noble, as if there were two tables, or one dish over another. These stands are made round, or six or eight squares … Now when they are thus squared, they are termed a square, or hexagon, or octagon,

stand for a dish".[4] The flat bevel along the outer edge of the top of the Somerset stand allows a dish to be placed flat on top of it, while the centre, engraved with the duke's armorials, is slightly dished to prevent wear or scratching. Its sturdiness would easily support a heavy dish holding one of the elaborate food creations of the time.

"Stands for the table" are mentioned in seventeenth-century inventories done at Knole, the house of the Sackvilles in Kent, and in October 1705 "a pair of stands" were included in a parcel of plate sent by that family to the silversmith Anthony Nelme, presumably for refashioning.[5] In 1685 the London goldsmith William Fowle supplied "2 Stands 2 Ladles and a Sett of Casters wtt 76–4".[6] A variant of the stand was the "dish ring" which appears frequently in contemporary accounts and inventories. "Three rings for the table of French pewter" were bought for the dining room at Kingston Lacey in 1693.[7] Not only did both these stands and rings allow for more dishes, but they protected the table top from heat. The natural progression was the addition of a spirit lamp to the centre of the ring, examples of which have survived in small numbers from the eighteenth century.[8] The "dish ring" enjoyed continued popularity in Ireland later in the eighteenth century.

Charles, 6th Duke of Somerset, "the Proud Duke" was born in 1662 and succeeded to the dukedom, one of the richest in England, in 1678. He made two rich marriages: the first, to Elizabeth, Countess of Ogle, took place when she was sixteen, although she had already been twice widowed. The marriage brought him Alnwick Castle, the Petworth estate, Syon House outside London and Northumberland House on the Strand.[9] She died in 1722 and the duke proposed marriage to the newly-widowed Sarah, Duchess of Marlborough: "If I were young and handsome as I was", she wrote in reply, "instead of old and faded as I am, and you could lay the empire of the world at my feet, you should never share the heart and hand that once belonged to John, Duke of Marlborough".[10] Instead, Somerset married, in 1725, Charlotte, daughter of the 7th Earl of Winchelsea.

The Duke of Somerset is perhaps best remembered as the creator of Petworth House as it appears today. During the 1680s and 1690s he built the west front in classical style; and it was at Petworth in 1703 that he played host to the King of Spain. After the elaborate formalities were concluded, supper was "served up with so much splendour and profusion, yet with so much decency and order that I never saw the like", remarked an observer.[11] As an officer of state, it was in playing such roles that he excelled; Macaulay remarked in the nineteenth century that "he was a man in whom pride of birth and rank amounted almost to a disease".[12] Horace Walpole was particularly savage, as one would expect him to be with such a staunch Tory: "His whole stupid life was a series of pride and tyranny".[13] The duke is said to have insisted that his children stood in his presence, and to have cut off the inheritance of one of his daughters after he fell asleep and woke to find her sitting down, and his second duchess, on tapping him on the shoulder with her fan, was told "Madam my

The south and west fronts of Petworth House, Sussex by an unknown artist, circa 1700.
British Library, London

Pair of candlesticks, silver,
c. 1689/90. Engraved with
the crest and coronet of the
6th Duke of Somerset.
Christie's, New York

first wife was a Percy, and she never took such
a liberty". Yet as Mark Girouard has observed,
"… the point about the Duke of Somerset was not
perhaps that he was proud but that he was old. He
lived until he was eighty-five, and died in 1750.
In the 1740s and even in the 1730s, the kind of
protocol that had reigned in 1703, when the King
of Spain came to Petworth, was beginning to
seem a little absurd".[14]

Plate made for the 6th Duke during his long life
covers the great change in style and fashion that
took place in English silver between the 1680s
and the middle years of the eighteenth century.
The bold gadrooning and emphasis on line of this
stand are typical of the ponderous classicism of
Louis XIV's reign. In contrast, a rococo soup
tureen of 1742 in the Cleveland Museum of Art
and the ladle of the same year in this collection
(no. 43) show the duke to have been an active
patron of silversmiths well into old age.

This stand bears the maker's mark attributed by
Jackson to Pierre Harache the elder, a Huguenot
who came from a long line of silversmiths in
Rouen. Unlike most of the Huguenots who
arrived in England later, Harache evidently
managed to leave France with many of his assets,

as on October 20, 1681 he is recorded as being
granted customs-free delivery of plate brought by
him from France, presumably on his arrival as an
immigrant.[15] Harache appears in the Denization
List for June 26, 1682 and was admitted,
apparently as the first Huguenot, to the
Goldsmiths' Company on July 21 of the same
year, as "lately come from France for to avoid
persecution and live quietly".[16] His mark appears
as early as 1683 on a set of candlesticks made for
Lord Spencer[17] and on a chocolate pot in a private
collection but there is considerable confusion
regarding Harache's date of death. When the
higher silver alloy known as Britannia was
introduced in 1697, a Pierre Harache entered a
new mark, but it is likely that this belonged to his
son, who was born about 1653. Heal records a
"Mrs. Harrache, silversmith", with an address in
Great Suffolk Street, in 1699, thereby suggesting
that Harache the elder was dead by that date.[18]

The Petworth Archives provide us with a clue, as
frustrating as it is tantalizing, for in the same
account cited earlier, "Mrs. Harrache" supplies a
dish weighing 39 ounces,[19] suggesting that
Harache the elder was in fact dead as early as 1690
and that his widow continued to operate the retail
shop by Charing Cross. A Pierre Harache appears
in the records of several churches as an elder
between 1689 and 1694.[20] This could be Harache
the younger who may have been in business on
his own account by 1691 when the following
entry appears in the records of Swallow Street
Church: "La coupe d'argent qui servit à la
communion a esté desrobée chez Mr. Harache par
les voleurs entrés par les fenestres de sa chambre
…",[21] while an entry in the same registers for
January 8, 1693 records a Pierre Harache giving
his daughter Fabrielle in marriage to one Antoine
Morgan, so it is possible there may have been
three generations of Pierres and the mark entered
in 1697 may be that of Pierre III.

Silver from the Harache workshop is among the
best produced during the last decades of the
seventeenth century and is characterized by its

massiveness. The use of bold cast gadroons, as on the foot of this stand, is typical. Identical gadrooning appears on a pair of unmarked candlesticks engraved with the Duke of Somerset's crest and coronet,[22] which are now here attributed to the Harache workshop and may have formed part of the same order as the present stand. By the end of the century the Haraches' gadrooning had grown considerably lighter, as for example on the feet of a pair of ewers of 1697, now at Temple Newsam House, Leeds[23] and on a box of about the same date, struck with the Britannia standard maker's mark only, at Williamsburg.[24] Both of these were made for the members of the Capel family, who were among the Haraches' richest patrons. Other families that patronized the workshop included the Dukes of Devonshire, to whom they supplied a sideboard dish and ewer (now in the Wilding Bequest at the British Museum) and a gold ewer and basin, still at Chatsworth.

John Davis has drawn attention to the distinctive style of the engraved scratch weights on pieces from the Harache workshop. This stand is engraved *58 on*, using an unusual abbreviation for ounce which also appears on the candlesticks at Althorp and on a cup of 1686 at Bruton parish church, Williamsburg, Virginia, given to the College of William and Mary in 1775.[25]

Marks
Struck under the base with hallmarks (leopard's head, lion passant, date letter) and with maker's mark

Provenance
Charles Seymour, 6th Duke of Somerset (1662–1748)
Subsequent provenance unknown until property of a Lady, sale, Christie's, London, December 16, 1904, lot 79
Mallet & Co. Ltd, London
Lord Astor of Hever
H. R. Jessop Ltd

Hilmar Reksten, Bergen, Norway
The Reksten Collection, sale, Christie's, London, May 22, 1991, lot 144

Bibliography
Michael Clayton, *The Collector's Dictionary of the Silver and Gold of Great Britain and North America*, 1985 edn, p. 86, illus. fig. 121
Christopher Hartop, "An Exceptional Year" in *Christie's Review of the Season*, 1992, p. 185, illus. pl. 188

Notes
[1] No reference to it is to be found in the Jewel House accounts.
[2] Now in the West Sussex Record Office, Chichester. I am grateful to the Earl of Egremont for permission to quote from these papers, and to Alison McCann, the Chief Archivist, for her help.
[3] "… the Accompte of John Bowen Gent. Servant to his Grace the Duke of Somerset and Payor and disbursor of sondry household payments … for one whole year endes the 29th day of March 1690", Petworth Papers, 172.
[4] Chapter 14.
[5] Sackville Papers, West Kent Archive Office, Maidstone, U269/E79.
[6] David Mitchell, "Dressing Plate by the unknown London silversmith 'WF'", *The Burlington Magazine*, June, 1993, p. 400.
[7] Sarah Paston-Williams, *The Art of Dining*, 1993, p. 195.
[8] Several examples are known by Paul de Lamerie including one of 1724 at Williamsburg (John D. Davis, *English Silver at Williamsburg*, 1976, no. 167), another of 1740, exhibited in 1956 (Houston, *Silver by Paul de Lamerie in America*, 1956, no. 42), and one of 1727 sold Christie's, New York, April 29, 1987, lot 346.
[9] G.E. Cokayne, ed., *The Complete Peerage*.
[10] Quoted in Reese, *The Royal Office of Master of Horse*, 1976, p. 207.
[11] *Annals of the Reign of Queen Anne*, 1704, vol. II, appendix 3.
[12] Lord Macaulay, *History of England*, vol. II, p. 271.
[13] Letter to Mann, December 26, 1748, *Correspondence*, vol. XX, p. 18.
[14] Mark Girouard, *Life in the English Country House*, 1978, p.182.
[15] Cal. Treasury Books 1681–5, p. 279, quoted in Hugh Tait, "London Huguenot Silver" in *Huguenots in Britain and their French Background, 1550–1850*, I. Scouloudi, ed., 1985, p. 93.
[16] Arthur Grimwade, *The London Goldsmiths 1697–1837*, rev. edn, 1990, p. 533.
[17] Formerly at Althorp; Arthur Grimwade, "Silver at Althorp – II", *The Connoisseur*, March, 1963, p. 159.
[18] Sir Ambrose Heal, *The London Goldsmiths 1200–1800*, 1935, reprinted 1972, p. 169.
[19] n. 3.
[20] These are references gleaned by Robin Glynn and first published by Hugh Tait, *op. cit.*, p. 93.
[21] *Huguenot Society Proceedings*, no. XXXV, quoted in Grimwade, *The London Goldsmiths 1697–1837*, rev. edn., 1990, p. 543.
[22] Christie's, New York, October 29, 1987, lot 520.
[23] James Lomax, *British Silver at Temple Newsam and Lotherton Hall*, 1992, no. 39.
[24] Davis, *op. cit.*, no. 211.
[25] Davis, *op. cit.*, p. 195; interestingly, it also appears on the salver of 1702 from the Willaume workshop (no. 2).

FOUR SALT CELLARS

16

Silver (Britannia standard)
Maker's mark of Thomas Prichard (Grimwade, no. 2219)
Hallmarks: London, 1701–2

Of circular form on spreading bases chased with a band of dentilation, the bowed sides with a band of bold gadrooning, with gilt wells, the undersides with traces of an erased crest

As early as 1631 the Haddon Hall accounts record the exchange of a great gilt standing salt for 4 "trencher salts" and other articles.[1] By the end of the seventeenth century the salt cellar had lost all of its former ceremonial status and was reduced to a functional object. However, superstitions surrounding salt, the gift of God, lingered on, as in the story of the marquis de Montrevel, a Marshall of France famous for his bravery, who died of fright in 1716 when a servant spilled the contents of a salt cellar over him.[2]

The word cellar is a corruption of the French word *salière*, a salt holder, so the term "salt cellar" is in fact a tautology. Small salts like these, often called "trencher" salts, were intended to be placed close to each place setting or "trencher". The Society of the Middle Temple purchased "12 Rounde Poll Salts wt. 39.2 dwt" on May 4, 1708/9 for a total of £12 13s 9d.[3]

Thomas Prichard was admitted free of the Goldsmiths' Company in 1695 and entered a mark as a smallworker in 1697. He appears to have specialized in supplying small silverware like salt cellars. Salts like this with heavy dentilation around the edges appear as early as 1694–5 on a pair from the Harache workshop.[4]

Marks
Struck under base with hallmarks (lion's head erased, Britannia, date letter) and with maker's mark

Provenance
Asprey, London

Notes
[1] H.H. Mulliner, *The Decorative Arts in England 1660–1780*, 1923, p. 101.
[2] Maguelonne Toussaint-Samat, *The History of Food*, 1987, p. 475.
[3] Treasurer's Account Book, p. 40, cited in B. Williamson, *Catalogue of Silver Plate of the Hon. Society of the Middle Temple*, 1930, p. 133.
[4] Sotheby's, London, December 4, 1969, lot 212.

Height: 1⅛ in (2.6 cm)
Diameter: 3 in (7.6 cm)
Weight: 19 oz 8 dwt (604 g)

Spice Box and Nutmeg Grater

17

Silver, the interior gilt, steel
Maker's mark of Pierre Platel (Grimwade, no. 2200)
Hallmarks: none
c. 1714

Of oval form, raised on four compressed ball feet,
with two hinged covers with cast bold dentilated rim
and removable central oval nutmeg grater with
conforming border and compressed ball finial, the
oval grater pierced, each cover opening to reveal a
gilt compartment, one with central divider, engraved
with a circular coat-of-arms within a foliate scroll
cartouche

Heraldry
The arms are those of Courtenay, probably as
borne by Sir William Courtenay (1675–1735) of
Powderham Castle, Devon.

Detail of cover

The spice box is a French form which is
extremely rare in English silver and the three
examples in the Hartman Collection show three
quite distinct styles. The compartments were
intended for salt and pepper, the latter available in
a number of varieties – often extremely costly –
during the early eighteenth century. They seem to
have been called "salt boxes" during the early
eighteenth century; "2 salt boxes" were supplied
to Sir William Irby by Edward Wakelin in 1749.[1]
Nutmeg enjoyed such a great vogue at the end of
the seventeenth century that the French poet
Nicolas Boileau wrote in *The Ridiculous Repast*:
"Do you like nutmeg? It's in everything!" Nutmeg
was also an essential ingredient of punch and
other warm alcoholic drinks.

This spice box is the only one of this form known
in English silver, although French-made examples
are common. A virtually identical box, made
in Paris in 1702–3 and with the maker's mark
of Sébastien Leblond, is in the Louvre.[2] Two
similar plain oval examples are known without
feet, both of which have the maker's mark of
Francis Garthorne.[3]

Height: 2½ in (6.4 cm)
Width: 5 in (12.7 cm)
Depth: 3¼ in (8.2 cm)
Weight: 12 oz 2 dwt (379 g)

Salver, 1714–15, maker's mark of Pierre Platel, silver-gilt. Along with the spice box, it evidently formed part of Sir William Courtenay's order to Platel in 1714–15.
British Museum, London

This spice box probably formed part of the Courtenay family's same order of silver from Platel's workshop which included a silver-gilt salver, now in the British Museum, with hallmarks for 1714–15 and Platel's mark.[4] The engraving of the arms and surrounding cartouche is virtually identical. On such a small item as a spice box Platel obviously avoided paying the duty, striking his mark on it but omitting to send it to Goldsmiths' Hall for assay along with the rest of the order. The Courtenay arms also appear on a series of four silver-gilt hexagonal dishes with elaborate chased borders after designs by Stefano della Bella, two of which are in the Gilbert Collection.[5]

Sir William Courtenay was MP for Devon and married Lady Anne Bertie, daughter of the Earl of Abingdon in 1704.

Pierre Platel, born in 1664, was the youngest son of Jean-Baptiste Platel du Plateau of Erize St Dizier near Bar Le Duc, Lorraine. He arrived with his brother in the train of William III in 1668. He was made freeman of the Goldsmiths' Company by order of the Court of Aldermen on June 14, 1699. His best-known apprentice was Paul de Lamerie.[6]

Spice box, maker's mark of Sébastien Leblond, Paris, 1702–3, silver.
Louvre, Paris, Collection Puiforcat/RMN, Martine Beck-Coppola

Marks
Struck with maker's mark on interior

Provenance
Probably Sir William Courtenay (1675–1735), subsequent provenance unknown until Anonymous sale, Ader Tajan, Paris, March 28, 1995

Notes
[1] Sotheby's, London, June 13, 1983, lot 46, where the entry in Wakelin's Gentlemen's Ledger is cited.
[2] Collection Puiforcat, OA 9645.
[3] Christie's, London, June 25, 1975.
[4] British Museum, MLA1969, 7-5, 26.
[5] Timothy Schroder, *The Gilbert Collection of Gold and Silver*, 1988, no. 35.
[6] Information from Miss K. Christmas, quoted in S. Hare, "Paul de Lamerie: a retrospective assessment", *Huguenot Society Proceedings*, XXV, no. 3, 1991, p. 220.

SIX SHELL-SHAPED DISHES

18

Silver
Maker's mark of John Bache (Grimwade, no. 118)
Hallmarks: none
c. 1718

Realistically raised and chased as scallop shells,
with flutes and matting

Provenance
Possibly Sir John Curzon, 3rd Bt (d. 1727)
Then by descent to the Viscount Scarsdale and the
Kedleston Trustees, sale, Christie's, London,
March 7, 1990, lot 180
S.J. Phillips Ltd, London

Shell-shaped dishes appear in documents in the early seventeenth century. In 1637 the Goldsmiths' Company Court Minutes listed "6 scallop shell dishes" among the plate earmarked for the melting pot.[1] Several silver examples survive from the end of the seventeenth century[2] but this set appears to be the only surviving between the 1690s and 1727. In that year the Earl of Chesterfield received "sevon scallop shells" as part of his allowance of plate on his appointment as ambassador to the Hague (see pp. 98–101). Shells start to appear in increasing numbers in the 1730s and are quite common from the second half of the century.

The function of shell-shaped dishes has caused confusion among silver scholars. "Butter shells", the name given them by twentieth-century dealers and auction-house cataloguers, seems more likely to reflect a modern-day adaptation. In an inventory made for the 2nd Duke of Beaufort at Badminton in 1705 there is listed a sweetmeat stand with seven dishes and "mustard saucers" but we do not know what these looked like.[3] Two mid-eighteenth century epergnes are known

Height: 1¼ in (1.3 cm)
Width: 4¾ in (12 cm)
Depth: 4¾ in (12 cm)
Weight: 25 oz (778 g)

which are fitted with shell-shaped dishes,[4] while the ledgers of the silversmith George Wickes record that John Trevor purchased "5 scollops for oysters" in 1740. This function is borne out by the inventory of the possessions of Jean-Baptiste Oudry, the painter, done in Paris in 1755, which lists *"quatre coquilles pour accommoder les huîtres"*.[5] It seems most likely that dishes like these were not used for serving raw oysters, but for minced oysters or other shellfish, probably pickled, which would be placed around a table as side dishes. For example, Lord Fermanagh and his family at Claydon in Buckinghamshire received a shipment of assorted seafood from the coast. They were "highly feasted" and "put half of them into pickle".[6] "Caveached" fish was another popular way of serving shellfish during a period when effective refrigeration was difficult.

As these dishes are struck only with Bache's maker's mark, and lack hallmarks, it is impossible to date them precisely, although they cannot date after 1720 when Bache entered a new, sterling standard, maker's mark at Goldsmiths' Hall. It is possible that these dishes were ordered by Sir John Curzon, 3rd Bt, when he inherited Kedleston and the family estates in Yorkshire in 1718. He sat as MP for Derby from 1701 until his death in 1727.

Marks
Struck with maker's mark on valves

Notes
[1] *Paul de Lamerie, the Work of England's Master Silversmith*, exh. cat., Goldsmiths' Hall, London, 1990, p. 120.
[2] A set of c. 1675 is on loan to the Royal Scottish Museum; a set of ten of 1675, maker's mark of Samuel Hood, is in the Al-Tajir Collection; others by Hood are recorded.
[3] A.J.H. Sale, "Records of Plate of the Beaufort Family", *The Silver Society Journal*, 7, Autumn, 1995, p. 387.
[4] One is in the Chicago Art Institute, the other in the Hermitage.
[5] H. Havard, *Dictionnaire de l'Ameublement*, 1880, p. 972.
[6] Sara Paston-Williams, *The Art of Dining*, 1993, p. 149.

CRUET STAND

19

Silver (Britannia standard), glass
Maker's mark of Charles Adam (Grimwade, no. 25)
Hallmarks: London, 1718–19

Raised on three bun feet supporting a superstructure flanked at the front with two octagonal stopper holders, the centre with a partly-fluted baluster stem and double ring handle; fitted with three octagonal baluster casters with pierced covers, and two bottle-shaped cut-glass bottles with faceted silver covers; the larger caster engraved with a circular coat-of-arms within a foliate scroll and shell cartouche surmounted by a crest, the rest engraved with the same crest

Heraldry
The arms are those of Bathurst quartering those of Horden, probably as borne by Edward Bathurst (1680–1772) of Wilmington, and subsequently Finchcocks, Kent .

Marks
Struck on top of frame and under bases of casters with hallmarks (lion's head erased, Britannia, date letter) and with maker's mark; flange of larger caster, bottle covers and handle with lion's head erased and maker's mark, smaller caster covers with maker's mark struck twice

The idea of grouping various casters and condiment jars into one stand dates back to the early seventeenth century, although virtually none have survived from before the end of the century (see p. 31) By the time this cruet stand was made, fashionable tables of the aristocracy would have been furnished with a *surtout*, or centrepiece, fitted with cruet stands for oil and vinegar (such as no. 22), but multi-purpose cruet stands like this example became a common feature of the dining tables of the gentry and prosperous middle class during the early part of the eighteenth century. Owing to their functional nature, few have survived intact.

Edward Bathurst was a descendant of Paul Bathurst of Horsmanden, Kent who married Elizabeth, the daughter and co-heiress of Edward of Horden, in 1568. Bathurst inherited the manor of Finchcocks from his uncle and rebuilt it "at great expense in the most stately manner", according to Hasted in his *History of Kent*. He was a Senior Bencher of the Middle Temple and died on August 1, 1772.

Provenance
Anonymous sale, Christie's, Australia, September 4, 1992, lot 539

Height: 8¼ in (21 cm)
Width: 6 in (15.2 cm)
Depth: 7 in (18 cm)
Weight (without bottles): 42 oz (1345 g)

SIX SALT CELLARS

20

Silver (Britannia standard)
Maker's mark of Benjamin Pyne (Grimwade, no. 2245)
Hallmarks: London, 1719–20

Height: 2 in (5 cm)
Width: 4¼ in (11 cm)
Depth: 3¾ in (9.5 cm)
Weight: 67 oz 14 dwt (2108 g)

Of massive rectangular form with canted corners,
the spreading sides cast and chased with a band of
gadrooning, rising to everted rims formed of ovolo

Rectangular salts with cut corners were popular during the first half of the eighteenth century but most modest examples were made from thin sheets of silver. By contrast these salts are cast and are of exceptional size and weight. Sets of salt cellars were popular from the seventeenth century onwards, enabling one to be placed in front of, or between, diners, but few sets of six have remained intact.

Benjamin Pyne was one of the most successful of the native English silversmiths of the period. He was apprenticed to the German immigrant craftsman, George Bowers, and made Free of the Company in 1676. His clients included Samuel Pepys, to whom he sold "a chocolate dish" in 1685. He was Subordinate Goldsmith to the King for the coronation of George I and served as Prime Warden of the Goldsmiths' Company in 1725 but at the end of his life he seems to have suffered a reversal of fortunes, for in 1727, when he must have been seventy-five, he petitioned the Company for the

post of beadle, and after his death in 1732 his children applied to the Company for charity as they were destitute and although "educated … not brot. up to any business".[1]

Doubtless due to his early training in Bowers's workshop, Pyne's work incorporates bold moulding, cast components and generous use of silver, all trademarks of the German immigrant school. From the work bearing his mark it is clear that he must have employed Huguenots and other immigrants as journeymen in what must have been a workshop of considerable scale.

Marks
Struck under bases with hallmarks (lion's head erased, Britannia, date letter) and with maker's mark

Provenance
Anonymous sale, Sotheby's, London, October 22, 1970, lot 206
An Iowa Collector, sale, Christie's, New York, April 29, 1987, lot 527
S.J. Phillips Ltd, London

Bibliography
Vanessa Brett, *The Sotheby's Directory of Silver*, 1986, p. 146, illus. no. 538

Note
[1] Grimwade, *The London Goldsmiths 1697–1837*, rev. edn, 1990 p. 635; Benjamin Pyne has been the subject of considerable research by E.J.G. Smith, publication forthcoming.

SPICE BOX

21

Silver (Britannia standard), the interior gilt, the exterior with traces of gilding
Maker's mark of Paul de Lamerie (Hare, no. 2)
Hallmarks: London, 1721–2

Of rectangular form with sloping sides and canted corners, raised on four scroll feet applied with stylized shells and terminating in oval pads, the cover with two hinged covers, each engraved with a border of birds, shells and amorini *supporting baskets of fruit, the centres with a crest, each interior compartment divided in two*

Heraldry
The crest is that of Howard, probably as borne by Thomas Howard, 8th Duke of Norfolk (1683–1732).

The solid, plain appearance of this spice box is enlivened by the bands of characterful engraving around the covers, based on designs by Daniel Marot. Nude cherub figures feature also in the printed designs of Simon Gribelin, which enjoyed great success at the beginning of the eighteenth century.

This box was probably one of the "4 Salt boxes" which are listed as part of the *surtout*, or centrepiece "containing Table, Body and Basonm, 2 sets of Castors, 4 saucers, 4 Branches, 4 Pans, 4 Nosels, 4 salt boxes, 4 Crewet Stands, 4 Crewet

tops with Handles, 2 Mustard Spoons" weighing a total of 807 ounces listed in an inventory of the Norfolk plate done after the death of Edward, 9th Duke of Norfolk in 1777. The centrepiece, and its smaller companion, must have appeared totally out of fashion by this date and were no doubt part of the old silverware given to Rundell and Bridge, the Royal Goldsmiths, after the death of the 10th Duke in 1815 in part payment for an extensive dinner service in the latest taste, struck with the maker's mark of Paul Storr, much of which remains at Arundel Castle.

Paul de Lamerie supplied George Treby with "2 Doble Salts for ye Surtout" weighing 27 oz 10 dwt in 1721[1] which were probably similar to this spice box. The only other spice boxes known bearing Lamerie's mark are a pair dating from 1727.[2]

Marks
Struck under the base with hallmarks (lion's head erased, Britannia, date letter) and with maker's mark

Provenance
Apparently Thomas Howard, 8th Duke of Norfolk (1683–1732)

Height: 2¼ in (5.6 cm)
Width: 5 in (12.2 cm)
Depth: 3¼ in (8.2 cm)
Weight: 14 oz 10 dwt (451g)

By descent to Edward, 10th Duke of Norfolk
(1720–1786)
Subsequent provenance unknown until the Earl
of Ducie, sale, Christie's, London, October 7,
1959, lot 86
H.J. Oppenheim, Esq., sale, Christie's, London,
May 13, 1964, lot 131
S.J. Shrubsole, Ltd, London
A Private collection, sale, Sotheby's, New York,
April 6, 1989, lot 218

Detail of cover

Notes
[1] P.A.S. Phillips, *Paul de Lamerie, his Life and Work*, 1935, p. 47.
[2] J. Ortiz-Patiño Collection, illustrated in *Paul de Lamerie, the Work of England's Master Silversmith*, exh. cat., Goldsmiths' Hall, London, 1990, no. 47.

OIL AND VINEGAR STAND

~

22

Silver (sterling standard), gilt
Maker's mark of Paul Crespin (Grimwade, no. 406)
Hallmarks: London, 1723–4

Formed of two square frames with canted corners, joined together and raised on four scroll and pad feet, the sides pierced and engraved with continuous foliate scrolls flanked by ewers and enclosing female masks, baskets of fruit or a wild mask, with ribbed side handle; fitted with two facet-cut colourless glass club-shaped bottles each with applied octagonal neck mount engraved with alternating panels of diaperwork, stylized foliage and fretwork, with scalloped leaves below, the hinged domed covers with conforming decoration and ball finials, each with a ribbed scroll handle

Frames like this originally formed part of a centrepiece or *surtout de table* similar to the centrepieces of 1730–1 and 1742–3 illustrated on p. 33. The Kirkleatham centrepiece of 1731, struck with the makers' marks of David Willaume II and Anne Tanqueray, now at Temple Newsam House, Leeds, still retains its original oil and vinegar bottle frames akin to the present example, in addition to a central soup tureen and six spice, or sugar, casters. Additionally, it is fitted with branches that can alternately hold candle sockets or circular dishes. Some cruet frames still retain the bracket underneath that held them in place on a centrepiece, such as an example of 1723–4

with the maker's mark of Lamerie. Perhaps the most extraordinary "centrepiece" or domestic cruet stand is of 1721–2, also with the mark of Crespin, at Colonial Williamsburg. This is in the form of a square tray fitted at each corner with two mounted glass bottles similar in form to those of the present example alternating with two octagonal casters. The centre is fitted with a spice box with double-hinged cover.

A similar cruet stand of the same date and with Paul Crespin's maker's mark is known[1] while others with Paul de Lamerie's mark are at Ickworth, made for the Hervey family in the same year, and one of 1727–8 in the Ashmolean Museum, Oxford. The superb quality of the engraving and piercing on this example, however, is exceptional. The wild masks which alternate with the female faces are decidedly whimsical.

Marks
Struck under base with hallmarks (leopard's head, lion passant, date letter) and with maker's mark

Note
[1] *Works of Art from the Bute Collection*, sale, Christie's, London, July 3, 1996, lot 99.

Height: 8¼ in (21 cm)
Width: 5¾ in (14.6 cm)
Depth: 4¾ in (12.2 cm)
Weight (without bottles): 17 oz (529 g)

Detail of piercing

PAIR OF SAUCEBOATS

23

Silver (sterling standard)
Maker's mark of Augustine Courtauld (Grimwade, no. 385)
Hallmarks: London, 1725–6

Of oval double-lipped form on spreading oval bases, with scalloped moulded rims, each long side with two waisted multi-scroll handles; each one engraved on the side between a spout and handle with a coat-of-arms within foliate scroll and fish-scale mantling surmounted by a stylized shell

Heraldry
The arms are those of Mills impaling those of another.

Augustine Courtauld, born in 1685–6, was the son of Augustine Courtauld, merchant of St Pierre in the Ile d'Oleron. Tradition has it that the young Augustine was smuggled into England by his family in a basket of vegetables. He was apprenticed to Simon Pantin in 1701 and was made Free of the Goldsmiths' Company in 1708. His workshop produced mostly domestic plate of high quality, of which these sauceboats, based on French originals, are a typical example.

A pair of sauce boats of similar form of 1724–5 and 1727–8, with the same maker's mark, was sold by Sotheby's, New York, June 16, 1988, lot 216.

Marks
Struck under bases with hallmarks (leopard's head, lion passant, date letter) and with maker's mark

Provenance
Lord Hillingdon, sale, Christie's, London, June 21, 1933, lot 62
William Comyns & Son Ltd, London
Anonymous sale, Sotheby's, London, November 17, 1988, lot 96
S.J. Shrubsole Corp., New York

Height: 4⅜ in (11 cm)
Width: 9¼ in (23.5 cm)
Depth: 7¾ in (19.7 cm)
Weight: 38 oz 4 dwt (1190 g)

SET OF THREE CASTERS

24

Silver (Britannia standard)
Maker's mark of Paul de Lamerie (Hare, no. 3)
Hallmarks: London, 1725–6

Comprising a large and pair of smaller examples,
each of octagonal baluster form on spreading
octagonal bases; the high domed octagonal covers
pierced and engraved with alternating panels of
foliate scrolls and bellflowers and diaperwork
enclosing, on the larger, draped masks and baskets
of flowers and, on the smaller, with profile heads,
each with octagonal baluster finial; engraved on one
side with a coat-of-arms within an asymmetrical
foliate and scroll cartouche with rocaille *below and*
surmounted by a bishop's mitre, and on the other
side with the initials AR in script

The larger with scratch weight 25=12 and No. 2;
the smaller examples with 13=14, No. 2 and 14=3,
No. 3; the covers numbered 2, 1 and 2 respectively

Heraldry
The arms are those of the See of Oxford impaling
those of Secker, as borne by Thomas Secker
(1683–1768), Bishop of Oxford from 1738
to 1758.

Initials
The initials are those of Archibald Philip
Primrose, 5th Earl of Rosebery (1847–1929).

Thomas Secker was born in 1683 at Sibthorpe,
Nottinghamshire and was first destined for a
medical career, studying medicine in London and
Paris. In 1723, however, he was ordained and two
years later married Catherine, sister of the Bishop
of Gloucester. In 1732 he was made a Chaplain to
the King, largely through the influence of Sarah,
Duchess of Marlborough. He became Bishop of
Bristol in 1734 and was translated to Oxford in
1737. In large part Secker owed his success to his
diplomacy and his friendship with George II. The
Dictionary of National Biography describes Secker
as "a favourable specimen of the orthodox
eighteenth-century prelate". He was in favour of
granting the episcopate to the American colonies
and in 1753 he, rather half-heartedly, supported
the repeal of the Jews' Naturalization Bill. In 1758
he was created Archbishop of Canterbury. The
arms on these casters were added between 1738
and 1758 during the time of his episcopacy at
Oxford and were most probably added in 1745, as

Height of largest: 9 in (23 cm)
Width: 3½ in (9 cm)
Depth: 3½ in (9 cm)
Weight: 50 oz (1568 g)

Salver, silver, London,
1745–6, maker's mark of
Paul de Lamerie, engraved
with the arms of Thomas
Secker, as Bishop of Oxford.
Al-Tajir Collection

Thomas Secker (as Archbishop of Canterbury), artist unknown, c. 1765.
National Portrait Gallery, London

Dish, silver, London, 1730–1, maker's mark of Paul de Lamerie, engraved with the arms of Thomas Secker as Bishop of Oxford.
Christie's, London

in that year Secker purchased a large salver from Lamerie's workshop, also engraved with his arms impaled by his see.[1] Secker died in 1768.

How Secker's casters entered the Rosebery collection is not recorded but they may have been acquired by the 5th Earl, whose collecting activities during the last century are well known.

Two sets of octagonal casters from Lamerie's workshop, of 1723–4, were made for the 1st Earl of Bristol and are at Ickworth, Suffolk.[2]

Marks
Struck under bases with hallmarks (lion's head erased, Britannia, date letter) and with maker's mark; the cover of the larger caster with lion's head erased and maker's mark

Provenance
Thomas Secker (1683–1768), Bishop of Oxford (1738–58), Archbishop of Canterbury (1758–68)

Subsequent provenance unknown until Archibald Philip Primrose, 5th Earl of Rosebery (1847– 1929)
5th Earl of Rosebery's Trust Settlement, sale, Sotheby's, London, February 28, 1991, lot 207

Notes
[1] The salver is now in the Al-Tajir Collection, London, and was previously sold Sotheby's, New York, June 4, 1974, lot 68 and again Christie's, Geneva, May 13, 1986, lot 132; *The Glory of the Goldsmith*, Christie's, London, 1990, exh. cat., no. 93; other Lamerie silver engraved with Secker's arms includes a fluted dish of 1730–1, Sotheby's, London, June 20, 1974, lot 190 and resold Christie's, London, July 10, 1996, lot 180 and a sweetmeat basket of 1745–6 in a private collection.
[2] *Paul de Lamerie: the Work of England's Master Silversmith 1688–1751*, exh. cat., Goldsmiths' Hall, London, 1990, no. 42; a single example of 1724 was sold Sotheby's, New York, December 13, 1984, lot 138.

PAIR OF SAUCEBOATS

25

Silver (Britannia standard)
Maker's mark of Paul de Lamerie (Hare, no. 3)
Hallmarks: London, 1729–30

Of oval form on spreading oval bases, engraved under the scalloped rim with panels of diaperwork and bellflowers on a matted ground enclosing female portrait busts in oval cartouches, under the lip with a shell, and above the lip with similar diaperwork and a bellflower, each with a multi-scroll handle headed by engraved diaperwork; each on one side engraved with a coat-of-arms within a foliate scroll cartouche flanked by demi-putti holding bellflowers

Numbered under the bases 7 and 11

Heraldry
The arms are those of Rudge impaling those of Reynardson, as borne by the Reverend Benjamin Rudge (b. 1684).

Benjamin Rudge was Rector of Thornshugh, Northamptonshire. He married in 1714, as his second wife, Elizabeth, daughter of Jacob Reynardson of Bristol, who bore him five sons. The Reynardson arms appear, impaling those of another, on a salver from the Lamerie workshop.[1] They appear impaled by those of Staughton on a pair of casters, also with Lamerie's mark, of 1728–9.[2]

The style of the engraving around the lips of these sauceboats, incorporating heads within cartouches, has often been called "Hogarthian". Heads of this type do appear in the engravings of William Hogarth and they seem to be typical of the output of the workshop of his former master, Ellis Gamble, with whom Lamerie was in partnership between 1723 and 1728 (see p. 49).

Marks
Struck under bases with hallmarks (lion's head erased, Britannia, date letter), with maker's mark

Provenance
The Reverend Benjamin Rudge (b. 1684)
Subsequent provenance unknown until Crichton Bros. Ltd, London, c. 1929
Anonymous sale, Christie's, London, December 12, 1930, lot 57
S.J. Phillips Ltd, London, c. 1980

Exhibited
25 Park Lane, London, *Loan Exhibition of Old English Plate*, 1929, cat. no. 188

Notes
[1] P.A.S. Phillips, *Paul de Lamerie, his Life and Work*, 1935, plate LV.
[2] Christie's, New York, April 17, 1996, lot 191.

Height: 4 in (10.2 cm)
Width: 7¾ in (19.5 cm)
Depth: 3¾ in (9.5 cm)
Weight: 24 oz 12 dwt (765 g)

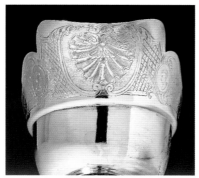

Detail of engraving

BASKET

26

Silver (Britannia standard)
Maker's mark of Paul de Lamerie (Hare, no. 3)
Hallmarks: 1731–2

Of oval form, the sides realistically pierced and chased to resemble basketweave with ropetwist and tied-reed at the shoulder, the foot pierced with ovolo within tied-reed bands, with two handles formed of ropetwist, the interior engraved with a continuous pattern of diaperwork divided into four parts by foliate strapwork enclosing bellflowers, the centre engraved with a coat-of-arms within foliate scroll mantling

Engraved under the base with scratch weight 41=5

Heraldry
The arms are those of Maxwell of Pollock House, Renfrewshire.

The small number of silver baskets made before the 1730s all tend to be large in scale (such as no. 7), although Lamerie's workshop as early as 1724–5 produced a pair of this much lighter form for George Baillie of Jerviswood.[1] Lamerie produced a large number of the same form at the beginning of the 1730s,[2] including some with a swing handle.[3] The whole group is characterized by the fine quality of the engraving to the interior which incorporates arms within a broad band of interlacing or brickwork.

Without any impalement, it is not possible to be sure to which member of the Maxwell family these arms pertain. Sir John Maxwell, 1st Bt, died July 4, 1732 and was succeeded by his cousin, John Maxwell, and it is tempting to assume that this basket is part of plate ordered at the time of John Maxwell's succession. The absence of a baronet's badge, however, is puzzling.

Mark
Struck under the base with hallmarks (lion's head erased, Britannia, date letter) and with maker's mark

Provenance
Anonymous sale, Phillips, London, October 19, 1990, lot 201
E. & C.T. Koopman Ltd, London

Notes
[1] One is in the Minneapolis Institute of Arts, cat. no. 4; the other was sold Sotheby's, London, July 18, 1974, lot 263.
[2] One made for Sir Robert Walpole, in the Gilbert Collection; at Ickworth; Goldsmiths' Company, London; Ashmolean Museum, Oxford; Duke of Devonshire, Chatsworth, and a pair in the Metropolitan Museum of Art, New York.
[3] The Dowty Collection, sale, Christie's, New York, April 22, 1993, lot 54; one, formerly in the Rothermere Collection, and one sold from the collection of Archer M. Huntington, Anderson Galleries, New York, March 5–6, 1926, lot 219.

Height: 3⅛ in (8. cm)
Width: 13 in (33 cm)
Depth: 9¼ in (23.2 cm)
Weight: 40 oz 4 dwt (1253 g)

PAIR OF SAUCEBOATS

27

Silver (sterling standard)
Maker's mark of George Wickes (Grimwade, no. 918)
Hallmarks: London, 1731–2

Of oval form, on spreading oval feet cast and chased with a band of palmettes, applied under the scalloped rims with alternating vertical straps of foliate scrolls and shells, with leaf-capped multi-scroll handles, engraved under the lips with a crest and viscount's coronet

Engraved under the bases with the numbers 1 and 2 and with scratch weights 18 12 and 19 0 respectively

Heraldry

The crest and coronet appear to be those of a Viscount Combermere, a title created in 1827.

These sauceboats are almost totally baroque in feeling, the only suggestion of the rococo being the gentle undulation of the rims but the effect of even this is perfect symmetry. The applied straps, which had first appeared at the beginning of the century, must have seemed a little old-fashioned by the 1730s.

Marks

Struck under bases with hallmarks (leopard's head, lion passant, date letter) and with maker's mark

Provenance

S.J. Shrubsole Corp., New York, c. 1955
Mrs. R.M. Robertson, Cambridge, Ontario, sale, Christie's, New York, October 27, 1987, lot 432

Exhibited

New York, Art Treasures Exhibition, 1955, no. 12, exhibited by S.J. Shrubsole Corp., New York
Royal Ontario Museum, Toronto, *English Silver*, 1958, no. G13, exhibited by Mrs R.M. Robertson

Bibliography

Elaine Barr, *George Wickes, Royal Silversmith* 1980, p. 87, illus. fig. 45

Height: 4½ in (11.5 cm)
Width: 8¾ in (22 cm)
Depth: 4½ in (11.5 cm)
Weight: 35 oz (1091 g)

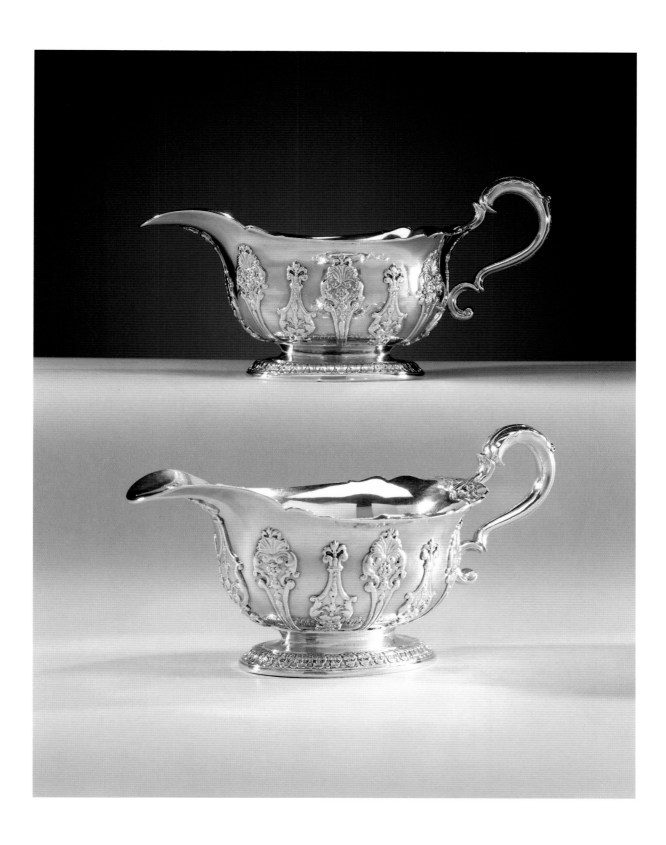

FOUR FLUTED DISHES

28

Silver (sterling standard), gilt
Maker's mark of Paul Crespin (Grimwade, no. 2143a)
Hallmarks: London, 1734–5

Of circular form with scalloped rims, each chased with eighteen flutes, the interior of the rim engraved with alternating panels of interlaced strapwork on a matted ground and trelliswork enclosing pateræ, the centres engraved with an oval coat-of-arms within a tied foliate branch cartouche surmounted by a basket of flowers

The reverses numbered 1 to 4 and with scratch weights 21=1½, 20=18, 20=16½ and 21=2 respectively

Heraldry
The arms are those of Edgcumbe, probably as borne by Richard Edgcumbe (1680–1758).

Richard Edgcumbe was the son of Sir Richard Edgcumbe of Mount Edgcumbe, Cornwall. He succeeded his brother to the family estates in 1694 and sat as an MP from 1701 until his elevation to the peerage as Baron Mount Edgcumbe in 1742. In 1715 he had married Matilda, daughter of Sir Henry Furnese. She died in 1721, which explains the absence of any impalement on the coat-of-arms.

Circular fluted dishes of this form are often called "strawberry" dishes but this is most likely a name they acquired in the nineteenth century. In the Wickes ledgers, such dishes are often called "sallet dishes", sallet referring in the eighteenth century to cooked, as well as raw, vegetables.

In 1800 Lord Mount Edgcumbe's son, who had been created Earl of Mount Edgcumbe in 1789, decided to have these outmoded "sallet" dishes form the basis of a gilt dessert service from Wickes's successors, the fashionable firm of Wakelin and Garrard, who refurbished and gilded the dishes and used them as the model to make a further six in the same taste[1] as well as two "small

Height: 2 in (5 cm)
Diameter: 9¾ in (24.6 cm)
Weight: 73 oz (227 g)

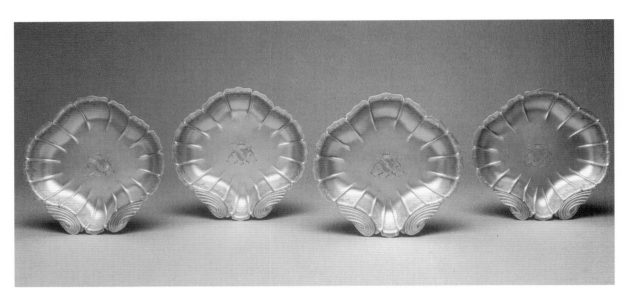

Four shell-shaped dishes, silver-gilt, London, 1800–1,
maker's mark of Wakelin & Garrard, engraved with
the same arms.
Christie's, New York

Detail of coat-of-arms

basons & covers with partitions and stands" which also match the decoration of these dishes.[2] The earl's account with the silversmiths, in their Gentlemen's Ledger which forms part of the Garrard ledgers now in the Victoria and Albert Museum, records the following:

Earl of Mount Edgcumbe[3]

	Oz	£	s	d
1800 Feb\y 8				
To 2 Escallop dishes with rich chased borders	42-	28	14	-
To 4 Shell shaped ditto	73.7	47	13	6
To engraving 6 coats, Suppr. & Corts		2	2	0
To smoothing and polishing four old dishes			10	0

Earl of Mount Edgcumbe[4]

To amount brought from Folio 11				
1800 Feb\y 8				
To gilding the new dishes in the best manner in two colours		28	15	-
d\o the old	80.15	14	-	-

Gilding "in two colours" appears regularly in the ledgers of Wickes and his successors. It was done to highlight engraved decoration, and in the case of these dishes and the Patiño set it is possible to see a different colour in the gilding over the arms and the panels of decoration in the flutes.

Marks
Struck on reverses with hallmarks (leopard's head, lion passant, date letter) and with maker's mark

Provenance
Probably Richard Edgcumbe (1680–1758)
By descent to Richard, Earl of Mount Edgcumbe (1720–95)
Subsequent provenance unknown until Lord Sieff, c. 1970
Spink & Son Ltd, London

Notes
[1] Four were sold from the collection of the late Antenor Patiño, Christie's, New York, October 28, 1986, lot 23.
[2] Christie's, London, July 12, 1995, lot 97.
[3] Victoria and Albert Museum, Gentlemen's Ledger, GL 21AS f. 11.
[4] *ibid* f. 13.

BASKET

29

Silver (sterling standard)
Maker's mark of John Pero (Grimwade, no. 1571)
Hallmarks: London, 1735–6

Of shaped oval form on spreading foot with flat rim, the foot and sides pierced and engraved with alternating panels of foliate scrolls and diaperwork enclosing stylized rosettes, applied each end with a cast bearded male mask issuing from an asymmetrical rocaille cartouche, the long sides applied with similar cartouches enclosing a later coat-of-arms, the corner panels with asymmetrical cartouches engraved with a coat-of-arms, with rosette border and everted rim cast and chased with foliage and scrolls, the shaped swing handle engraved with a band of trellis

Heraldry

The arms in the corner panels are those of Palffy of Erdőd, Hungary; the later arms are those of Vachell with those of Lloyd on an escutcheon of pretence.

This basket is a good example of the unusual form and bold ornament that characterizes work from Pero's workshop. A candelabrum of 1733 in the form of a blackamoor is in the Royal Scottish Museum, Edinburgh[1] which, like the vigorous heads on this basket, shows that Pero, or someone working for him, was an accomplished modeller. A similar head appears on a silver-gilt ewer of the same year as this basket which was supplied, with its accompanying basin, by George Wickes to Bristol Corporation, and it may be that both Wickes and Pero used the same modeller. The head is reminiscent of a river god[2] which one would expect to adorn a ewer, but its presence is puzzling on a bread basket, where Ceres, the goddess of harvest would be more likely (see no. 39).

The arms of the Hungarian family of Palffy of Erdőd appear on a number of London-made pieces of silver dating from the eighteenth century,[3] The family descended from Paul Palffy III of Dereszika who married Calire, daughter of Nicholas Bakács of Erdőd, at the end of the fifteenth century. The Vachell arms appear to have

Height: 11 in (28 cm)
Width: 12¾ in (32.5 cm)
Depth: 11 in (28 cm)
Weight: 90 oz (2799 g)

Detail of applied mask

Detail of piercing

Detail of arms on applied
cartouche

been added at the beginning of the nineteenth
century.

Marks
Struck under base with hallmarks (leopard's head,
lion passant, date letter) and with maker's mark

Provenance
The Executors of the late Dr Julius Grant, sale,
Sotheby's, London, June 10, 1993, lot 421

Notes
[1] A1963.453.
[2] Elaine Barr, "The Bristol Ewer and Basin" in *Art at Auction*,
1982–3, p. 287.
[3] Two flagons, one 1710–11, maker's mark of Edmund Pierce,
Royal Scottish Museum, Edinburgh (A1956.1382); the other
1742–3, Thomas Whipham, Sotheby's, London, October 15,
1970, lot 45; an oval dish, 1730–1, Anne Tanqueray, in *Silver at
Partridge*, October, 1991; twelve dinner plates, 1788–9, Fogelberg
and Gilbert, Sotheby's, New York, November 23, 1989, lot 307.

PAIR OF SAUCEBOATS

30

Silver (sterling standard)
Maker's mark of Paul de Lamerie (Hare, no. 4)
Hallmarks: London, 1735–6

Cast as shells, each on four ribbed scroll feet terminating in quatrefoils, the handles formed as dolphins with their tails entwined in a scroll that forms the lower part, engraved each side with a circular coat-of-arms within a foliate scroll and rocaille cartouche

Engraved under bases with scratch weights 22 × 3 and 21 × 2

Heraldry

The arms are those of Congreve impaling those of Stawell, as borne by Ralph Congreve (d. 1775).

Interestingly, not only do Ralph Congreve's arms impale the Stawell arms, but they also appear on an escutcheon of pretence, as one would expect in view of the fact that Congreve married an heiress. She was Charlotte, daughter of William, 3rd Lord Stawell. This marriage brought Congreve considerable estates in Hertfordshire. The arms appear on a waiter struck with Lamerie's mark of the same year as these sauceboats, in the Gilbert Collection,[1] a lobed salver of 1744–5 also from Lamerie's workshop,[2] and a two-handled cup and cover of c. 1670, which was presumably

Detail of handle

Height: 5 in (12.7 cm)
Width: 8¼ in (21 cm)
Depth: 4¾ in (12.1 cm)
Weight: 41 oz 10 dwt (1291 g)

Sauceboat, one of a set of
four, silver, London,
1738–9, maker's mark of
Paul de Lamerie.
Christie's, New York

engraved during the 1730s or 1740s.[3]

Paul de Lamerie's workshop produced a small
number of sauceboats of this form during the
1730s. Like the cream jug from Willaume's
workshop (no. 67), their use of undiluted
auricular forms found in the designs of the van
Vianen family sets them somewhat apart from
English silver of the period. Some (for example, a
pair of sauceboats of 1738, illustrated above),
have the addition of a Bacchic mask under the lip
which has nothing to do with the van Vianens.
These, like another pair of the same date formerly
in the Swaythling Collection, have dolphin
handles more closely based on the van Vianen
originals[4] but the individuality of the dolphins on
the present sauceboats, and the way in which
their tails entwine the scrolls at the bottom of the
handles, are the works of a virtuoso.

Marks
Struck under bases with hallmarks (leopard's
head, lion passant, date letter) and with
maker's mark

Design for a bowl from
Modelles Artificiels by
Adam van Vianen,
engraved by Theodora van
Kessel, Utrecht, 1650.
Victoria and Albert
Museum, London

Provenance
Ralph Congreve (d. 1775)
Subsequent provenance unknown until E. & C.T.
Koopman Ltd, London, 1990

Notes
[1] Timothy Schroder, *The Gilbert Collection of Gold and Silver*,
1988, no. 55.
[2] Illustrated in P.A.S. Phillips, *Paul de Lamerie, his Life and Work*,
1935, pl. CXLIV, now in the Al-Tajir Collection.
[3] Christie's, New York, October 30, 1991, lot 306.
[4] Christie's, London, May 6, 1924, lot 18; now in a private
American collection.

SOUP TUREEN

~

31

Silver
Maker's mark of Benjamin Godfrey (Grimwade, no. 170)
Hallmarks: none
c. 1735

Of oblong form with shaped ends, raised on four lion's paw feet with entwined tails and headed by lion masks, the sides applied with alternating vertical straps and bellflowers against a matted ground with an upper border of ogee arches, the rim applied with dot-and-dash band, with two double-scroll pendant ring handles issuing from a cartouche of rocaille and scrolls against matting; applied underneath with a circular drop with dot-and-dash and radiating acanthus leaves, the domed cover applied with similar straps and with gadrooned rim, surmounted by a double-scroll unscrewing handle on a circular pedestal with dot-and-dash and radiating acanthus leaves

Two almost identical tureens and covers were ordered by Sir Robert Walpole, the Prime Minister, from George Wickes in 1738. One bears Paul Crespin's mark, and the hallmarks for 1733–4, and was sold as "an old tureen"; Wickes supplied a new one made to match that bears his mark and the date letter for 1738–9.[1] The present tureen, while identical in form and decoration, is slightly taller than the Walpole tureens. It is tempting to think that it may have also belonged to Walpole, but it does not appear among Walpole's extensive orders of plate in George Wickes's ledgers, nor does it appear, as the other two do, in the sale of much of the Walpole silver held at Strawberry Hill in 1842.

The heaviness of Crespin's tureens for the Earl of Chesterfield (no. 8) has been lightened somewhat by the ogee outline and arcading under the rim on this example and those made for Walpole, but the overall effect is still monumental. The tureen presents a curious mixture of styles; the bellflowers and straps are positively baroque, while the radiating acanthus leaves below and around the handle on the top hark back to late

Height: 12½ in (31.6 cm)
Width: 14¼ in (36 cm)
Depth: 10¼ in (25.7 cm)
Weight: 148 oz 18 dwt (4613 g)

Tureen, silver, London,
1740–1, maker's mark of
George Wickes, supplied
by Wickes to Sir Robert
Walpole, the Prime
Minister. Wickes made it
to match a second-hand
example he supplied
Walpole, which bears the
maker's mark of Paul
Crespin and hallmarks
for 1733–4.
Private collection

seventeenth-century embossing and chasing. Early stirrings of the rococo can be seen in the asymmetrical *rocaille* applications by the two side handles. Despite these disparate styles, however, the tureen is firmly in the tradition of the sculptural, imposing forms promoted by the architect William Kent, who designed silver for George II, Lord Montford and other grandees.[2] The use of a sarcophagus form is typical of Kentian Palladianism and is inspired by the work of Giulio Romano and others.[3] Lion-mask-headed paw supports appear as early as 1731 on a tureen bearing the maker's mark of Paul Crespin.[4]

Marks
Struck on rim four times with maker's mark (thrice indistinctly)

Provenance
A Corporate Trustee, sale, Christie's London, March 23, 1966, lot 32
S.J. Shrubsole Corp, New York
Emil Schmitt, Palm Beach
Anonymous sale, Sotheby's, New York, November 5, 1986, lot 186

Bibliography
Elaine Barr, *George Wickes, Royal Goldsmith*, 1980, p. 24, illus. fig. 7b
Michael Clayton, *The Collector's Dictionary of the Silver and Gold of Great Britain and North America*, 1985 edn, p. 268, illus. fig. 534

Notes
[1] Sotheby's, London, July 9, 1964, lot 102; illustrated and discussed in Elaine Barr, *George Wickes, Royal Goldsmith*, 1980, p. 24.
[2] Kent's assistant, John Vardy, published *Some Designs of Mr. Inigo Jones and Mr. William Kent* in 1744.
[3] I am grateful to Cinzia Sicca for this suggestion.
[4] Christie's, London, July 10, 1984.

FOUR SAUCEBOATS

32

Silver (sterling standard)
Maker's mark of Paul Crespin (Grimwade, no. 2143a)
Hallmarks: London, 1735–6

Each of oval lipped form raised on four lion's paw feet entwined with tails and headed by lion masks, the sides applied with garlands of grapevine and fruit, with ribbed scroll serpent-form handles, the interior of the scalloped rims engraved with panels of diaperwork, foliate scrolls and rocaille; engraved under the lips, c. 1870, with an earl's armorials.

Heraldry
The arms are those of Archibald Philip Primrose, 5th Earl of Rosebery (1847–1929).

These sauce boats follow the boat-shaped form that had become standardized by the early 1730s. Lion mask supports were a popular feature from the mid-1730s onwards (see nos. 31 and 35) while the ribbed serpent handles, based on auricular designs by the van Vianens, are identical to ones used by the Lamerie workshop (see p. 176). The applied floral festoons are another popular feature of the 1730s and 1740s but interestingly, like the motifs, they too derive from designs of the previous century. Similar sauceboats with the maker's mark of Paul de Lamerie are known,[1] although on these the lion masks are more characterful.

Marks
Struck under bases with hallmarks (leopard's head, lion passant, date letter) and with maker's mark

Provenance
Archibald Philip Primrose, 5th Earl of Rosebery (1847–1929)
The 5th Earl of Rosebery's Trust Settlement, Sotheby's, London, February 28, 1991, lot 206

Note
[1] A pair of 1734 sold Sotheby's, London, February 6, 1986, lot 174 and a pair of 1733, illustrated in Arthur Grimwade, *Rococo Silver, 1727–1760*, 1974, p. 118.

Detail of foot

Height: 4⅜ in (11.6 cm)
Width: 9½ in (24 cm)
Depth: 4½ in (11.5 cm)
Weight: 91 oz 10 dwt (2848 g)

FOUR SALT CELLARS

33

Silver (sterling standard), the interiors gilt
Maker's mark of Paul de Lamerie (Hare, no. 4)
Hallmarks: London, 1735–6

Of circular form, each raised on four scroll feet terminating in lobing and headed by trefoils, each side applied with a shell, with everted wavy gadrooned rims

The circular cauldron-form salt raised on four legs became standardized by the 1730s. The sides between the supports could be chased or applied with floral motifs or occasionally, as on these examples, with stylized shells. Several sets of this form are known with Lamerie's mark.[1]

Marks
Struck underneath with hallmarks (leopard's head, lion passant, date letter) and with maker's mark

Provenance
Spink & Son Ltd, London

Note
[1] Four of 1737, Farrer Collection, Ashmolean Museum, Oxford, illus. in *Paul de Lamerie, the Work of England's Master Silversmith*, exh. cat., Goldsmiths' Hall, London, 1990, no. 78; four of 1739, Christie's, New York, October 30, 1991, lot 247.

Height: 2⅜ in (5.6 cm)
Diameter: 3⅜ in (8.5 cm)
Weight: 29 oz 10 dwt (917 g)

SPICE BOX

34

Silver, gilt
Maker's mark of Charles Kandler (Grimwade, no. 689)
Hallmarks: none
c. 1735

Of shaped oval form with straight sides, raised on four scroll feet terminating in rocaille, *with moulded base, the sides flat-chased with scrolls,* rocaille *and panels of diaperwork, the top with two hinged covers opening to reveal two chambers, one divided into two, similarly chased within applied borders of scrolls, leaves and with a shell at each end, the centre with circular compartment with removable shell-chased cover with ball finial, each cover engraved amid the scrolling with shields bearing the arms of England and France, one side engraved twice with gothic upper-case initials GB under a ducal coronet*

Initials
The engraved initials seem to date from the end of the eighteenth century and Michael Clayton has suggested that they may be those of Georgiana, wife of the 6th Duke of Bedford, whom she married in 1786.[1]

The overall appearance of this spice box, with its swirling *rocaille* decoration imposed on severe, straight lines, is decidedly Germanic, a common feature in Kandler's silver (see pp. 52–3). The circular cap in the centre was probably originally fitted with a nutmeg grater (see no. 17).

Marks
The base struck with maker's mark

Provenance
Anonymous sale, Sotheby's, London, March 31, 1966, lot 110
Anonymous sale, Sotheby's, New York, April 6, 1989, lot 234

Bibliography
Michael Clayton, *The Collector's Dictionary of the Silver and Gold of Great Britain and North America*, 1985 edn, p. 368, illus. fig. 548

Note
[1] The box does not appear in any plate inventory at Woburn Abbey, the seat of the Dukes of Bedford. I am grateful to Lavinia Wellicome for this information.

Height: 2½ in (6.4 cm)
Width: 5 in (12.6 cm)
Depth: 3⅞ in (9.9 cm)
Weight: 18 oz 12 dwt (581 g)

PAIR OF SAUCEBOATS

35

Silver (sterling standard)
Maker's mark of Peter Archambo I (Grimwade, no. 2127)
Hallmarks: London, 1736–7

Of oval lipped form, each raised on three lion's paw feet with entwined tails and headed by lion masks, engraved under the scalloped rims with a band of foliate scrolls and rocaille *enclosing panels of diaperwork and, under the lips, with baskets of flowers, with leaf-capped multi-scroll handles headed by acanthus, one side engraved with a duke's armorials, the other with three crests and duke's coronet, engraved underneath with the initials F & C under a baron's coronet*

Numbered underneath 6 and 8

Heraldry
The arms are those of Osborne impaling those of Townsend, as borne by George Osborne, 6th Duke of Leeds (1775–1838). The initials *F.* and *C.* and coronet are those borne by his descendant Marcia Amelia, Baroness Fauconberg and Conyers (1863–1926) who married Charles, 4th Earl of Yarborough in 1886.

These sauceboats lack the lightness of touch of the set of four from Crespin's workshop (no. 32), made the year before. Their generous proportions give them a monumentality, and the only concession to the rococo is the *rocaille* engraving around the rims. The lions, however, have a grandeur that is lacking in the Crespin set.

Marks
Struck under bases with hallmarks (leopard's head, lion passant, date letter) and with maker's mark

Provenance
George Osborne, 6th Duke of Leeds (1775–1838)
By descent to Marcia Amelia, Baroness Fauconberg and Conyers (1863–1926)
By descent to an anonymous owner, sale, Henry Spencer and Sons, Retford, November 17, 1983, lot 361
Anonymous sale, Sotheby's, London, June 19, 1987, lot 67

Height: 4½ in (11.5 cm)
Width: 9½ in (24 cm)
Depth: 5⅛ in (13 cm)
Weight: 41 oz 12 dwt (1296 g)

SOUP TUREEN

36

Silver (sterling standard)
Maker's mark of Paul de Lamerie (Hare, no. 4)
Hallmarks: London, 1736–7

Of oval bombé *form, raised on four lion's paw feet entwined with tails and headed by lion masks, the tied-reed rim with* rocaille *at intervals, with two double-scroll and foliate handles issuing from stylized sea-monster heads amid scalework, shells and foliage, the domed cover engraved with bands of scrolls and* rocaille *enclosing panels of trelliswork and surmounted by a handle formed as two lion masks amid scrolls,* rocaille *and foliage issuing from a calyx of applied foliate scrolls,* rocaille, *lion and bird masks, each side of the cover engraved, c. 1780, with a shield enclosing a crest*

Heraldry
The crest, that of an arm embowed holding a sword, pertains to numerous families and replaces earlier engraving.

Marks
Struck under base with hallmarks (leopard's head, lion passant, date letter) and with maker's mark; the interior of cover with lion passant, leopard's head and date letter

The borders of engraved scrolls and *rocaille* – as on this tureen – which first appear in the early 1730s as the only rococo elements on much of the silver from Lamerie's workshop, by 1736 seem decidedly staid alongside the cast ornament that was emerging. The contrast is well illustrated by the cover of this tureen; the bold naturalism of the shells which form part of the cast ornament around the handle is something quite new in Lamerie's output and suggests that he must have hired a skilled modeller about this time. The lion masks which surmount the feet are also quite different in character from the more ferocious faces which appear on work from the workshops of Archambo and others during the period. An idea of the original cost of this tureen is gleaned from a bill of John Craig and John Neville for "a ffine oval tureen & cover" bought by Lord Stanhope on August 25, 1736; weighing 121 ounces 2 pennyweights, which cost £45 13s 2d.[1]

Provenance
S.J. Phillips Ltd, London

Note
[1] Stanhope Papers, West Kent Archive Office, Maidstone, U1590/E13.

Height: 9¾ in (24.6 cm)
Width: 16½ in (42 cm)
Depth: 10 in (25.5 cm)
Weight: 134 oz 18 dwt (4197 g)

Detail of cover

LADLE

37

Silver (sterling standard)
Maker's mark of Paul de Lamerie (Hare, no. 4)
Hallmarks: London, 1737–8

*With oval bowl and tubular handle terminating
in an eagle's head*

A few ladles of this form were produced in
Lamerie's workshop but this appears to be
the earliest recorded. One dating from 1742 is at
Sidney Sussex College, Cambridge, and two of
1743–4 formed part of a dinner service supplied
by Lamerie to the Earl of Thanet between 1742
and 1746.[1] The same form was also sold by
George Wickes, who supplied a tureen and eagle-
headed ladle to Sir Lister Holte in 1742.[2]

Marks
The side of the bowl struck with hallmarks
(leopard's head, lion passant, date letter) and
with maker's mark

Provenance
Anonymous sale, Sotheby's, New York, October
12, 1978, lot 343

Notes
[1] R.A. Crichton, *Cambridge Plate*, exh. cat., Fitzwilliam Museum,
Cambridge, 1975, no. B06; the Thanet service was sold, Sotheby's,
London, November 22, 1984.
[2] Elaine Barr, *George Wickes, Royal Goldsmith*, 1980, p. 152.

Length: 13½ in (34.2 cm)
Weight: 8 oz 10 dwt (265 g)

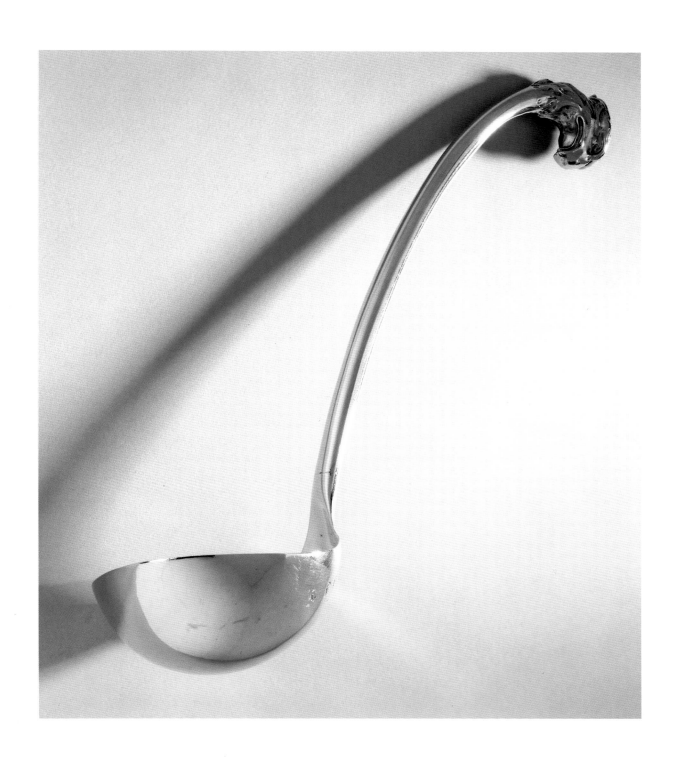

PAIR OF SAUCEBOATS

38

Silver (sterling standard)
Maker's mark of David Willaume II (Grimwade, no. 517)
Hallmarks: London, 1739–40

Of oval form, each raised on three scroll feet headed by stylized shells, applied under the moulded wavy rims with floral sprays and rocaille asymmetrical cartouches on a matted ground, each headed by a lion mask, applied under the lip with a shell, with multi-scroll leaf-capped handles, each engraved on one cartouche with two crests

Marks
Struck under bases with hallmarks (leopard's head, lion passant, date letter) and with maker's mark

These sauceboats are among the purest examples of the rococo style in English silver and their lightness of touch is more typical of French sauceboats of the period.[1] They should be compared with the more ponderous sauceboats of a few years earlier, like nos. 25 and 27. Their low profile, however, makes them less capacious than more typical London-made examples of the period (see nos. 40 and 41) and one therefore wonders whether they could have been popular with the average English diner, given the English propensity at the time to pour great quantities of melted butter over their roast meats.

Provenance
Anonymous sale, Sotheby's, London, February 5, 1987, lot 114

Note
[1] cf. a pair of 1734–5 with the maker's mark of Jacques Roettiers, formerly in the Puiforcat Collection, illustrated in Faith Dennis, *Three Centuries of French Domestic Silver*, 1960, vol I, p. 200.

Height: 5½ in (14 cm)
Width: 9 in (22.8 cm)
Depth: 4½ in (11.5 cm)
Weight: 43 oz 2 dwt (134 g)

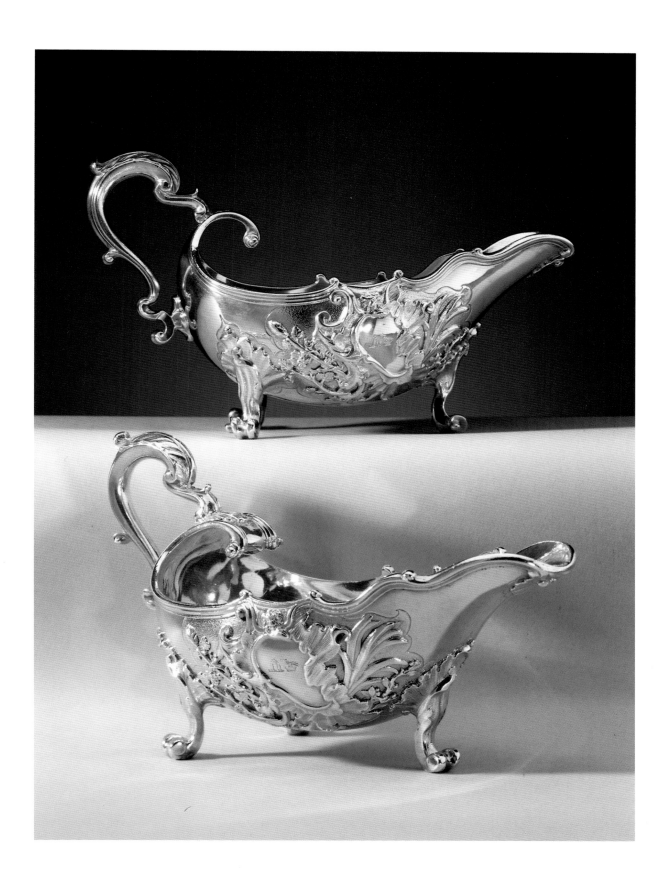

BASKET

39

Silver (sterling standard)
Maker's mark of Paul de Lamerie (Hare, no. 5)
Hallmarks: London, 1739–40

Shaped oval, raised on four lion's mask feet supporting openwork rocaille *and scroll decoration and joined by an openwork foliate scroll and* rocaille *apron enclosing, on each side, the head of Ceres; the everted sides pierced and engraved with foliate scrolls and flowerheads below an applied foliate scroll, flowerhead and* rocaille *rim; the centre flat-chased with a border of foliate scrolls and flowerheads within matting and enclosing a coat-of-arms and motto flanked by supporters and surmounted by an earl's coronet; the swing handle with foliate swags and* rocaille *issuing from putto terms; engraved under the base with two early twentieth-century crests*

Engraved under the base with Esther Hoblitzelle's inventory number EH-134.1 and painted with Dallas Museum of Art accession number 1987-105.1

Heraldry
The arms in the centre are those of Coote impaling those of Newport, as borne by Algernon Coote, 6th Earl of Mountrath (1689–1744).

The later crests are those of Heywood and Lonsdale.

This cake basket forms part of an important group of silver bearing Paul de Lamerie's mark, ordered by the 6th Earl of Mountrath between 1738 and 1742. Seen as a whole it well illustrates the early phase of English rococo silver.

The group comprises:

An epergne of 1738, engraved with the Earl's armorials.[1]

Two cake baskets of 1739, one of which is the present example.

A set of four candlesticks of 1740, engraved with the earl's crest and coronet.[2]

A ewer and dish of 1742, applied with the earl's armorials, the dish engraved: *This dish and Ewer, two Cups Covers and linings, with three Castors, were purchased from the Mountrath Collection, 1881, Also two Bread Baskets, and plain Cup and Cover.*[3]

A pair of salvers (18½ in diam.) of 1741 and 1742, engraved with the earl's armorials.[4]

Height: 11 in (28 cm)
Width: 14¾ in (37.5 cm)
Depth: 12 in (30.5 cm)
Weight: 62oz 10 dwt (1933 g)

Epergne, silver, 1738–9,
maker's mark of Paul de
Lamerie.
Christie's, London

Four candlesticks, silver,
1740, maker's mark of Paul
de Lamerie.
Al-Tajir Collection

Ewer and dish, silver,
1742–3, maker's mark of
Paul de Lamerie.
The Gilbert Collection,
photograph: Los Angeles
County Museum of Art

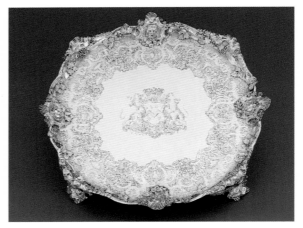

Salver (one of a pair), silver,
1741–2 and 1742–3, maker's
mark of Paul de Lamerie.
The Gilbert Collection,
photograph: Los Angeles
County Museum of Art

*Algernon Coote, 6th Earl of
Mountrath* by Jonathan
Richardson
(c. 1665–1745).
Private collection

*Diana, Countess of
Mountrath, wife of the 6th
Earl* by Charles Jervis
(c. 1675–1739).
Private collection

Two cups and covers, 1742, applied with cast
armorials.[5]

Further pieces, including a fish slice, remain in
a private collection.

A further group appears to date from after the
6th Earl's death and may have been
commissions that were not delivered until
after his death; it includes: a pair of salvers
(10 in diam.) of 1745, engraved with the 6th
Earl's armorials (illus. p. 366).[6]

A pair of waiters (6¼ in diam) of 1745,
engraved with the Coote crest and Earl's
coronet (no. 94 in this catalogue).[7]

Other Lamerie pieces, engraved with the Coote
crest and earl's coronet, were evidently made for
the 7th Earl.[8]

The 6th Earl of Mountrath was one of the group
of anti-Walpolean Whigs who patronized Lamerie
during the 1730s and 1740s. Other members of
the group included Admiral George Anson and
his father-in-law the Earl of Hardwicke, who was
the Lord Chancellor, and Benjamin Mildmay, Earl
Fitzwalter, owner of the tureen (no. 11).[9]

Mountrath was educated at St. Paul's School and
Trinity College, Cambridge and appointed a Privy
Councillor in 1723. The following year he was
returned as MP for Castle Rising, Norfolk, where
his family had an estate. He represented Castle

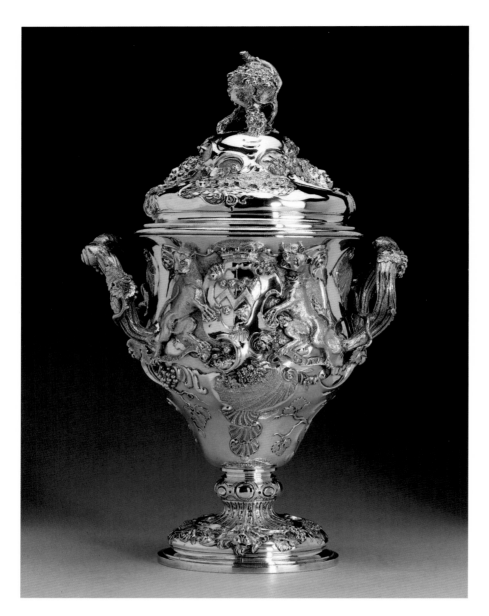

**Cup and cover, silver,
1742–3, maker's mark of
Paul de Lamerie.**
Indianapolis Museum of
Art, photograph: Christie's,
New York

Rising until 1734; he did not return to Parliament
until 1742 when he was elected MP for Hedon in
Yorkshire, which he represented until his death
two years later.[10]

Mountrath married Diana, the youngest daughter
of Richard, 3rd Earl of Newport, who brought
with her a considerable dowry. The marriage took
place soon after he succeeded to the earldom, on
November 28, 1721. She bore him one son,
Charles, who succeeded to the earldom on the

death of his father on August 27, 1744. In his will, dated July 26, 1744, the 6th Earl left his "Dear Wife Diana Countess of Mountrath all her Jewells and all my Rings, Plate, household Goods, Furniture and Pictures …" It is interesting to note that one of the earl's executors was Benjamin Mildmay, Earl Fitzwalter.[11]

The Dowager Countess of Mountrath, as a friend of Lord Hardwicke, the Lord Chancellor, was the target of some of Horace Walpole's most bitter jibes: "That reverend head of the Law is frequently shut up here (at Twickenham) with my Lady Mountrath, who is as rich and as tipsy as Cacofogo in the comedy. What a jumble of avarice, lewdness, dignity – and claret!" Three days after her death he wrote to Lord Holland "My Lady Mountrath is dead, and has made as drunken a will as you could expect." Her will, dated June 9, 1766, was indeed extremely complex and rambles over some fourteen pages. She left the sum of £2,500 for a monument to be erected in Westminster Abbey for herself and her husband. Her son was to receive £30,000 and an annuity of £1,000, while Lord George Cavendish was to receive £40,000 and a lifetime interest in her estate at Twickenham, which included the deer park there. Her two physicians were each to receive £1,000, while her apothecary, one Thomas Rayor, was to receive £8,000. She specifically requested that "my own mare Fanny and also my black mare Mary continue to be taken care of at Twickenham Park aforesaid so long as they live … and that the dogs there may continue and be taken care of in the same manner as they are or shall be during my life and that my body may not be buried or put into a coffin (if it may be avoided) for the space of ten days at the most next after my decease."

The Countess left her "Japan china and trinkets" to the Duchess of Montrose, but the plate, furniture and other effects in her house in Grosvenor Square were bequeathed to Caroline, Lady Milton: "… and my will and desire is that the said plate pictures jewels furniture and linen may be delivered to the said Caroline Lady Milton as soon after my decease as it can be done with courtesy and convenience and that the said silver and gilt plate shall and may continue to be used by the said Caroline Lady Milton and her children respectively with the same arms and crests as are now engraved thereon without being erased or altered …"[12]

Caroline, Lady Milton was the daughter of Lionel, 1st Duke of Dorset (see no. 7), and the wife of Joseph Damer, another Whig who had opposed Walpole, created Baron Milton in 1753. She was bequeathed the silver-gilt toilet service, (no. 110), by her mother in 1768 and died in 1775. Her husband was created Earl of Dorchester in 1792 and died in 1798, when he was succeeded by his eldest surviving son, George, who died unmarried in 1808, whereupon the Damer property, together with the Mountrath silver, passed to his sister, Lady Caroline Damer. She in turn died unmarried in 1829 when the property passed to the children of John Dawson, 1st Earl of Portarlington, son of the 1st Viscount Carlow by Mary, the elder sister of Joseph Damer mentioned above. The Mountrath silver then descended to Henry, 3rd Earl of Portarlington, born in 1822, who disposed of some of it in 1881.[13]

The Mountrath plate (which combines pieces purely for display, like the cups and covers, and also table silver, like the epergne) is united by a common decorative scheme of elaborate rococo imagery illustrative of Ceres, the goddess of the harvest, and Bacchus, the god of wine. This combination of food and drink was a fitting motif for dining room plate and symbolizes Terence's celebrated line "Sine Cerere et Tempero friget Venus" – love withers without the stimulus of wine and feasting. The lion heads which support the basket, symbolic of earth, whence food comes, are another common motif on dining table silver of the period, but their significance is twofold for they also represent might subdued by the power of love. They are akin to those that appear as feet on the Mountrath salvers in the

Basket, interior

Gilbert Collection;[14] similarly, the Ceres heads set against shells which are applied at each end of the present basket appear at intervals on the borders of the matching salvers. Similar piercing and decoration appears on another basket by Lamerie of 1740–1 in the Museum of Art, Birmingham, Alabama[15] and another of 1744–5 in the Sterling and Francine Clark Art Institute, Williamstown, Massachusetts.[16]

The engraving of the 6th Earl's arms on the present basket is obviously by the same hand as that on the salvers in the group and, as Timothy Schroder has observed discussing the Gilbert salvers, "The style of the engraved cartouches (repeated on the smaller salvers of 1745) is not typical of Lamerie's workshop at this time. Although tighter and more symmetrical than usual, they are, in fact, very similar to those on a number of George Wickes's more important commissions … The individuality of this

Basket, detail of foot

Basket, detail of mask and piercing

engraver was noted by Oman ... but he suggested no identification."[17] Indeed, it is interesting to compare these armorials with the engraving of the royal arms on a series of silver-gilt dishes struck with Wickes's maker's mark, dating from 1739, one of which is in the Gilbert Collection, while others are at Williamstown, and in the collection of the Marquess of Cholmondeley at Houghton, Norfolk.

The arms engraved on the Mountrath plate may owe their survival to the Countess of Mountrath's request in her will that the silver be used by Lady Milton and her children "with the same arms and crests as are now engraved thereon without being erased or altered".

Marks
Struck under base with hallmarks (leopard's head, lion passant, date letter), and with maker's mark

Provenance
Algernon Coote, 6th Earl of Mountrath (1689–1744)
Bequeathed in 1744 to Diana, Dowager Countess of Mountrath (c. 1700–66)
Bequeathed in 1766 to Caroline, wife of Joseph Damer, afterwards Lord Milton, (d. 1775)
Then by descent to the Earl of Portarlington
Sold about 1881 to Arthur Pemberton Heywood-Lonsdale of Shavington, Shropshire
Then by descent to Lieutenant-Colonel Arthur Heywood-Lonsdale, sale, Christie's, London, June 27, 1956, lot 125 (a pair)
Esther Thomas Hoblitzelle, Dallas, Texas
Bequeathed in 1987 to The Dallas Museum of Art
Property from the Hoblitzelle Collection, Dallas Museum of Art, sale, Christie's, New York, April 22, 1993, lot 44 (the other of the pair retained by the museum)

Bibliography
Mary L. Kennedy, *The Esther Thomas Hoblitzelle Collection of English Silver*, 1957, p. 46, illus. pl. 58

Exhibited
Museum of Fine Arts, Houston, *Paul de Lamerie in American Collections*, 1956, cat. no. 72
High Museum of Art, Atlanta, *The Esther Thomas Hoblitzelle Collection of English Silver*, 1975, cat. no. 10

Notes
[1] Sold by the 7th Earl of Portarlington and the Hon. John Dawson-Damer, Christie's, London, December 27, 1986, lot 240, now in the Kerry Packer Collection.
[2] Formerly in the collections of the Hon. W.F.B. Massey-Mainwaring, Pierpont Morgan and J. P. Morgan, sold by the Morgan family, Christie's, New York, October 26, 1982, lot 39, now in the Al-Tajir Collection, London.
[3] Sold by Lieutenant-Colonel A. Heywood-Lonsdale, Christie's, London, June 27, l956, lot 126, purchased by Sir George Dowty, sold to J. H. Bourdon-Smith, London, 1971, now in the Gilbert Collection.
[4] Formerly in the collection of Mr. and Mrs. Frank E. Zorniger, Wilmore, Kentucky, now in the Gilbert Collection.
[5] Sold by Lieutenant-Colonel A. Heywood-Lonsdale, Christie's, London, June 27, 1956, lot 124; Esther Thomas Hoblitzelle, Dallas, Texas, given to the Dallas Museum of Art, 1987, one of the pair now in the Indianapolis Museum of Art.
[6] Sold Sotheby's, London, November 17, 1960, lot 153 and again from the estate of the late Donald S. Morrison, Sotheby's, New York, June 6, 1980, lot 27.
[7] Sold Sotheby's, London, November 17, 1960, lot 154 and again from the collection of Hilmar Reksten, Christie's, London, May 22, 1991, lot 53.
[8] These include a pair of sauceboats of 1749–50, illus. p. 366, and soup ladle of 1748 in a private collection.
[9] See Christopher Hartop, "Admiral Anson and his Paul de Lamerie Silver," *Antiques*, June, 1994.
[10] G. E. Cokayne, ed.: *The Complete Peerage*.
[11] Public Record Office, London, P.C.C., 219 Anstis.
[12] Public Record Office, London, P.C.C., 420 Tyndall.
[13] The Dorset toilet service mentioned here (no. 110), was given or bequeathed by Lady Milton to her brother Lord George Sackville and descended in the Stopford-Sackville family.
[14] Timothy Schroder, *The Gilbert Collection of Gold and Silver*, 1988, no. 66.
[15] Bequest of Frances Oliver Estate, 1972.287.
[16] Inv. no. 414.
[17] Schroder, *op. cit.*, pp. 257–8.

PAIR OF SAUCEBOATS

40

Silver (sterling standard)
Maker's mark of Paul de Lamerie (Hare, no. 5)
Hallmarks: London, 1740–1

Of oval lipped form, each raised on four splayed shell-form feet, realistically chased to represent shells and applied with flowers, shells and leaves, chased under the lips with rocaille *and scalework, the handles formed as putto busts issuing from lion masks, engraved under the lips with a crest and motto*

Heraldry
The crest and motto are those of Gordon.

Detail of handle

The stylized shell which forms the body of these sauceboats derives from the auricular designs of the van Vianens (see no. 67), and the lion mask is a standard motif of the 1730s. The bold modelling of the shellwork and the putto handles are more firmly in the rococo repertoire but they lack the lightness and movement characteristic of that style.

When these sauceboats were sold at Sotheby's in 1985, the following lot was a pair made to match in 1823–4 with the maker's mark of Robert Garrard, engraved with the same crest.[1]

Marks
Struck under bases with hallmarks (leopard's head, lion passant, date letter) and with maker's mark

Provenance
A Lady, sale, Sotheby's, London, October 24, 1985, lot 403

Note
[1] A pair of sauceboats of similar form was sold Sotheby's, New York, September 16, 1972, lot 499.

Height: 5¹/₁₆ (12.8 cm)
Width: 9 in (22.5 cm)
Depth: 4½ in (11.4 cm)
Weight: 45 oz 14 dwt (1423 g)

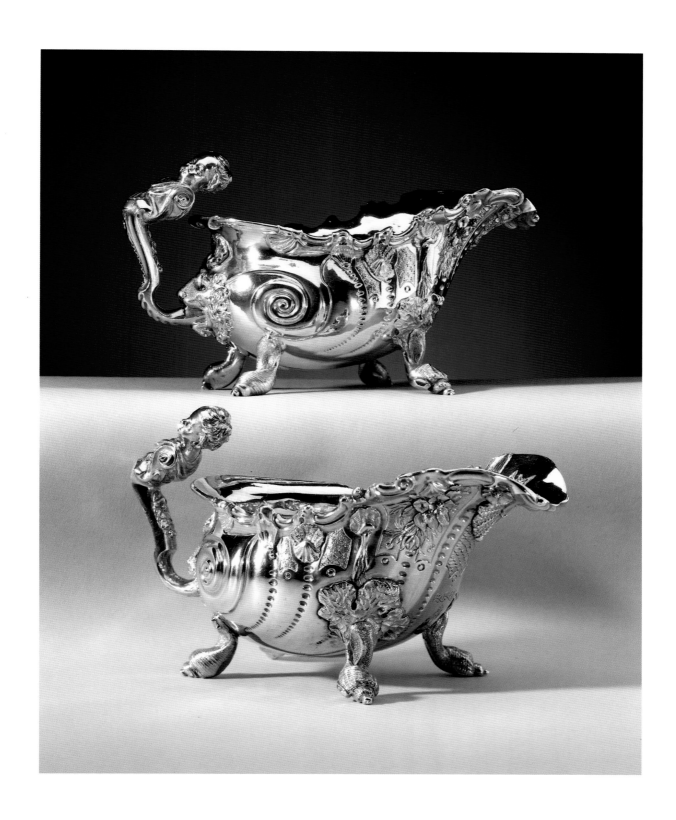

PAIR OF SAUCEBOATS

41

Silver (sterling standard)
Maker's mark of Peter Archambo I (Grimwade, no. 2128)
Hallmarks: London, 1741–2

Of oval double-lipped form, each raised on four lion's paw feet entwined with tails and headed by lion masks, with wavy gadrooned rims and central high double-entwined snake handles, engraved each side with a coat-of-arms within the garter of the Order of the Bath, flanked by supporters with a motto below

Each numbered underneath 567 and with scratch weights 27=1 and 26=15

Heraldry
The arms are those of Stanhope within the motto of the Order of the Bath, probably as borne by Sir William Stanhope. Sir William Stanhope, a Knight of the Bath, was brother of Philip, 4th Earl of Chesterfield. He married Susannah, daughter of John Rudge in 1721.

The double-lipped form of sauceboat was virtually replaced by the single-lipped version (no. 25) by the 1730s, but a small number of double-lipped examples continued to be made into the 1740s. Instead of twin scroll handles along each side, these later versions usually gain delicacy with a single, overhead scroll handle, in this case formed of two serpents. The castings of the lion mask feet are identical to those found on the pair of 1736–7 also from Archambo's workshop (no. 35). Four sauceboats of similar form of 1744–5, maker's mark of Thomas Gilpin, are also recorded;[1] these also have what appear to be identical cast feet and it may be that all of them were supplied by the same specialist workshop.

Marks
Struck under bases with hallmarks (leopard's head, lion passant, date letter) and with maker's mark

Provenance
Sir William Stanhope (b. 1702)
Subsequent provenance unknown until Archer M. Huntington, sale, Anderson Art Galleries, New York, March 5–6, 1926, lot 216 (as a set of four)
Henry Walters, Baltimore
Mrs Henry Walters, sale, Parke Bernet, New York, December 3, 1943, lot 890[2]
Jessie Woolworth Donahue, sale, Sotheby's, New York, April 28–9, 1972, lot 87
Spink & Son Ltd, London

Notes
[1] Christie's, New York, December 6, 1978, lot 123.
[2] The other pair, the preceding lot, is now in the Chrysler Museum, Norfolk, Virginia.

Height: 7¾ in (19.5 cm)
Width: 9 in (23 cm)
Weight: 53 oz 14 dwt (1670 g)

Left: detail of foot of no 41. Right: detail of foot of no. 35.
The casting is identical. Both may have been supplied by
the same specialist workshop.

SAUCEBOAT

~

42

Silver (sterling standard)
Maker's mark of Frederick Kandler (Grimwade, no. 691)
Hallmarks: London, 1742–3

Of oval lipped form raised on a shaped oval base cast and chased with naturalistic foliage and shells on a granulated ground rising to three cast mermaid-form supports with entwined bifurcated tails, the body applied with trailing foliage on a matted ground and applied each side with an oval cartouche enclosed by crustacea and surmounted by a wild mask with tongue protruding, with foliate scroll rim, the handle formed as a winged gryphon semé with dots, one cartouche engraved with a coat-of-arms, the other with a crest

Heraldry
The coat-of-arms appears to be eastern European, and was probably added in the nineteenth century.

This sauceboat was originally one of a pair, separated some time after the 1928 auction; the other is now in the Metropolitan Museum of Art, New York.

The striking sculptural form of this sauceboat is typical of much of the silver produced in the Kandler workshop. We now know them to have been related to the famous family of Meissen modellers (see pp. 52–3) and one can see several Meissen-like motifs in the decoration of this sauceboat, such as the dragon-form handle. Paradoxically, though, the inspiration for such dragons is silver made in France at the end of the seventeenth century, where they appear on vessels in the paintings of Desportes,[1] and ultimately they derive from Chinese lacquer panels brought to Europe earlier in the century. Dragons appear filling the corners or perched on flimsy ledges in Jean Berain's designs, but the Kandler dragons are fierce and vigorously modelled. The Kandler model may have been a design for a sauceboat with similar dragon handle and shell body published in Nuremburg about 1740. Kandler used similar dragon-form handles on a number of sauceboats[2] and used dragon-form feet on a brazier of 1742–3 in the Metropolitan Museum.[3]

Height: 8 in (20.4 cm)
Width: 9½ in (24 cm)
Depth: 4¼ in (10.6 cm)
Weight: 39 oz 18 dwt (1243 g)

Engraving for a sauceboat,
Nuremburg, c. 1740

**Brazier, silver, London,
1742–3, maker's mark of
Frederick Kandler.**
Metropolitan Museum of
Art, New York, gift of Irwin
Untermyer, 1974
(1974.28.179)

Motifs of fruit and *rocaille*, typical of London-made silver of the 1740s, adorn the body, whose shell shape is perhaps symbolic of Venus. The theme of love is continued with the faces of recumbent lions, which have been subdued by love, and by the central support formed of three mermaids, which appears to be unique in Kandler's work. The model for this appears to be English. William Kent, inspired by Italian designs of the sixteenth century, used similar mermaids repeatedly in his work for the English court, as on his Venus fountain and his "Candlesticks for the King", designs for both of which were published in 1744 but were doubtless well known during the early 1740s.

Marks
Struck under base of body with hallmarks (leopard's head, lion passant, date letter) and with maker's mark

Provenance
The late Mrs. William Salomon, sale, American Art Association, New York, January 4–7, 1928, lot 334 (a pair)
Anonymous sale, Sotheby's, London, April 20, 1972, lot 147

Bibliography
Vanessa Brett, *The Sotheby's Directory of Silver*, 1986, illus. p. 196, fig. 831

Design for the Venus Fountain, by William Kent, from John Vardy, *Some Designs of Mr. Inigo Jones and Mr. William Kent*, London, 1744

Sauceboat, silver, c. 1740, attributed to Frederick Kandler. Ashmolean Museum, Oxford, Conway Bequest

Notes
[1] For example a tureen with dragon handles in Desportes's *Buffet with Silver Vessels* in the Metropolitan Museum of Art, New York, illus. p. 69.
[2] Such as a pair in the Ashmolean Museum, Oxford, another of 1743–4 in the National Gallery of Victoria, Australia, and another, of the same date, sold Christie's, London, November 22, 1995, lot 120.
[3] Gift of Irwin Untermyer, 1974.

LADLE

43

Silver (sterling standard)
Maker's mark of Paul Crespin (Grimwade, no. 2149)
Hallmarks: London, 1742–3

The back of the deep bowl applied with flutes, the shaped stem engraved with ruled compartments and applied at the end with an asymmetrical rocaille and scroll cartouche engraved with the Seymour crest and earl's coronet

Heraldry
The crest and coronet are those borne by Charles Seymour, 6th Duke of Somerset (1662–1748).

The 6th Duke of Somerset was an active buyer of silver right up to the end of his long life. As a young man he had re-built Petworth, his house in Sussex, in the baroque style, but despite

Soup tureen and stand, silver, London, 1740–1, maker's mark of Paul Crespin. Toledo Museum of Art, Ohio

his reputation as a staunch conservative (see no. 15) he clearly espoused the rococo style in the 1740s. In 1740 he commissioned from Crespin a remarkable soup tureen and stand in the most advanced rococo style,[1] and it is tempting to think that this ladle may have been ordered from Crespin to accompany it. Unfortunately there are few lists of plate from this period in the Petworth Papers. The weight of this ladle is exceptional, caused for the most part by the applied flutes on the bowl. Soup ladles with shell-shaped bowls are common from mid-century onwards, but usually the fluting is chased rather than applied.

Marks
Struck on stem with hallmarks (leopard's head, lion passant, date letter) and with maker's mark

Provenance
Charles Seymour, 6th Duke of Somerset (1662–1748)
Subsequent provenance unknown until Sir Sidney Nolan, OM, AC, CBE, sale, Christie's, London, July 14, 1993, lot 71

Note
[1] Originally sold by the Duke of Somerset at Christie's in 1888, it was subsequently in the collection of Mrs James de Rothschild and sold Christie's, London, May 13, 1964, lot 104; it is now in the Toledo Museum of Art, Ohio.

Length: 15¼ in (38.7 cm)
Weight: 16 oz (497 g)

BASKET

44

Silver (sterling standard)
Maker's mark of Peter Archambo I (Grimwade, no. 2128)
Hallmarks: London, 1743–4

Of shaped circular form raised on four scroll and rocaille feet, the sides pierced and engraved with foliate scrolls and rocaille, the rim cast and chased with foliage, rocaille, wheat ears, scrolls and, along each side, with the head of Ceres, the centre flat chased with a border of scrolls, rocaille and flowers on a matted ground, the swing handle cast and chased with a stylized eagle's head amid foliage, with a putto and scroll term on each side, the centre engraved with an asymmetrical foliate scroll and rocaille cartouche enclosing a mirrored cypher

Initials
The cypher engraved in the centre of the cartouche is unidentified.

Overhead view

The extravagant sculptural qualities of this basket make it one of the most rococo pieces of English silver from the 1740s. The basic shape of an oval, however, is not a rococo form and is an adaptation of earlier, symmetrical, baskets such as the one with Paul de Lamerie's mark of 1731–2 (no. 26). The head of Ceres, the goddess of the harvest, appears on each side amid wheat sheaves, flowers and rocaille, which, together with the eagle and putti on the handle, continue the theme of peace and plenty. A similar basket of 1741–2 bearing Archambo's mark is in the J. Paul Getty Museum, Malibu, California.[1]

Marks
Struck under base with hallmarks (leopard's head, lion passant, date letter) and with maker's mark

Provenance
Anonymous sale, Sotheby's, New York, December 15, 1981, lot 273

Note
[1] 78. DG. 136.

Height: 12½ in (31.7 cm)
Width: 16 in (39.8 cm)
Depth: 11 in (28 cm)
Weight: 98 oz 14 dwt (3072 g)

SAUCEBOATS, STANDS AND LADLES

45

Silver (sterling standard)
Overall weight: 85 oz (2643 g)

Sauceboats:
Marks: none
c. 1746
Height: 6¼ in (15.9 cm)
Width: 8 in (20.3 cm)
Depth: 4 in (10.2 cm)
Stands:
Maker's mark of Nicholas Sprimont
(Grimwade, no. 2102)
Hallmarks: London, 1746–7
Width: 11¾ in (29.8 cm)
Ladles:
Marks: none
c. 1745
Length: 8 in (20.3 cm)

In the form of a shell, the flutes either polished plain or cast with shells and seaweed issuing from the scroll backs, the scroll handles formed of double-entwined serpents, on shaped oval bases cast and chased with similar flutes and shellwork; engraved under the lips with an earl's armorials

The shaped oval stands formed of a border of similar alternating rockwork and plain radiating flutes, with stylized rocaille *at each end, the plain centres engraved with a crest within foliate sprays under a marquess's coronet*

The ladles with fluted bowls in the form of a shell, the shaped stems with reeded stems terminating in foliate cartouches engraved with a crest and marquess's coronet

The sauce boats and ladles unmarked; the stands struck underneath with hallmarks (leopard's head, lion passant, date letter) and with maker's mark; the stands also numbered 2 and 3

Heraldry
Sauceboats: The arms are those of Watson quartering those of Wentworth and impaling those of Finch, as borne by Thomas Watson (1693–1750), as Marquess of Rockingham (so created in 1746).
Stands and ladles: The crest and coronet are those borne by Thomas Watson (1693–1750) as Earl of Malton (so created in 1734).

Thomas Watson was a typical Whig grandee who greatly increased his wealth and position by supporting the oligarchy throughout his career. The considerable quantity of silver he bought in the 1740s in the latest French rococo style, like these sauceboats, tends to contradict the assumption, so often made, that the rococo was very much a style of the Tory opposition. Watson represented the "pocket borough" of Malton in Yorkshire until 1727 when, in the peerages conferred at the time of George II's coronation, he was created Baron Malton and took his seat in the House of Lords. In 1734 he was created Earl of Malton and finally, on April 19, 1746, he was created Marquess of Rockingham. The sauceboats and ladles, although without hallmarks, were evidently supplied before this date as they are engraved with an earl's coronet; the stands, with

Sauceboat, silver, made for the court of Portugal, present whereabouts unknown, from Germain Bapst, *L'Orfèvrerie Française à la Cour de Portugal au XVIIIᵉ siècle*, 1892.

Sauceboat, porcelain, c. 1753, Derby. Victoria and Albert Museum, London

Dish, porcelain, c. 1750, Chelsea Factory. Christie's, New York

the full armorials of a marquess, were commissioned after this date (the sauceboats and ladles show considerably more wear than the stands). Included in the 1948 Christie's sale were seven sauce boats, four stands, four ladles and a small cream boat of the same form.[1]

Much of the work attributed to Sprimont, like these sauceboats, is virtually identical to that bearing Paul Crespin's, and given the close proximity of their workshops in Soho, it is unlikely that each establishment carried out all the stages of production independently. Between the two workshops there must have been some pooling of resources, such as modelling or casting. The same duplication of designs and craftsmanship is found on the soup tureen and stand made for the Duke of Somerset (illus. p. 212) of 1740–1, bearing Crespin's mark, the centrepiece of 1741–2, also with Crespin's mark, in the Royal Collection, and the Ashburnham centrepiece of 1747–8, which bears Sprimont's mark. It was suggested some years ago by Charles Oman that the first of these was in fact made in Sprimont's workshop but submitted for assay by Crespin as Sprimont had not yet entered his own mark at Goldsmiths' Hall.[2] A set of sauceboats of the same form as these Sprimont examples is known, however, bearing Crespin's mark and date letters for 1746–7 and 1752–3,[3] well after Sprimont had registered his mark, which appears to contradict this theory. The truth of the matter may be that Sprimont acted as a sub-contractor to Crespin and other members of the Lamerie group, and "made up" finished articles from the group's components during busy times. It is unlikely that Sprimont, newly-arrived from the Low Countries and – from the mid-1740s onwards – heavily involved with the new Chelsea porcelain factory, could have had the type of workshop necessary to cast and produce objects of the scale of the Ashburnham centrepiece. The connection with Crespin is strengthened by the presence of Lord Malton's arms on a centrepiece of 1742–3, bearing Crespin's maker's mark.

The sauceboats follow the form of French examples of the late 1730s; perhaps the closest parallel is one formerly in the Portuguese royal collection, now lost, but evidently supplied, along with other silver, by Germain. The use of the Venus shell as the body of a sauce boat was well established in London-made silver by the early 1740s, and applied bands of shells and seaweed often appear on work struck with Crespin's mark, such as the teapot of 1740 (no. 76). By the mid-1740s silver forms were being used in porcelain made by the Chelsea factory,[4] while fluted shell-shaped boats similar to these silver examples were being made in the 1750s by William Ball's factory at Liverpool, as well as at Chelsea and Derby, although the intricacy of the shell and seaweed decoration is somewhat watered down. The shaped oval stand, though, did translate into

porcelain in virtually identical form, and was one of the most popular models produced by Chelsea during the 1750s.

Provenance
Thomas Watson, Marquess of Rockingham (1693–1750)
Then by descent to Lady Anne Watson-Wentworth, his daughter, who married William, 3rd Earl Fitzwilliam
Then by descent to the 8th Earl Fitzwilliam, DSC, sale, Christie's, London, June 9, 1948, part of lot 81 or 82
Jessie and Sigmund Katz, New Orleans
Museum of Fine Arts, Boston, gift of Mrs. S.J. Katz (1969–71)
Property of the Museum of Fine Arts, Boston, sale, Sotheby's, New York, April 27, 1990, lot 405

Bibliography
Arthur Grimwade, *Rococo Silver 1727–1765*, 1974, illus. pl. 32B
Elizabeth Adams, *Chelsea Porcelain*, 1987, illus. pl. 7

Exhibited
University Art Museum, University of Texas, *100 Years of English Silver 1660–1760*, 1969, exh. cat., no. 83 (a sauceboat and stand from the set)
Frick Collection, New York, *English Silver*, 1978–9, exh. cat., no. 14
Victoria and Albert Museum, London, *Rococo Art and Design in Hogarth's England*, 1984, exh. cat., no. G19 (a sauceboat and stand from the set)

Notes
[1] The Museum of Fine Arts, Boston retained four sauce boats, two stands and two ladles.
[2] Arthur Grimwade, "Crespin or Sprimont? An unsolved problem of Rococo silver", *Apollo*, August, 1969.
[3] Christie's, London, March 26, 1976, lot 73; an unmarked pair of sauceboats of the same form, engraved with the arms of the 3rd Earl of Scarbrough, is cited in the 1990 Sotheby's catalogue entry, and an identical, unmarked, cream boat was sold from the collection of Colonel Tipping, Christie's, London, May 15, 1911, lot 28.
[4] A sauceboat example following a silver shape with applied floral swags, which may be as early as 1744, is illustrated in Elizabeth Adams, *Chelsea Porcelain*, 1987, fig. 19.

PAIR OF MEAT DISHES

46

Silver (sterling standard)
Maker's mark of Paul de Lamerie (Hare, no. 5)
Hallmarks: London, 1748–9

*Of shaped oval form, the rims applied with a band
of rosettes with scroll, blossom and rocaille motifs
at intervals, the borders engraved on each side with
a crest*

*Numbered 10 and 11 and with scratch weights
26*13½ and 25*11½ respectively*

Heraldry
The crest is that of Sneyd, probably as borne by
Ralph Sneyd (1723–93).

Ralph Sneyd of Keele Hall, Staffordshire,
married Barbara, the daughter of Sir Walter
Wagstaffe Bagot, Bt, in 1749 and placed what
must have been a large order of plate with Paul de
Lamerie's workshop, including a pair of cake
baskets (which evidently was supplied by
Lamerie from stock, as they are hallmarked for
1747–8),[1] and a pair of large candlesticks.[2] The
Sneyds were a high Tory landowning family who
had supported the 1715 Jacobite uprising. They
seem to have recovered rapidly, however, and
Ralph's father served as High Sheriff of
Staffordshire in 1720. By the middle of the
century they were making a considerable income
from their coal and iron interests in north

Staffordshire and Ralph reportedly had "a genius
for making improvements, with discretion
enough to keep it within bounds".[3]

As Timothy Schroder pointed out in his 1983
catalogue of an exhibition of the Dowty
Collection, "The style of these meat dishes – both
their shape and decoration – suggests a rather
earlier date than the hallmarks. In all probability,
they were made to enlarge a dinner service already
supplied. The rosette pattern of the border is
already found in the late 1720s, for example, on a
snuffer stand of 1727, while the applied shell and
scroll moulding is paralleled in a slightly more
austere form on the Walpole salver of 1728. The
shape of the border is unusual but stylistically
more in keeping with the early 1730s rather than
the 1720s." The numbers engraved on this pair
suggest that the set was once much larger. These
two dishes are part of a set of four sold in 1924.[4]

Dishes like these examples, in varying sizes, were
usually the most expensive part of a "laying
down" of plate in the eighteenth century because
of the amount of silver necessary. A service
supplied by George Wickes to the Duke of
Leinster between 1741 and 1747, much of which
has survived intact, included thirty oval meat

Width: 12½ in (31.7 cm)
Depth: 8⅞ in (22.7 cm)
Weight: 50 oz 12 dwt (1573 g)

dishes, in addition to seven and a half dozen dinner plates and eighteen soup plates. It is evident that plates were changed with each course, or "remove".[5] These dishes do not appear in the "List of Plate at Keele Hall 11 April, 1854", but they may be part of the "13 Shaped gad'n flat silver dishes" listed in the "Inventory of Plate left at Messrs. Garrard & Co., Panton St., London" dated June 16, 1849. Presumably this was silver left with Garrard's and used by the family when in London for the season.[6]

Marks
Struck on reverses with hallmarks (leopard's head, lion passant, date letter) and with maker's mark

Provenance
Probably Ralph Sneyd (1723–93)
By descent to the Sneyd Heirlooms, sale, Christie's, London, June 24, 1924, lot 88 (a set of four)
Anonymous sale, Christie's, London, April 28, 1965, lot 113
Sir George Dowty

Cake basket (one of a pair), silver-gilt, London, 1747–8, maker's mark of Paul de Lamerie. Ralph Sneyd purchased elaborately decorated rococo silver from Lamerie's workshop as well as severely plain, functional pieces.
Colonial Williamsburg Foundation

The Dowty Collection, sale, Christie's, New York, April 22, 1993, lot 48

Bibliography
Timothy Schroder, *The Dowty Collection of Silver by Paul de Lamerie*, exh. cat., Cheltenham Art Gallery, 1983, p. 14

Exhibited
Cheltenham, Art Gallery, 1983, cat. no. 8

Pair of candlesticks, silver, London, 1748–9, maker's mark of Paul de Lamerie.
Sotheby's, New York

Notes
[1] These were lot 64 in the 1924 Christie's sale and are now at Colonial Williamsburg.
[2] Lot 78 in the 1924 sale, subsequently sold from the collection of Mrs. Fay Plohn, Sotheby's, London, July 16, 1970, lot 96; then in the E.W. Davidson Collection.
[3] J.M. Kolbert, *The Sneyds & Keele Hall*, 1967, p. 3.
[4] The other pair of meat dishes was sold from the Plohn Collection, Sotheby's, London, July 16, 1970, lot 95 and is now in the Ortiz-Patiño Collection; these meat dishes were exhibited in *Paul de Lamerie: the Work of England's Master Silversmith*, Goldsmiths' Hall, London, 1990, no. 118.
[5] The Leinster service is in the Al-Tajir Collection; for a discussion of it, see Elaine Barr, *George Wickes, Royal Goldsmith*, 1980, pp. 197–205.
[6] Sneyd MSS, Keele University, MT Box 79.

PLATEAU

~'

47

Silver (sterling standard)
Maker's mark of Paul Crespin (Grimwade, no. 2149)
Hallmarks: London, 1749–50

Of shaped oval form, on four large fluted scroll feet,
the upcurved border cast and pierced with
gadrooning, shells and foliage, the field engraved with
a similar band enclosing a coat-of-arms surmounted
by an earl's coronet within a rococo cartouche

Heraldry
The arms are those of Stanhope, probably as borne
by Philip, 2nd Earl Stanhope (1714–1786).

The plateau is typical of the rich, sculptural
rococo of the later phase of English rococo
silver. It was probably intended as the base for a
centrepiece or *surtout* which would have held
casters, spice boxes and cruet bottles. A
centrepiece on four scroll feet of 1742–3, also with
Crespin's maker's mark, in the Museum of Fine
Arts, Houston, has very similar decoration and it
gives us an idea what this plateau would have
looked like with its epergne.[1] The Houston
centrepiece has no arms engraved on it and its
early provenance is unknown, and unfortunately
the arms engraved on this plateau do not pinpoint

which Earl Stanhope may have commissioned it.

The rococo cartouche in the centre of the plateau
was intended for a coat-of-arms, but the engraver
has attempted to fit into it a coat surmounted by a
coronet and enclosed in its own, rococo,
cartouche. The effect is awkward and it is possible
that the arms were engraved at a later date,
although there is no sign of an erasure under
the engraving.

By the end of the century, *surtouts* were outmoded
and it may be that the "large Epargne" weighing
266 ounces which Lord Stanhope sent to the
retailer Richard Heming (the brother of Thomas)
in 1793 as part of a parcel of plate to be melted
down was the centrepiece which had sat on this
plateau. Stanhope's bill for £227 9s 10d of new
silver was settled with a quantity of old, outmoded, pieces for which he was credited a total of
£224 14s d.[2] In 1794 the plateau itself appears in
an inventory of plate at Chevening, when its
original function evidently escaped the valuer,
who referred to it as a "large Dish for Venison".[3]

Height: 2¼ in (5.6 cm)
Width: 23¼ in (59 cm)
Depth: 18½ in (47 cm)
Weight: 134 oz (4167 g)

Centrepiece, silver,
London, 1742–3, maker's
mark of Paul Crespin.
Museum of Fine Art,
Houston, Texas

Marks
Struck under base with hallmarks (leopard's
head, lion passant, date letter) and with maker's
mark

Provenance
Probably Philip, 2nd Earl Stanhope (1714–1786)
By descent to the Earl Stanhope, sale, Christie's,
London, October 26, 1960, lot 170
Hilmar Reksten, Bergen, Norway
The Hilmar Reksten Collection, sale, Christie's,
London, May 22, 1991, lot 144

Notes
[1] Anonymous loan, 193-80.
[2] Stanhope Papers, West Kent Archive Office, Maidstone,
U1590/E14/2.
[3] "Account of Sundry Plate weigh'd and valued for The Rt Honble.
Earl Stanhope by Rundell & Bridge, Ludgate Hill, March 1794",
Stanhope Papers, U1590/E13.

TABLE SERVICE

48

Silver (sterling standard), steel
Maker's mark of Frederick Kandler (Grimwade, no. 691)
Hallmark: London sterling standard mark (lion passant), pre-1756
c. 1750

Knives:
Width: 10¾ in (27.7 cm)
Depth: 1½ in (3.8 cm)
Spoons:
Weight of spoons: 72 oz 10 dwt (2266 g)
Forks:
Weight of forks: 73 oz (2274 g)
Cases:
Walnut, oilcloth, silver (sterling standard)
Silver mounts: maker's mark CL (unidentified)
Hallmark: London sterling standard mark
(lion passant), pre-1756
c. 1750

Comprising 24 table forks, 24 tablespoons and 24 table knives, the spoons and four-tined forks with tapering stems divided into two compartments and interrupted by a stylized wave, the terminals and the backs of the spoon bowls and tines with a shell; the knives with pistol handles chased with scrolling foliage, with steel scimitar-shaped blades

In two cases, the sloping-front case fitted for the knives raised on three shell and ball-and-claw feet, that for the spoons and forks on four similar feet; the sides and lids of both applied with a swing scroll silver handle with shaped shell and scroll backplate, the fronts with similar escutcheon plates

When this table service was sold in Amsterdam in 1992, the previous lot from the same owner was a similar Dutch table service made in the Hague in 1753. The interior of the case for the latter was fitted with similar galooning. From this we might suppose that the Kandler service was supplied by Kandler to a Dutch client. By the eighteenth century, England had become a major exporter of finished silverware, not only to its American colony, but to many of the European countries including Russia and France.

Almost no services of silver cutlery survive from before the eighteenth century, although sets of spoons, usually with apostle terminals, were made. A personal set of flatware, called in French a *couvert*, was carried when travelling and often accompanied a guest invited to dine at a great house or castle, but it was not until the early eighteenth century that flatware became impersonal enough to be made in large sets. This service is rare, not only because of its exceptional quality and virtually mint condition, but because the decoration of the spoons and forks is quite unusual. London-made silver cutlery of this period is particularly dull, with plain unadorned stems in what Victorian dealers dubbed "Hanoverian" pattern. Occasionally a patron like the Earl of Chesterfield would purchase more elaborate flatware from Parisian silversmiths, and commission London makers to copy it (see p. 101), but for the most part early Georgian table silver is not as imaginative as this set.

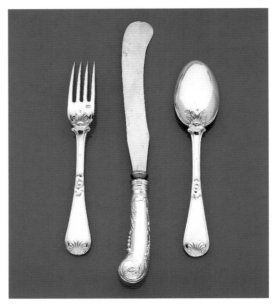

The knives follow the more standard eighteenth-century form, with pistol-shaped handles and scimitar blades.

The identification of the maker's mark on the mounts is uncertain. Several smallworkers with the initials CL are known from the post-1770 period, but a positive identification with a maker of the 1750s has not been made. Only one name emerges from the surviving registers of makers' marks at Goldsmiths' Hall. Charles Laughton registered marks in 1739 and 1741, but both of those are quite different from the mark on these case mounts.[1]

Marks
The spoons struck on the backs of the bowls with hallmark (lion passant); ten also struck with maker's mark

The forks struck on the back of the tines with hallmark (lion passant); nine also struck with maker's mark

Eleven of the knives struck at the top of the handles with hallmark (lion passant); two with traces of maker's mark

The knife case mounts struck with hallmark (lion passant), and with maker's mark; the spoon and fork case mounts struck with hallmark (lion passant); the lock plate and one handle plate with maker's mark

All components and mounts also struck with Dutch mark of old work of Dutch origin, 1853–1927 (an axe), and with post-1953 Dutch control marks[2]

Provenance
Anonymous sale, Christie's, Amsterdam, December 3, 1992, lot 1054

Detail of a mount on one of the cases

Notes
[1] I am grateful to David Beasley, Librarian of the Goldsmiths' Company, for this information.
[2] According to the standard reference work, *Nederlandse verantwoordelijkheidstekens sinds 1797*, "the lack of knowledge of old marks had caused this mark to be sometimes struck on old foreign objects", (1995, pp. 44–5).

BASKET

49

Silver (sterling standard)
Maker's mark of Samuel Courtauld I (Grimwade, no. 2489)
Hallmarks: London, 1750–1

Of circular form on moulded spreading foot, the everted sides cast and pierced with interlaced basket weave and wheat ears with sheaves and sickles at intervals; the slightly domed centre engraved with a coat-of-arms within a foliate scroll and rocaille *cartouche flanked by wheat sheaves*

Inscription
Outside of the foot rim engraved: "The Bequest of The Right Honble. Frederick Vane who died April 27th 1801 to Sir Ralph D'Arcy Hildyard Bart."

Heraldry
The arms are those of Vane, probably as borne by Frederick Vane (1732–1801).

This basket is unusual, for most baskets of the mid-century are oval and have an overhead swing handle. The idea of imitating basketweave in silver appears as early as the sixteenth century. It appears in a slightly different form on the basket of 1731–2 from Lamerie's workshop (no. 26), where the sides are chased from sheet and pierced to give the impression of woven straw. The result is one-sided, for the decoration is only on the outside. Both interior and exterior of this basket's sides are detailed and applied with harvest symbols of

sheaves and sickles. As a result, the basket is just as decorative empty as full of bread.

Frederick Vane, a politician, was the second son of Henry, 3rd Baron Barnard. He married Henrietta, sister of Sir William Meredith, Bt, in 1758. After his wife's death, he married, in 1797, Jane, eldest daughter of Arthur Lysaght, but had no other issue.

Samuel, the second son of Augustine Courtauld, was born in 1720. He served his apprenticeship with his father and continued to work with him for another five years before finally entering his own mark with the Goldsmiths' Company in 1746. From this we can deduce that he was a practising silversmith, not merely a retailer. Work bearing his mark is consistently of a high standard.

Marks
Struck under base with hallmarks (leopard's head, lion passant, date letter) and with maker's mark

Provenance
Frederick Vane (1732–1801)
Bequeathed to Sir Ralph d'Arcy Hildyard, Bt
Subsequent provenance unknown until Asprey, London, 1990
S.J. Phillips Ltd, London

Height: 4 in (10 cm)
Diameter: 11 in (28 cm)
Weight: 60 oz (1866 g)

Detail of side

Detail of interior

FOUR DISHES

50

Silver (sterling standard)
Maker's mark of Frederick Kandler
Hallmarks: London, 1752–3

Of shaped circular form, the raised sides chased with spiral flutes, with gadrooned rim, the centres engraved with a coat-of-arms against drapery mantling

Heraldry
The arms are those of Weddell impaling those of Ramsden, as borne by William Weddell of Newby.

Dishes of this type were known as "sallet" or salad dishes and were used to serve cooked vegetables or fresh salads, both of which were known by the term "sallet".

As William Weddell married Elizabeth, daughter of Sir John Ramsden, Bt, in 1771, the engraving of the arms must be from after this date. The style of the drapery mantling, however, is typical of the mid-century and it may be that only the shield in the centre was re-engraved at that time.

Marks
Struck on reverses with hallmarks (leopard's head, lion passant, date letter) and with maker's mark

Provenance
Anonymous sale, Christie's, London, March 17, 1987, lot 320

Height: 1½ in (3.8 cm)
Width: 9⅜ in (23.8 cm)
Depth: 9⅜ in (23.8 cm)
Weight: 76 oz (2363 g)

BASKET

51

Silver (sterling standard)
Maker's mark of Phillips Garden (Grimwade, no. 2185)
Hallmarks: London, 1755–6

Formed as a shell and raised on three feet cast as wriggling dolphins, the scrolling upright handle cast as a mermaid terminating in twin tails amid marine ornament, the undulating rim applied with shells and sea foam and pierced within with foliate scrolls

Venus shell baskets like this, intended to be filled with either bread or grapes to illustrate Terence's line: "Sine Cerere et Tempero friget Venus", were a speciality of the Lamerie group. Examples with the marks of Lamerie,[1] of William Cripps, who is known to have made finished silver for Garden (see p. 52),[2] and of Thomas Heming are known,[3] but the largest group has Garden's mark on them.[4] A pair of 1747–8 with the maker's mark of Edward Wakelin is also known.[5] The graceful form of these baskets prompted Philip A.S. Phillips to remark that "… nothing more successful as table ornaments ever emanated from the goldsmith's workshop".[6]

Marks
Struck underneath with hallmarks (leopard's head, lion passant, date letter) and with maker's mark.

Provenance
Anonymous sale, Sotheby's, London, May 14, 1959, lot 115
Anonymous sale, Sotheby's, London, February 8, 1962, lot 130
Hilmar Reksten, Bergen, Norway
The Hilmar Reksten Collection, sale, Christie's, London, May 22, 1991, lot 48

Notes
[1] One is in the Philadelphia Museum of Art (gift of Mrs. Widener Dixon and George D. Widener, 1959-151-6) whose date is generally given as 1743–4, but as the others of this group date from after 1747, this may be a mis-reading of the date letter. The marks on this type of basket are often cut by the pierced decoration, as evidently the finished shell was submitted to the assay office for marking before the delicate work of piercing was carried out; a pair of 1747–8 is in the Ashmolean Museum, one of which was exhibited in *Paul de Lamerie: the Work of England's Master Silversmith*, exh. cat., Goldsmiths' Hall, London, 1990, no. 113.
[2] One of 1746 was sold Christie's, New York, October 21, 1993, lot 544, and a pair of 1750–1 is in a private collection.
[3] One of 1763–4 was sold Sotheby's, London, June 17, 1971, lot 34.
[4] One of 1750–1 is at Polesden Lacey, Surrey, see Michael Clayton, "Silver at Polesden Lacey" in *Apollo*, May, 1965, pp. 380; another of 1751–2 is in the Royal Collection and illustrated in E.A. Jones, *The Gold and Silver of Windsor Castle*, 1911, p. 84; another of 1754–5 was sold Christie's, London, July 12, 1995, lot 119; a pair of 1754–5 is in a private European collection.
[5] Sold Sotheby's, London, December 12, 1974, lot 142.
[6] *Paul de Lamerie, Citizen and Goldsmith of London*, 1935, p. 109.

Height: 9 in (22.8 cm)
Width: 14¾ in (37.5 cm)
Depth: 11 in (28 cm)
Weight: 61 oz (1897 g)

THREE CASTERS

52

Silver (sterling standard), the interiors gilt
Maker's mark of Phillips Garden (Grimwade, no. 2185)
Hallmarks: London, 1757–8

Comprising a large and a pair of smaller examples, egg-shaped, each on spreading domed bases flat-chased with foliage, rising to knopped stems chased with small vertical flutes, the bodies chased with vertical panels of flowers, the lower part with vertical lobes in two sizes; the removable covers of shaped square form, applied with straps chased with foliage and pierced with foliate scrolls between, the larger surmounted by a finial cast as an insect atop a flower, the smaller with insect finials, the fronts engraved with a vacant asymmetrical foliate scroll cartouche

The egg-shaped form of these casters is unusual; one other set is known, of 1756–7, with the maker's mark of Pierre Gillois. Some printed designs by Thomas Johnson and John Linnell, from the mid-century, illustrate vases with exotic outlines, and it may be that these casters were originally condiment vases and the covers have been pierced at a later date. Sets of condiment vases were usually intended for mustard (sprinkled as a powder over food), sugar and pepper and were often accompanied by small pierced ladles.[1]

Set of three casters, silver, London, 1756–7, maker's mark of Pierre Gillois.
I. Freeman & Son, New York

Marks
Struck on inside of foot rims with hallmarks (leopard's head, lion passant, date letter) and with maker's mark; the flanges of the covers struck with lion passant and maker's mark; both parts also struck with modern French control marks

Provenance
E. & C.T. Koopman Ltd, London

Note
[1] Michael Snodin, "Silver Vases and their Purposes" *Connoisseur*, January, 1977, pp. 37–42.

Largest:
Height: 7¾ in (19.7 cm)
Width: 3⅛ in (7.7 cm)
Depth: 3⅛ in (7.7 cm)
Total weight: 28 oz (870 g)

PAIR OF SAUCEBOATS AND LADLES

53

Silver (sterling standard)
Maker's mark of Edward Wakelin (Grimwade, no. 656)
Hallmarks: London, 1757–8

The sauce boats boat-shaped on spreading shaped oval bases cast and chased with scrolls, shells and gadrooning, the bodies cast and chased as overlapping cabbage leaves, with leaf-clad scroll handles, engraved with the initials HSE under an earl's coronet

The undersides engraved with scratch weights, one illegible, the other 23-17

The ladles with fluted shell bowls, the shaped stems terminating in leaves and engraved with the same initials and coronet

Initials
The initials and coronet are those borne by Hannah Sophia Cecil, Dowager Countess of Exeter (1702–65).

There is little symbolism in a sauce boat formed of cabbage leaves, and these examples show the movement away from classical imagery towards the picturesque that took place in the middle of the eighteenth century. Unlike Sprimont's sauceboats (no. 45), these come without the baggage of classical symbols which could be "read" by the educated consumer. Instead, they rely for their effect on the transformation, from nature to silver, of the leaves. Sauceboats of this form, which represent the last phase of the rococo in English silver, are rare: another pair of 1756–8, with the same maker's mark, is in the M.H. de Young Memorial Museum, San Francisco. The form was to be a popular one in porcelain. As early as the mid-1740s the Chelsea factory was producing wares formed of what is commonly known as the "strawberry leaf" pattern,[1] and by the 1760s a host of factories, including Longton Hall and Derby, were producing sauceboats and other wares formed of leaves.

Hannah Sophia, Countess of Exeter, married Brownlow, 8th Earl of Exeter in 1724. She was the daughter and co-heiress of a rich London merchant, Thomas Chambers. Lord Exeter died in 1754 and his widow continued to make extensive purchases of silver from Edward Wakelin during the next few years. Wakelin's "Gentlemen's

Sauceboats:
Height: 6¼ in (15.9 cm)
Width: 9¼ in (23 cm)
Depth: 4⅛ in (10.5 cm)
Ladles:
Length: 7½ in (19 cm)
Total weight: 51 oz 7 dwt (1598 g)

Teapot, porcelain, in the
"strawberry leaf" pattern,
Chelsea Factory,
c. 1744–9.
Colonial Williamsburg
Foundation

Coffee jug, silver, London,
1753–4, maker's mark of
Edward Wakelin.
H.S. Wellby Ltd

Ledger" for 1757 records the purchase of these sauceboats:

The R^t. Honble. The Countess Dowager of Exeter
1757
Oct.25

To a p^r. Leaf Saucebooats
                    48-1 @ 10/6   £25-4-6
To a p^r. of Shell Saucespoons
                    6-2 @ 6/-   1-16-8
To making   1-4
To Graving + Cyphers + Cor^{ts}.   10-

The two sauce boats were charged at 10s 6d per ounce, while the ladles, which required less work, cost only 6s per ounce. The surviving ledgers of George Wickes and his successors provide us with useful information regarding not only the business practices of the day, but also the prices of various types of silverware. A comparison of prices between then and today is always dangerous as relative values have changed so drastically, but it is evident from contemporary accounts that, after land, silver could represent the largest capital expenditure for an individual. The lion's share of the cost was in the raw material, which, of course, could always be readily converted back to cash. By comparison, the skilled labour was cheap: to engrave the sauceboats and ladles cost 10s, approximately a day's wages for a journeyman. An agricultural worker might earn £1 a week. By contrast, the widowed Countess of Exeter spent several hundred pounds with Wakelin on table silver and, a few years later, the Countess of Mountrath bequeathed her apothecary £8,000.

Marks
Sauceboats:
Struck under lips with hallmarks (leopard's head, lion passant, date letter) and with maker's mark
Ladles:
Struck on stems with hallmarks (one illegible, the other with leopard's head, lion passant, date

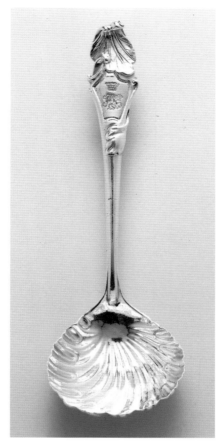

Detail of ladle

letter), both with maker's mark

Provenance
Hannah Sophia, Countess of Exeter (1702–65)
Then by descent to the Most Hon. The Marquess of Exeter, sale, Christie's, London, July 17, 1959, lot 66
Anonymous sale, Sotheby's, London, April 24, 1986, lot 149

Bibliography
Arthur Grimwade, *Rococo Silver 1727–1765*, pl. 35B
Elaine Barr, *George Wickes, Royal Goldsmith*, 1980, p. 109, illus. fig. 63

Note
[1] Elizabeth Adams, *Chelsea Porcelain*, 1987, illus. p. 28, figs. 15, 16.

SOUP TUREEN

~

54

Silver (sterling standard)
Maker's mark of Thomas Heming (Grimwade, no. 2797)
Hallmarks: London, 1758–9

Of shaped oval bombé *form, raised on four scroll feet headed by emerging hounds and stags, chased with spiral fluting under a gadrooned rim, the handles formed as heraldic wyverns, the domed cover with similar fluting and wyvern's head finial, the body engraved each side with a coat-of-arms within the Order of the Bath, with helm, motto and supporters*

Heraldry
The arms are those of Warren with those of Revel on an escutcheon of pretence, as borne by Sir George Warren, a Knight of Bath.

Heming's workshop produced silver in the French style during the 1750s and 1760s, much of it, like this tureen, taken from the published designs of Pierre Germain. Most of the silver objects which appear around the border on Heming's trade card (p. 54) are copied directly from designs in Germain's *Eléments d'Orfèvrerie*, which appeared in 1748 and was followed by additional designs two years later. This soup tureen follows a design for a *bombé* tureen illustrated as plate 80 in the 1750 edition of Germain's designs, although on the silver example wyverns, the heraldic beasts which support Warren's coat-of-arms, have been used as the handles for the body and the cover. Warren ordered a pair of wine coolers from Heming at the same time which not only have wyverns as the handles, but also closely follow another one of Pierre Germain's designs. Warren's arms also appear on a salver with the maker's mark of John Hugh Le Sage, of 1747–8.[1]

The source of Sir George Warren's wealth lay in his marriage to Jane, the daughter and co-heiress of a rich Surrey landowner, Thomas Revel. During

Height: 8½ in (21.6 cm)
Width: 17½ in (44.4 cm)
Depth: 9¼ in (23.5 cm)
Weight: 112 oz (3483 g)

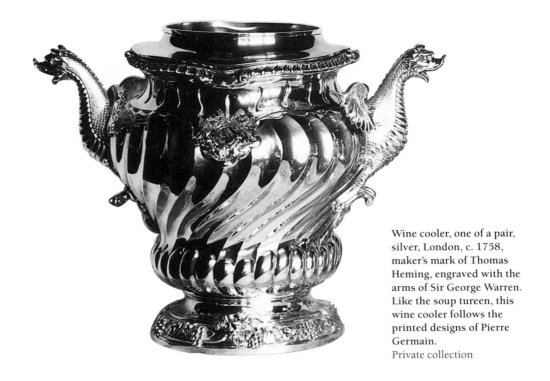

Wine cooler, one of a pair, silver, London, c. 1758, maker's mark of Thomas Heming, engraved with the arms of Sir George Warren. Like the soup tureen, this wine cooler follows the printed designs of Pierre Germain.
Private collection

Salver, silver, London, 1747–8, maker's mark of John Hugh Le Sage, engraved with the arms of Sir George Warren.
Christie's, New York

Design for a soup tureen
by Pierre Germain from his
Eléments d'Orfèvrerie of
1750.

his career as a soldier, Warren continued to buy land, mostly in his native Cheshire. He had one child, a daughter, Elizabeth Harriet, who married Thomas, Lord Bulkeley in 1777. She inherited the Warren estates, and as a result of this Lord Bulkeley assumed the name and arms of Warren in 1802. On her death in 1826 Lady Bulkeley left the Warren estates (amounting to some 2,500 acres in Cheshire) to a stranger, Frances Maria, Lady Vernon, in the mistaken belief that they were related. In fact, there was no evidence to support this apart from an erroneous pedigree in Watson's *House of Warren*.[2]

Marks

Struck under base and on cover flange with hallmarks (leopard's head, lion passant, date letter) and with maker's mark

Provenance

Sir George Warren, KB
Subsequent provenance unknown until anonymous sale, Sotheby's, New York, June 17, 1981, lot 64

Notes
[1] Christie's, New York, October 18, 1995, lot 390.
[2] G. E. Cokayne, ed., *The Complete Peerage*.

FOUR BASKETS

55

Silver, gilt
Maker's mark of John Parker and Edward Wakelin
Hallmarks: none
c. 1766

Of circular form, on spreading rim feet, the everted sides and feet pierced to resemble basket weave and applied on the outside with grape vine, the rims with flower and foliage applied borders

These baskets probably formed part of a dessert service and were intended to be arranged on a table, filled with fruit, nuts or sweetmeats. Foreign visitors often remarked on the English custom of removing the table cloth after the first two courses (which would have been served on white silver) and placing a dessert in silver-gilt dishes on the polished mahogany of the table top.[1] A set of four oval silver-gilt baskets, which appear to have been part of the same service, is also known. The oval baskets, engraved with armorials which appear to have been altered in the early nineteenth century, are also struck with Parker and Wakelin's mark; three have hallmarks for 1766, and the fourth, like these circular examples, is only struck with the maker's mark three times. It is clear that only part of the dessert service was submitted by Parker and Wakelin for assay at Goldsmiths' Hall and the duty paid on that part only. The rest, struck with their mark three times, would have appeared at first glance to have been hallmarked too.

Marks
Struck under bases with maker's mark struck three times; also numbered with dots 1–4

Provenance
Hilmar Reksten, Bergen, Norway
The Reksten Collection, sale, Christie's, London, May 22, 1991, lot 37

Note
[1] See François de la Rochefoucauld, *A Frenchman in England, 1784*, 1933, pp. 29–31.

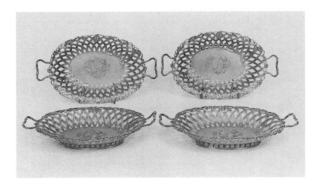

Four baskets, silver-gilt, London, 1766–7, maker's mark of Parker and Wakelin.
Sotheby's, New York

Height: 5 in (12.7 cm)
Diameter: 7 in (17.9 cm)
Weight: 66 oz (2052 g)

SILVER for DRINKING

The Brothers Clarke and Other Gentlemen taking Wine by Gawen Hamilton (c. 1697–1737), c. 1730. Yale Center for British Art, Paul Mellon Collection

TANKARD

56

Silver (sterling standard)
Maker's mark WI above a mullet in heart-shaped punch, possibly for William Jennings
(Jackson, p. 137, line 9)
Hallmarks: London, 1686–7

Of tapering cylindrical form raised on three massive cast dolphin feet, with moulded base rim and applied moulded mid-rib, the handle cast in the form of a serpent and scroll, the hinged domed cover chased with a band of oval lobes with acanthus between and surmounted by a baluster finial issuing from a calyx of chased swirling acanthus, with entwined dolphin thumbpiece; the front engraved with a coat-of-arms, helm and crest within foliate scroll mantling

Heraldry
The arms are those of Courthoppe, as borne by one of the two sons of Sir George Courthoppe, George Courthoppe (1646–1714) or Edward Courthoppe (b. 1651).

Sir George Courthoppe of Whiligh in Sussex was born in 1616. In 1643 he purchased, as his father had done before him, a lucrative sinecure from the Crown, the Commission of Alienations, for which he paid £1,300. During the Commonwealth he served as one of the Knights of the Shire for Essex but at the Restoration of Charles II in 1660 his loyalty to the crown was rewarded by a knighthood. He sat as MP for East Grinstead during much of Charles's reign and died in 1685. Interestingly, his wife, Elizabeth, who had died in 1660, left her daughter a silver "scallop shell sugar box".[1] Sir George left two sons, either of whom may have purchased this tankard in 1686, the year following his death. George Courthoppe, the eldest son, was Sheriff of Sussex in 1691 and died in 1714, aged 68, at Ticehurst, where there is a monument to him in the church. The younger son was Edward Courthoppe, who had been born at Ticehurst in 1651. He succeeded his father as Commissioner of Alienations and walked as a Gentleman Pensioner at the coronation of James II on the right hand of the king. He is believed to have committed suicide. In the absence of any mark of cadency, it seems most likely that the tankard was owned by Sir George Courthoppe's eldest son, who succeeded to his father's estates. In his will, Sir George directs his son "to give his Dear Mother one of y[e]. roomes with all such furniture as she shall best like & halfe of y[e]. plait duering her widdowhood & also such pieces as have been given to her to dispose of forever".[2]

The lack of many records from before 1697 at Goldsmiths' Hall in London makes identification

Height: 8 in (20.3 cm)
Width: 8¾ in (22.3 cm)
Depth: 7¼ in (18.5 cm)
Weight: 48 oz (1501 g)

Tankard, silver, London, 1675,
maker's mark *IH*, fleur-de-lys
between pellet below (Jackson,
p. 138, line 21).
Christie's, New York

of most makers' marks of this period impossible.
In only a few cases can a corpus of work with the
same maker's mark be matched to an individual
with the same initials. In this case, the identity of
the silversmith who used the mark *WI* is
unknown. A William Jennings is listed by Heal as
a goldsmith in Pall Mall in 1686. He was admitted
a freeman of the Goldsmiths' Company on March
15, 1692/3,[3] but there is insufficient evidence to
make a definite attribution.

The style and methods used in the manufacture of
the tankard, however, provide us with a clue.
Most London-made tankards of the period are
plain cylinders, quite often of thin-gauge silver,
with decoration limited to an occasional band of
naively chased foliage. By contrast, this tankard,
with its boldly modelled handle and feet, is
technically far in advance of the work of most

Dressing glass, silver, walnut,
London, 1692–3, maker's mark
WI, star below, possibly for
William Jennings.
Museum of Fine Arts, Boston

English silversmiths of the period. Similar cast
handles appear on north German tankards of the
same period and were introduced to England by a
small group of immigrant craftsmen. This group
includes Jacob Bodendick,[4] who came from
Limburg in Germany, and Wolfgang Howzer, a
Swiss. Yet the style of this tankard is quite distinct
from work bearing Bodendick's and Howzer's
marks. Grotesque handles and unusual cast feet
in the form of animals also appear on tankards
bearing the maker's mark of a native-born master,
Thomas Jenkins, suggesting that he may have
employed foreigners, or "strangers" in his
workshop.[5] Another group of tankards is also
known with cast eagle feet and thumbpieces, all
bearing the maker's mark *IH* with a
fleur-de-lys, which is also unattributed.[6]

Other pieces struck with the maker's mark *WI* are

also firmly in the Germanic style. A dressing glass
frame of 1692–3 in the Museum of Fine Arts,
Boston, is surmounted by putti modelled with the
same vigour as the dolphins supporting this
tankard. The frame is in the foliate baroque style,
with elaborately chased foliate scrolls around the
border, and Ellenor Alcorn has drawn attention to
similarities with mirrors struck with the maker's
mark of Jacob Bodendick.[7] Two tazze, or salvers,
of 1686 also with the same maker's mark, set with
plaques depicting mythological scenes, are in the
Ashmolean Museum, Oxford. Plaques like these,
some of which appear to be chased and some cast,
are often found set into components of toilet
services of the period and may have been supplied
by one workshop. Whether these plaques, like the
cast components of this tankard, were imported
from the continent or made in London, most
probably by "stranger" craftsmen, is not known.[8]
It may be that Jennings employed immigrant
journeymen, or else operated a retail shop selling
their work.

Marks
Struck on rim by handle and on cover flange with
hallmarks (leopard's head, lion passant, date
letter) and with maker's mark

Notes
[1] Philippa Glanville, *Silver in Tudor and Stuart England*, 1990,
p. 366.
[2] Courthoppe Papers, East Sussex Record Office, Lewes,
SAS/CO/106.
[3] Sir Ambrose Heal, *The London Goldsmiths 1200–1800*, 1935,
p. 183; intriguingly this mark does not appear on the surviving
copper plate of pre-1697 makers' marks (I am grateful to David
Beasley, Librarian of the Goldsmiths' Company, for this
information).
[4] For examples of his work see Ellenor M. Alcorn, *English Silver in
the Museum of Fine Arts, Boston*, vol I, 1993, nos. 56, 59, 64 and
"English Silver 1660–1760", *The Museum of Fine Arts, Houston,
Bulletin*, Fall, 1987, p. 13.
[5] Judith Bannister, "The Master Craftsman", *The Proceedings of the
Society of Silver Collectors*, vol. II, p. 187; a pair of tankards of
1675–6 with this maker's mark is at Dunham Massey, Cheshire.
[6] See Christie's, New York, December 15, 1986, lot 330.
[7] Alcorn, *op. cit.*, p. 190.
[8] See David Mitchell, "Dressing Plate by the 'Unknown' London
Silversmith 'WF'", *The Burlington Magazine*, June, 1993,
pp. 386–400.

MONTEITH

57

Silver (Britannia standard)
Maker's mark of William Gibson (Grimwade, no. 824)
Hallmarks: London, 1698–9

Of circular form on spreading base chased with a broad band of gadrooning, the sides chased with long spiral scrolls forming nine panels with pendant bellflowers and stylized leaves on a matted ground between, the shaped rim applied with a border of gadrooning with female masks against shells at intervals; five of the panels containing engraved armorials

Heraldry

The bowl bears five coats-of-arms showing a line of descent from about 1699 to after 1821; they are the arms of:

1. French with those of Farrell on an escutcheon of pretence, as borne by Christopher French of Tyrone who married Margery, daughter of Iriel Farrell of Cloonyquin in county Roscommon, about 1699.
2. French impaling those of Usher, as borne by Arthur French, the son of Christopher French, who married Olivia, eldest daughter of John Usher, Governor of county Galway and Vice Admiral of Connaught, on January 23, 1736.
3. French impaling those of Farrell.

4. St George quartering those of French and impaling those of Bingham, as borne by Arthur French St George, formerly Arthur French, who married Anne, eldest daughter of Henry Bingham of Newbrook, county Mayo, in 1778. Arthur French was granted the right to bear the surname St George in compliance of a settlement made by his forebear George, Lord St George, by a Royal Licence of 1811.
5. St George quartering others and impaling those of St Lawrence, as borne by Arthur French St George, who married Harriet, second daughter of William St Lawrence, Earl of Howth, in 1801. The use of the supporters which flank this shield was granted to Arthur St George by a Royal Licence in 1821.

The repetition of the arms of French impaling those of Farrell in no. 3 is unexplained. Stylistically, the asymmetrical cartouche surrounding this shield dates from the 1740s and may have been added by Christopher French late in life.

Height: 8⅛ in (20.6 cm)
Diameter: 13⅛ in (33.7 cm)
Weight: 58 oz (1804 g)

1

2

3

4

5

Arms engraved on the monteith

Detail from *A Rake's Progress* by William Hogarth (1697–1764) c. 1735, showing a monteith presented as a race prize

The monteith is an invention of the late seventeenth century which served the dual purpose of punch bowl and glass cooler. Its name is explained by the well-known entry in the journal of Anthony à Wood for December 1683: "this year in the summer-time came up a vessel or bason notched at the brim to let drinking vessels hang there by the foot, so that the body or drinking place might hang into the water to cool them. Such a bason was called a Monteigh from a fantastical Scott called Monsieur Monteigh who at that time or a little before wore the bottom of his cloake or coate so notched U U U U". Monteigh was evidently a fashionable man about town, described by Samuel Pepys as "a swaggering handsome young gentleman", who achieved immortality by giving his name to this type of bowl:

New things produce new words and so
                                                    Monteith
Has by one vessel saved himself from
                                                    Death

So wrote King in his *Art of Cookery* in 1707.[1]

The popularity of the monteith lasted until the 1720s when the fashion for chilling wines was superseded by a taste for fortified wines like port, drunk at room temperature, or hot punch or negus. Few are found with the marks of Huguenot makers which is perhaps explained by the fact that it is not a French form. The stylized foliage chased between the panels on this bowl retains some auricular elements popular in the middle years of the century, while the bold gadrooned decoration of the foot is produced by chasing rather than the casting one would expect on work bearing a Huguenot maker's mark. The only cast element is the rim which is applied with somewhat naive and poorly cast faces.

William Gibson was apprenticed to George Garthorne in 1682 and was admitted a freeman of the Goldsmiths' Company in 1690. The Garthorne family were among the more prosperous non-Huguenot silversmiths of the period and both George – and Francis, presumed to be his son – were signatories to the petition against "aliens and foreigners" in 1697. One of their main products was the monteith and it is hardly surprising that Gibson's monteith closely follows the output of his former master.

Gibson appears repeatedly in the parish registers of St Vedast, Foster Lane; after 1705 the entries refer to Mr William Gibson, "her Majties Lyon Keeper in the Tower" and, as Arthur Grimwade observes, "they provide evidence of the most unlikely change of occupation for a goldsmith one could imagine".[2]

Marks
Struck near rim with hallmarks (lion's head erased, Britannia, date letter) and with maker's mark.

Notes
[1] Georgina Lee, *British Silver Monteith Bowls*, 1978, p. 11.
[2] *The London Goldsmiths 1697–1837*, rev. edn, 1990, p. 522.

TANKARD

58

Silver (Britannia standard)
Maker's mark of Isaac Dighton (Grimwade, no. 476)
Hallmarks: London, 1699–1700

Of slightly tapering form on spreading moulded foot, the lower part of the body with applied rib, the tubular scroll handle issuing from cut-card stylized foliage and applied under the hinge with similar decoration, with shaped escutcheon-form terminal; the slightly domed cover with scalloped lip and a border of scribed concentric circles, with bifurcated scroll thumbpiece and ball finial issuing from a calyx of cut-card radiating foliage; the front engraved with a circular coat-of-arms within a cartouche of foliate scrolls, cornucopiæ and fish-scale

Heraldry
The arms, those of an eagle displayed, are borne by numerous families and in the absence of the tinctures being specified, precise identification is impossible.

This tankard is unusual in that it follows conventional form but is embellished with strapwork, more often found on ewers and cups. Tankards are seldom found bearing the marks of Huguenot makers, presumably as it was not a vessel used in France and by the end of the seventeenth century it had become a purely utilitarian object seldom made by the first rank of craftsmen whether English or foreign. Isaac Dighton was one of the signatories to the petition to the Goldsmiths' Company of 1703 which opposed marking foreigners' work, so we must assume that the high quality of the casting of the finial and thumbpiece is the product of native English workmen, possibly trained by the German "strangers" of some years earlier.

Mark
Struck on side by handle with hallmarks (lion's head erased, Britannia, date letter) and with maker's mark; the cover with maker's mark struck four times by thumbpiece, the handle with maker's mark struck once

Provenance
Lord McAlpine of West Green, sale, Sotheby's, West Green House, May 17, 1990, lot 798

Height: 8½ in (21.6 cm)
Width: 9 in (22.9 cm)
Depth: 5¾ in (14.6 cm)
Weight: 34 oz 14 dwt (1081 g)

MONTEITH

59

Silver (Britannia standard)
Maker's mark of Anthony Nelme (Grimwade, no. 68)
Hallmarks: London, 1705–6

Of circular form, on domed spreading foot, with two hinged baluster ring handles issuing from male masks and applied front and back with oval cartouches enclosed by scrolls and strapwork, one engraved with an oval coat-of-arms within a foliate scroll border surmounted by a shell, the other engraved with a crest within a similar border; the removable rim formed of eight trefoil panels with notches between, applied with granulated moulding and pendant bell flowers

Heraldry

The arms are those of Throckmorton, with those of Yate on an escutcheon of pretence, as borne by Sir Robert Throckmorton, 3rd Bt (1662–1720).

The Throckmortons were eminent Catholics and suffered many deprivations during the reign of Elizabeth I, having been involved in the so-called Throckmorton Plot of 1583 which had sought the overthrow of Elizabeth. Sir Robert's great-grandfather, Thomas, was repeatedly imprisoned and lost considerable property. Sir Robert succeeded to the baronetcy in 1680 on the death of his father and on January 15, 1682/3 was admitted to Gray's Inn. He partially rebuilt the family house at Weston Underwood in Warwickshire, and was remembered as a great benefactor to the surrounding region. He was one of the Catholic "nonjurors". He married Mary, second daughter and heiress of Sir Charles Yate, 3rd Bt of Buckland, near Farringdon, Berkshire. He died aged 58 in 1720 and was succeeded by his son, also Robert, who spent much of his time abroad on account of his religion; in Paris in 1729 he, and his three sisters who were all nuns of the Augustinian Convent in Paris, were each painted by Nicolas de Largillière.

Height: 9⅛ in (23.2 cm)
Diameter: 13⅕ in (33.5 cm)
Weight: 96 oz 4 dwt (2992 g)

A virtually identical monteith of 1722–3, bearing the same maker's mark, is at Clare College, Cambridge, given by George, Viscount Parker.[1]

This monteith makes an interesting comparison with no. 57. The sculptural quality of the rim mouldings, the armorial cartouche and the lion-mask handles are all elements found on many of Daniel Marot's designs for silver, while the quality of the castings is far superior to Edward Gibson's example. Although Nelme was vociferous in his opposition to the "necessitous strangers", it is known that he used German immigrant journeymen.

Marks

Struck under body and on removable rim with hallmarks (lion's head erased, Britannia, date letter) and with maker's mark; each handle struck with lion's head erased and Britannia

Provenance

Sir Robert Throckmorton, 3rd Bt (1662–1720) Subsequent provenance unknown until anonymous sale, Sotheby's, London, November 17, 1988, lot 85

Note
[1] Foster & Atkinson, *An Illustrated Catalogue of the Loan Collection of Plate exhibited at the Fitzwilliam Museum*, May, 1895, p. 64, no. 105.

WINE COOLER

60

Silver (Britannia standard)
Maker's mark of David Willaume I (Grimwade, no. 3194)
apparently overstriking that of another
Hallmarks: London, 1718–9

Of elongated octagonal form, the stepped base cast and chased with a border of stiff foliage, the tapering sides cast and chased with panels of diaperwork enclosing flowerheads and, on each end, with an alternating pattern of circles and flowerheads, all above a band of foliate scrolls on a matted ground, each upper corner with a flowerhead, applied front and back with a shaped fish-scale and laurel cartouche surmounted by an earl's coronet and engraved in the centre with an earl's armorials, the shoulder cast and chased with panels of crisscross and stylized flowerheads, the rim with a band of alternating flowers and lacing, with two reeded cast loop handles with double-acanthus and baluster heads, the interior fitted with a removable platform elaborately pierced with foliate scrolls

Scratched under the base with weight 105-16

Inscription
The inscription under the base reads: "Lord Camden [sic] was Babtized [sic] with water that was put into this July yᵉ 12 1740 at Blackheath."

Heraldry
The arms are those of Noel, Earls of Gainsborough.

In the absence of any impalement it is impossible to be certain by which earl the armorials on this wine cooler were added. The arms sit a little awkwardly in the oval cartouche, which is really intended to contain a coat-of-arms rather than an entire achievement and, somewhat needlessly, the coronet which appears above the cartouche is repeated in the engraving. The rather stiff handling of the supporters and the proportions of the supporters in relation to the coat-of-arms suggest a mid-eighteenth-century date. An inscription scratched under the base refers to Noel, 4th Earl of Gainsborough (the eldest son of the Earls of Gainsborough bore the courtesy title Viscount Campden). In fact it is possible that the wine cooler was given as a christening present and entered the family collection at that time, as Lord Campden's father, the 4th Earl, was only ten years old when the wine cooler was made in 1718, having succeeded to the earldom on the sudden death of his father of smallpox in 1714. By 1740 individual wine coolers like this were becoming outmoded and this may explain its use in that year as a christening font.

The individual wine cooler enjoyed a brief period

Height: 7½ in (19 cm)
Width: 12½ in (31.8 cm)
Depth: 7¼ in (18.5 cm)
Weight: 104 oz (3234 g)

of popularity from the end of the seventeenth century until the 1720s. Large wine "cisterns", usually oval and intended to sit on the floor, had been used to chill flasks or ewers of wine. All types of wine, including red, were drunk chilled.[1] The advent of the glass wine bottle at the end of the seventeenth century, and the increase in private, less formal dining, created the need for an individual bottle cooler which could be placed on the table. Wine coolers like this appear in Pierre Lepautre's engraving of Louis XIV's sideboard at Marly.[2] Among the earliest surviving English examples are a pair supplied by Willaume to the Duke of Devonshire in 1698[3] and a pair in gold made for the Duke of Marlborough about 1700 and now in the British Museum.

Few wine coolers appear to have been made after 1730,[4] and their decline in popularity is perhaps explained by the change in drinking habits that took place during the first half of the eighteenth century. Owing to the almost continual war with the French, and the favourable rates of duty given to Portuguese wines after the Methuen Treaty was signed in 1703, French wines all but disappeared from England by the 1720s. The fortified red wine known as "port", which under the Hanoverians became known as "the Englishman's wine", was drunk at room temperature. It was not until the 1770s, when the consumption of French wines

became widespread once again, and – perhaps most importantly – sparkling champagne became popular, that the custom of chilling wine revived.

This wine cooler belongs to a small group of English octagonal examples decorated with panels of diaperwork in the severest French taste. The recessed panels of crisscross with rosettes between contrast with the plain surrounds and create a tension of dynamic surfaces which is typically baroque. The panels, and the borders of rosettes within lacing, derive from the designs of Jean Berain of some thirty years earlier which were adapted by Daniel Marot and used in his pattern books *Vases de la Maison Royalle de Loo*, published about 1700, and *Nouveaux Livre d'Orfèvrerie* which appeared in 1712. Diaperwork appears on English silver as early as 1686, on a two-handled tray supplied by the Harache workshop to the Capel family,[5] and similar diaperwork panels within plain borders appear on a soup tureen supplied by the Paris silversmith Claude Ballin to the court of Bavaria in 1705, but the distinctive use of the octagon does not start until about 1712 in either France or England. The French court goldsmith Nicolas de Launay appears to have used these decorative motifs in conjunction with octagonal and other geometric forms in silver he designed for the Countess Oxenstierna-Steenbock, in the 1690s, the drawings for which exist in

Wine cooler (one of a pair),
silver, London, 1716–17,
maker's mark of William
Lukin, applied with the
arms of Sir Robert Walpole.
Metropolitan Museum of Art,
New York, gift of Irwin
Untermyer 1968
(68.141.129)

A pair of French gilt-metal wine coolers of identical form and decoration is known, as are two silver-plated low candlesticks with similar diaperwork panels. Both of these have traditionally been dated to 1700 but it seems unlikely that these are earlier than about 1715.[7] Only one pair of French silver wine coolers of similar form appears to have survived, however. They are a pair with marks for Paris, 1727–8, and were probably commissioned by Horace Walpole, younger brother of Sir Robert Walpole, when he was ambassador to Paris. They lack a maker's mark but have been attributed to Nicolas Besnier, from whom Walpole ordered a pair of *pots à oille* in 1726.[8] While following the form and basic decoration of the Gainsborough cooler, the Walpole examples have foliage and shellwork added at the corners, giving an early suggestion of rococo on an essentially baroque form.

Of the known English examples of this form, a pair of 1716–17 is in the Untermyer Collection at the Metropolitan Museum of Art, New York[9] with drop ring handles and with the applied arms of Sir Robert Walpole. This pair bears the maker's mark of a non-Huguenot, William Lukin, and may well have emanated from a Huguenot workshop and been retailed by Lukin. Two further examples, one of 1703, maker's mark of Pierre Platel, and one of 1716, maker's mark of Paul de Lamerie, are in the Philadelphia Museum of Art.[10]

The 4th Earl took as his wife, Elizabeth, the daughter of his gamekeeper, William Chapman. They were married in 1728 but the marriage was not declared until 1736.[11] Their first son, Noel,

Stockholm,[6] but perhaps the earliest surviving French silver pieces in this severely geometric style are a pair of double salt cellars, each formed of three octagons and with the same decoration as this wine cooler, bearing Paris marks for 1712–13 and with the maker's mark of Jacques Trouve. A gilt bronze inkstand in similar style is in the J. Paul Getty Museum, Malibu, California and has been dated about 1715.

Double salt with pepper box, silver, Paris, 1712–13, maker's mark of Jacques Trouve, formerly in the Jean Bloch Collection.
Sotheby's, Monaco

Wine cooler (one of a pair),
silver, Paris, 1727–8,
attributed to Nicolas
Besnier.
Sotheby's, New York

was educated at Eton and succeeded to the title as
5th Earl at the age of eleven in 1751. He died,
unmarried, at Geneva in 1759 and was succeeded
by his brother Henry as 6th Earl. This earl appears
to have had little taste for public life and died,
unmarried, in 1798. The lack of any impalement
on the coat-of-arms suggests an unmarried man
and it may be that the arms were added by this
holder of the title, sometime between 1759 and
1798.

Marks
Struck under base with hallmarks (lion's head
erased, Britannia, date letter) and with
maker's mark

Provenance
Baptist Noel, 4th Earl of Gainsborough
(1694–1759)
Then by descent to a Gentleman, sale, Christie's,
London, November 10, 1993, lot 250

Exhibited
Seaford House, London, 1929, *Queen Charlotte's
Loan Exhibition of Old Silver*, no. 461, p. 69, lent
by Major M.W. Noel

Notes
[1] It is interesting to read a letter written by George Washington in
1789 where he speaks of the need for "useful coolers for wine *at*
and *after* dinner" (Kathryn Buhler, *Mount Vernon Silver*, 1957, p.
50).
[2] James Lomax, *British Silver at Temple Newsam and Lotherton
Hall*, 1992, p. 60.
[3] Jackson-Stops *et al.*, *Treasure Houses of Britain*, exh. cat., 1985,
no. 117.
[4] An exception is the pair dating from the early 1740s at Blenheim
Palace which bear what appear to be transposed hallmarks
(probably "duty dodgers") and the maker's mark of Paul Crespin.
[5] The Meech Collection, sale, Sotheby's, New York, October 22,
1993, lot 50.
[6] *Versailles à Stockholm*, exh. cat., Hotel de Marle, Paris, 1985, pp.
199–204.
[7] Both are in the Puiforcat Collection in the Louvre and illustrated
in Gerard Mabille, *La Collection Puiforcat, Donation de Stavros
S. Niarchos au Département des Objets d'Arts*, 1994, nos. 46 and
47.
[8] The Ortiz-Patiño Collection, Sotheby's, New York, May 21,
1992, lot 114.
[9] Yvonne Hackenbroch, *English and other Silver in the Irwin
Untermyer Collection*, 1963, no. 43, illus. pls. 50 and 51.
[10] Gift of Mrs. Widener Dixon and George D. Widener (1959.151-
7, 8); these have plain diaperwork panels on the centre of each
side rather than an applied cartouche, although distortion on the
interiors suggests that they may originally have had applied arms
which have been removed. Like the present example they also
have an interior ledge to support a pierced strainer, which is now
missing.
[11] John Cannon, *Aristocratic Century*, 1984, p. 77; G.E. Cokayne,
ed. *The Complete Peerage*.

PUNCH BOWL

61

Silver
Maker's mark of Paul de Lamerie (Hare, no. 2)
Hallmarks: none
c. 1719

*Of circular form with moulded rim, on domed
spreading foot applied with a band of alternating
bellflowers and lobed straps on a matted ground, the
lower part of the body applied with palmettes on a
matted ground alternating with lobed key-hole
straps headed by scrolls on a fish-scale ground, the
two hinged scroll handles issuing from boldly cast
lion masks, engraved on one side with a viscount's
armorials and, on the other side, with a crest within
a foliate scroll, strapwork and bellflower cartouche
surmounted by a viscount's coronet*

Heraldry

The arms are those of Brownlow, as borne by Sir
John Brownlow, 5th Bt (1690–1754) of Belton
House, Lincolnshire. He was created Viscount
Tyrconnel in 1718.

Belton House in Lincolnshire was built in the
late seventeenth century by Sir John
Brownlow, 3rd Bt. Since then the house has
changed little (it now belongs to the National
Trust) but it is to Sir John's nephew, also John,
later Lord Tyrconnel, that it owes its superb
contents. Despite sales of pictures and plate in the
twentieth century, it remains one of the most
intact collections of the eighteenth century.

The young Sir John Brownlow married his cousin
in 1712, bringing together the property of the two
branches of the family. By 1718 he and his wife
were installed at Belton and in that year he was
elevated to the peerage as Viscount Tyrconnel. No
seat in the House of Lords came with this, an Irish
title, however, so Tyrconnel was able to retain his
seat in the House of Commons and continue his
political career there at the centre of the political
scene. Yet as Gervase Jackson-Stops remarked, "If
Lord Tyrconnel's professional activities as a
politician were scarcely remembered beyond his
own lifetime, we know him today as the first
member of his family to be recognized as a
collector".[1] Tyrconnel was a courtier and friend of
Frederick, Prince of Wales and very involved in
the artistic circles that surrounded the prince. His
place in the prince's circle, however, made him the
butt of Lord Hervey's caustic wit. Hervey, as
confidant to the Queen, naturally despised the
prince's friends, while George II himself described
Tyrconnel as "a puppy that never votes twice on
the same side".[2] He was famous for his love of
pomp and show, and when he had proposed to
Mary Pendarves, later Mrs. Delany, after the death
of his first wife, she refused him, saying that "he
had the character very justly of being silly". He
and his family appear in a group painted by

Height: 7⅝ in (19.4 cm)
Width: 11 in (28 cm)
Depth: 10½ in (26.6 cm)
Weight: 99 oz 14 dwt (3103 g)

Viscount Tyrconnel and his Family by Philippe Mercier (1689–1760), c. 1725.
Belton House, Lincolnshire: National Trust Photographic Library/John Hammond

Detail of punch bowl handle

Philippe Mercier about 1725 which still hangs at Belton and it is probably to Tyrconnel that Mercier owed his introduction to the Prince of Wales some years later.

The same applied vertical straps appear on an unmarked silver-gilt covered cup still at Belton, evidently ordered at the same time as the punch bowl. It bears Lord Tyrconnel's arms on one side and the arms of the 1st Baron Brownlow (after 1776) on the other. Evidently Lord Tyrconnel ordered a "laying-down" of plate in the years following his elevation to the peerage, and avoided paying the newly established duty of 6d per ounce on much of it, as the punch bowl is marked only with Lamerie's maker's mark and lacks the hallmarks which would have denoted that the duty had been paid. It seems likely that the unmarked cup[3] comes from the same workshop.[4] Other cups with the same applied decoration and Lamerie's maker's mark are known, including one of 1717–18 in the Gilbert Collection,[5] another of the same date in the Portland Art Museum, Oregon[6] and another of

1718–19 in the Al-Tajir Collection. A cup with the same decoration of 1716–17 and with the maker's mark of Lamerie's master, Pierre Platel, is in the Thyssen Collection.[7] These cups prompt the question, first posed by Timothy Schroder[8] whether the two cups bearing Lamerie's maker's mark were bought by him from Platel's estate in finished state and submitted by him for assay after he had added his own maker's mark. Another explanation, favoured by Schroder, is that Lamerie inherited his master's ornamental mouldings and continued to use them in his own workshop. This appears to be confirmed by the Brownlow punch bowl and the fact that it is a "duty dodger" and as such cannot be dated earlier than 1719, the year duty on wrought plate sent for assay was introduced.

The characterful lions' faces which hold the handles were to figure frequently in the work of Lamerie and others during the next two decades. A pair of sauceboats of 1733–4 from Lamerie's workshop, with feet headed by similar masks, is in the Gilbert Collection.[9]

The punch bowl does not appear in any of the early eighteenth-century inventories of plate at Belton (which are somewhat patchy) and it may always have been at the Tyrconnel's London house. An inventory done at Belton in 1772 lists "1 large Silver Punch Bowl L^d. T^s. Arms one Side Sir J^s. Arms the other Side"[10] which may be the present example, but, in the absence of any weight, it is impossible to be certain. The bowl may originally have been fitted with a detachable rim, now lost: a "monteith" is listed in Belton inventories of 1754 and 1772.[11]

Marks
Struck twice under base with maker's mark

Provenance
John Brownlow, Viscount Tyrconnel (1690–1754)
Then by descent to the Right Honourable Lord Brownlow, *Magnificent English Royal Plate*, sale, Christie's, London, May 29, 1963, lot 10
Spink & Son Ltd, London

Cup and cover, silver, London, 1717–18, maker's mark of Paul de Lamerie. Portland Art Museum, Oregon (W.H. Nunn Trust Fund, in memory of his wife, Alice B. Nunn)

Bibliography
P.A.S. Phillips, *Paul de Lamerie, Citizen and Goldsmith of London*, 1935, p. 81 and illus. pl. XXXV
Timothy Schroder, *The Gilbert Collection of Silver and Gold*, 1988, p. 154, illus. fig. 40
Susan Hare, ed., "Paul de Lamerie 1688–1751" in *Paul de Lamerie: the Work of England's Master Silversmith*, exh. cat., Goldsmiths' Hall, London, 1990, no. 14, the marks illustrated p. 9, fig. 1

Exhibited
25 Park Lane, London, 1929, cat. no. 775
Goldsmiths' Hall, London, 1990, *Paul de Lamerie: the Work of England's Master Silversmith*, cat. no. 14

Cup and cover, silver-gilt, c. 1719. Although unmarked, this cup probably formed part of the same order for plate from Paul de Lamerie about 1719.
Belton House, Lincolnshire: National Trust Photographic Library/Angelo Hornak

Notes
[1] *The Treasure Houses of Britain*, exh. cat., Washington, D.C., 1985, no. 166.
[2] Hervey, *Memoirs*, quoted in Earl of Ilchester, *Lord Hervey and his Friends 1726–1738*, 1950, p. 186n.
[3] The cup was exhibited in 1985 (*The Treasure Houses of Britain*, *op. cit.*, no. 112); it is mentioned in an inventory of plate drawn up on the death of Lord Tyrconnel in 1754 (Belton MSS).
[4] A pair of baskets which also appear to be "duty dodgers", bearing the maker's mark only of Lamerie's contemporary, Francis Nelme, and dating from the same period was included in the Brownlow sale in 1963.
[5] Timothy Schroder, *The Gilbert Collection of Silver and Gold*, 1988, no. 36.
[6] W.H. Nunn Trust Fund, 61.9.
[7] H. Muller, *The Thyssen-Bornemisza Collection: European Silver*, 1986, no. 6.
[8] "Paul de Lamerie: Businessman or Craftsman", *The Silver Society Journal*, 6, Winter, 1994, p. 267.
[9] Timothy Schroder, *op. cit.*, no. 53.
[10] Belton MSS, Lincolnshire Record Office, Lincoln, BNLW 2/2/5/27.
[11] *ibid*, BNLW 2/2/5/20 and 27. I am grateful to Chris Johnson for making these available to me.

PUNCH BOWL

62

Silver (Britannia standard)
Maker's mark of John East (Grimwade, no. 525)
Hallmarks: London, 1719–20

Of plain hemispherical form on spreading moulded foot, with moulded rim, engraved under the rim with an inscription terminating in a foliate paraph, the front engraved with a coat-of-arms, helm, crest and motto within foliate scroll mantling (with VIII below) and enclosed within a scribed circle

Inscription
The inscription reads: "Donum Lanæ Coactorum in Oppido Mancestriensi et Vicinia adjacenti Jeremiæ & Ellin Bower Anno Domini 1719 . Vivat Rex . ffloreat Artificium."

Heraldry
The arms are those of the Company of Haberdashers. The Roman numeral VIII in the mantling may refer to the fact that the Company is eighth in order of precedence among London livery companies.

The inscription translates: "The gift of the felt makers in the town of Manchester and vicinity Jeremy & Ellin Bower Year of the Lord 1719. Long live the King. May the craft flourish."

When sold in 1993 the word *Coactorum* in the inscription was translated as tax and it was thought that the bowl represented wool tax revenue in the area. It has been convincingly argued, however, by Dr J.D. Renwick that as the Latin for felt is *coactilis*, the author of the inscription combined this word with *lana*, or wool, to make up the word *lanæ coactor*, or feltmaker.[1]

The records of the London Company of Haberdashers do not appear to include this punch bowl, nor do they provide any clue to its presentation. No one by the name of Jeremy or Ellin Bower became Free of the Company during the period 1650 and 1725, nor did anyone of the name of Bradbury (the surname of the vendor in 1993 in whose family it had descended).[2] A Jeremy and Ellin Bower are recorded as the parents of a child christened in the parish church

Height: 7¼ in (18.5 cm)
Diameter: 12 in (30.5 cm)
Weight: 57 oz (1772 g)

Details of inscription

of Leek, Staffordshire on September 17, 1721, but no Bowers appear to have been prominent in business in the Manchester district.

John East's mark appears on workman-like plate in the English style. Not unsurprisingly he was apprenticed to George Garthorne, whose output is similar to his, and like his master he signed petitions railing against the competition of foreign workers.

Marks
Struck under base with hallmarks (lion's head erased, Britannia, date letter) and with maker's mark

Provenance
Anonymous sale, Lawrence of Crewkerne, April 27, 1993

Bibliography
Country Life, May 27, 1993, illus. p. 86

Notes
[1] *Country Life*, June 10, 1993.
[2] I am grateful to Dr. H.L. Bradley, Archivist of the Haberdashers' Company, for this information.

TANKARD

63

Silver (sterling standard)
Maker's mark of Thomas Tearle (Grimwade, no. 2938)
Hallmarks: London, 1726–7

Of slightly tapering form on spreading foot, with
applied moulded mid-rib and tubular scroll handle
with shield-shaped terminal, applied by the hinge
with a flattened baluster drop; the hinged domed
cover with scroll thumbpiece on tri-form support;
the front engraved above the rib with a galloping
racehorse with jockey up, and below The Bay Colt
Stourbridge Octbr. 11, 1726, *the handle engraved*
with the initials M *over* E I

The engraving of a racehorse and jockey on
this tankard is of a standard form which
frequently appears on racing prizes from the end
of the seventeenth century to the 1730s[1] and is
based on engravings in books such as Richard
Blome's *The Gentleman's Recreation* of 1686. This
book, which went through numerous editions and
was probably the most popular book on sport of
the period, has a plate devoted to *Horse Raceing*
engraved by Arthur Soly after Jan Wyck which
shows similar horses and riders. Another well-
known etching, *The Last Horse Race run before*
Charles the Second of Blessed Memory by Dorset
Ferry near Windsor Castle, published in 1687, also
shows similar horses.[2]

Racing had been organized at Croydon in the
sixteenth century but James I appears to have
been the first monarch interested in the sport. He
built a palace at Newmarket and was present at
the first race run there in 1619. The earliest prizes
were bells but after the Restoration racing was
enthusiastically patronized by Charles II, who
seems to have introduced the custom of

Height: 9¼ in (23.4 cm)
Width: 8½ in (21.6 cm)
Depth: 6 in (15.2 cm)
Weight: 45 oz 15 dwt (1424 g)

Tankard – detail of engraving

Arthur Soly after ?Jan Wyck, *Horse Racing*,
engraving from Richard Blome, *The
Gentleman's Recreation*, 1686.
British Library, London/Paul Mellon Centre for
Studies in British Art

Punch bowl, silver, London,
1728–9, maker's mark of
Edward Vincent.
Sterling and Francine Clark Art
Institute, Williamstown,
Massachusetts

presenting a substantial piece of plate, often a cup
or bowl to hold the "purse".

The *Racing Calendar* runs from 1727 and, with
the exception of the royal meetings like York and
Newmarket, records from before this date are
scant. According to the *Calendar*, the 1727
meeting at "Stowerbridge" was held on two days
in September, 1727. On the 27th "a prize of 20 *l*
value" was run for, on the following day "a plate
of 10 *l* value".[3] A tankard of this weight would
have cost between £15 and £20 at the time,
making it likely that this was the previous year's
version of the "prize of 20 *l* value". It is tempting
to speculate that the owner of the horse who won
the second race in 1727, a Mr. Machin, may have
won this tankard the previous year, and that the
initials of "E I M" which appear on the base of this
tankard are those of him and his wife.

Marks
Struck on rim by handle and interior of cover
with hallmarks (leopard's head, lion passant, date
letter) and with maker's mark; the handle struck
with maker's mark

Provenance
The Estate of J. Harold Crang of Toronto, sale,
Sotheby's, New York, June 16, 1988, lot 192
S.J. Shrubsole Corp., New York

Notes
[1] One of the earliest is a cup and cover of 1699, engraved
"Laleham Plate", Christie's, London, June 23, 1971; compare also
with two punch bowls of 1728–9 and 1730–1 given as "The
Kettering Plate" (Sterling and Francine Clark Art Institute,
Williamstown, Massachusetts, no. 84 and sold, Christie's London,
July 11, 1985, lot 316 respectively); a gold cup and cover, c. 1730,
made out of the Bramham Moor race cups of 1705 and 1708, sold
Sotheby's, New York, April 26, 1985, lot 125; another, 1713–14,
presented by Queen Anne and "run for at York by Six Years old
Horses Aug[st]. 3[d] 1713", sold Christie's, London, July 12, 1995,
lot 136.
[2] S. Deuchar, *Sporting Art in Eighteenth Century England*,
1988, p. 38.
[3] I am grateful to Mr. David Oldrey for this information.

PUNCH BOWL

64

Silver (sterling standard), interior gilt
Maker's mark of John White (Grimwade, no. 1735)
Hallmarks: London, 1736–7

Of hemispherical form on spreading stepped foot engraved with a band of shells and pateræ with oblong panels enclosing pateræ at intervals, with moulded lip, engraved below with four foliate scroll cartouches, two enclosing female masks and two wild masks, with four asymmetrical scroll and rocaille cartouches between two female and two male busts, all connected by panels of diaperwork

It was Arthur Grimwade who first drew attention to the work of John White's workshop: "John White is a mysterious figure, as his work, somewhat rare, is of high quality and Huguenot character, without there being any apparent connection in his training or parentage with the immigré school".[1] White was apprenticed to Robert Cooper, one of the most successful of the native English school craftsmen. He entered his first mark in 1719. By the 1730s White was part of the Lamerie group and it may be that objects like this punch bowl were produced in Lamerie's workshop and retailed by White (see p. 50) The use of engraved rather than chased ornament on this bowl is characteristic of silver from the Lamerie group of this time; it is in a curious mixture of baroque and rococo motifs, with the slightest hint of asymmetry. A larger

punch bowl of 1736–7, also with White's mark, is at Oriel College, Oxford. It has similar engraving and the addition of applied baroque straps.[2] Small punch bowls, probably intended to be used by two or at most three convivial drinkers, appear sporadically during the first half of the century but are rare compared with full-sized examples.

Marks
Struck under base with hallmarks (leopard's head, lion passant, date letter) and with maker's mark

Provenance
Goldsmiths' and Silversmiths' Co., Ltd, c. 1932
Anonymous sale, Christie's, London, November 4, 1936, lot 105
S.J. Phillips Ltd, London
The late Samuel Messer, sale, Christie's, London, May 13, 1992, lot 237
Asprey Ltd, London

Exhibited
Christie's, London, *Art Treasures Exhibition*, 1932, no. 533

Notes
[1] *The London Goldsmiths 1697–1830*, rev. edn, 1990, p. 698.
[2] E. Alfred Jones, *Catalogue of the Plate of Oriel College, Oxford*, 1944, illus. p. 40, pl. 15.

Height: 4¾ in (12 cm)
Diameter: 8¼ in (21 cm)
Weight: 29 oz (90 g)

Details of engraving

SILVER for
COFFEE, TEA
and CHOCOLATE

English Family at Tea,
English School, c. 1720.
Worshipful Company of
Goldsmiths, London

COFFEE POT

65

Silver (Britannia standard), fruitwood
Maker's mark of Richard Bayley (Grimwade no. 116)
Hallmarks: London, 1713–14

Of tapering octagonal form on stepped moulded foot,
the later wood scroll handle issuing from octagonal
sockets, at right angles to an octagonal swan-neck
spout with pendant drop, the hinged domed cover
with octagonal baluster finial, engraved under the
base with traces of initials ?F over WF

Engraved under the base with traces of scratch
weight ?1-3

The first coffee house had opened in London
in 1652 but the earliest known silver coffee
pot appears to date from 1681–2.[1] Its tall conical
form set the standard for the next half century.
This example, and the one following, are devoid
of any ornament and rely solely on their plain
reflective surfaces for effect. Many early
eighteenth-century examples, like this one, have
the handle at right angles to the spout.

Marks
Struck under base with hallmarks (lion's head
erased, Britannia, date letter) and with maker's
mark; the cover flange struck with lion's
head erased

Note
[1] Maker's mark of George Garthorne, in the Victoria and Albert
Museum, London.

Height: 9⅝ in (24.5 cm)
Width: 6 in (15.2 cm)
Depth: 6 in (15.2 cm)
Gross weight: 25 oz 4 dwt (784 g)

COFFEE POT

66

Silver (Britannia standard), fruitwood
Maker's mark of Simon Pantin (Grimwade, no. 2124)
Hallmarks: London, 1715–6

Of tapering octagonal form on stepped moulded base, the later wood scroll handle issuing from octagonal sockets, with octagonal swan-neck spout and hinged domed cover with octagonal baluster finial, the side engraved with a lozenge-of-arms within foliate scroll and bellflower mantling

Engraved under the base with scratch weight 34=10

Heraldry
The arms appear to be those of a lady of the Rolle family of Stevenston, Devon, or of its collateral branch of Lewknor, Oxfordshire.

T he fact that this coffee pot bears the mark of a Huguenot, and the preceding one that of a non-Huguenot, shows how widespread the plain geometric style was at the time. Its origins have nothing to do with the influx of Huguenots, for the popularity of totally plain, utilitarian silver was longstanding throughout Europe. Nor was it a style monopolized by the Huguenots. The geometric shapes are inspired by Oriental

porcelain, and seem to have been most popular for wares associated with the serving of coffee and tea.

Marks
Struck under base with hallmarks (lion's head erased, Britannia, date letter) and with maker's mark, the cover with lion's head erased and maker's mark

Provenance
Anonymous sale, Christie's, London, May 23, 1990, lot 216

Height: 9⅞ in (25 cm)
Width: 8½ in (21.6 cm)
Depth: 4½ in (11.5 cm)
Gross weight: 31 oz (965g)

CREAM JUG

67

Silver (sterling standard), gilt
Maker's mark of David Willaume I (Grimwade, no. 3194)
Hallmarks: London, 1721–2

The bowl formed of an auricular shell, raised on a dragon-form support on rectangular pedestal base with canted corners, applied under the lip with a bearded mask, with ribbed serpent scroll handle chased with continuous crescents

Considerable imagination was devoted to whimsical cream jugs to adorn the English tea table during the eighteenth century. The early years of the century saw the growing custom of taking milk or cream in tea.

This example is the earliest of a small group of similar pieces, a number of which bear David Willaume's mark although most are unmarked.[1] The jug presents a curious mixture of styles. The bowl and handle are based on the designs of the van Vianens, the Dutch family of silversmiths and designers who were instrumental in promoting the "auricular" style in silver during the first half of the seventeenth century. Their book of designs, published under the authorship of Adam van Vianen but in fact a compendium of the work of all of them, continued to provide motifs for English silversmiths and modellers well into the eighteenth century. A similar bowl formed of a shell appears on a ewer of 1614 bearing Adam's maker's mark in the Rijksmuseum. In total contrast, however, is the foot in the form of a dragon on this jug, which is positively Gothic. On an unmarked example formerly in the Pierpont Morgan Collection[2] the dragon even has wings.

Marks
Struck on rim by handle with hallmarks (leopard's head, lion passant, date letter) and with maker's mark

Notes
[1] Compare with an example of 1719–20 with Willaume's mark, Sotheby's, London, May 3, 1984, lot 56; a gilt example with Willaume's mark only, Christie's, New York, October 27, 1992, lot 375; a gilt unmarked example, Christie's, London, April 27, 1983. Three unmarked examples, all on oval bases, were sold from the collection of Hilmar Reksten, Christie's, London, May 22, 1991, lots 90–2.
[2] Burlington Fine Arts Club, London, *Exhibition of a Collection of Silversmiths' Work of European Origin*, exh. cat., 1901, no. 25, case P, p. 177.

Height: 4⅛ in (10.5 cm)
Width: 4 in (10.2 cm)
Depth: 2¼ in (5.4 cm)
Weight: 7 oz 18 dwt (247 g)

Ewer, silver-gilt, Utrecht,
1614, maker's mark of
Adam van Vianen.
Rijksmuseum, Amsterdam

CHOCOLATE POT

68

Silver (sterling standard), fruitwood
Maker's mark of David Tanqueray (Grimwade, no. 509)
Hallmarks: London, 1722–3

Of baluster form raised on three fish-form scroll feet,
the high short spout cast and chased with a stylized
shell at the base and headed by a dragon-mask, with
later wood scroll handle at right-angles to the spout,
with octagonal sockets, the lower socket, the feet
and the spout issuing from calyces of cut-card
stylized foliage; the domed cover with dentilated
hinge, with dentilated rim and scroll thumbpiece,
with unscrewing fluted baluster finial, the front
engraved with a viscount's armorials, with a female
mask below

Heraldry

The arms are those of Montagu impaling those of
Popham, as borne by Edward Montagu, Viscount
Hinchingbrooke (1692–1722).

Before the advent of new processes in the
1820s by which the cocoa fat was removed
from it, chocolate was prone to settle and
therefore required not only a spout set high up the
side of the pot but also an aperture in the cover to
accommodate a *molinet*, or "muddler". By the
beginning of the nineteenth century, however,
chocolate as a fashionable drink had all
but disappeared.

A few chocolate pots of this form survive in
English silver, including an exceptionally rare one
of 1683–4, with the maker's mark of Pierre
Harache, in a private American collection;
another from the Harache workshop, of 1695–6,
is known,[1] and one of 1697, maker's mark of
Benjamin Bradford, is in the Metropolitan
Museum of Art, New York.[2] These pots follow the
form of French chocolate or coffee pots of the end
of the seventeenth century. Virtually no French
examples have survived from before 1700[3] but the
form appears in the drawings of Louis XIV's silver
commissioned by the King of Sweden at the
beginning of the eighteenth century and in
Nicolas de Larmessin's engraving of an

Height: 8¾ in (22.2 cm)
Width: 6 in (15.2 cm)
Depth: 7¼ in (18.2 cm)
Gross weight: 28 oz 15 dwt (896 g)

Chocolate pot, silver,
fruitwood, London,
1695–6, maker's mark of
Pierre Harache II.
Sotheby's, New York

emblematic silversmith (see p. 42). Small bellied pots on three splayed feet, probably for cordials, survive in English silver of the 1680s[4] but full-size chocolate pots of this form are extremely rare. The more common coffee pot form, a tapering cylinder or octagon (see nos. 65 and 66) was also utilized for chocolate by the addition of an aperture in the cover and it may be that many surviving coffee pots of the early Georgian period were originally for chocolate and had the cover aperture removed when chocolate passed out of fashion. An example with its original molinet, of 1738–9, maker's mark of Paul Crespin, is in the Ashmolean Museum, Oxford.[5]

Edward Montagu, only son of Edward, 3rd Earl of Sandwich, bore his father's secondary title, that of Viscount Hinchingbrooke, as a courtesy title. He married Elizabeth, daughter of Alexander Popham of Littlecote, Wiltshire. As heir to an earldom, he divided his time between a colonelcy in the army and a seat in Parliament and in 1718 fought a duel with a fellow MP as a result of "warm words over the Spanish War".[6] He died at the age of thirty on October 3, 1722.

Chocolate pot, silver,
fruitwood, Paris, 1698–9.
Christie's, New York

Marks
Struck under base with hallmarks (leopard's head, lion passant, date letter) and with maker's mark, the cover flange struck with lion passant

Provenance
Anonymous sale, Sotheby's, London, July 4, 1989, lot 240

Bibliography
Joel Langford, *Silver: a Practical Guide to Collecting Silverware and Identifying Hallmarks*, 1991, illus. p. 93

Notes
[1] The Meech Collection, sale, Sotheby's, New York, October 22, 1993, lot 52.
[2] Gift of Irwin Untermyer, 1968.
[3] Except an example of 1698, sold from the Devine Collection, Christie's, October 15, 1985, lot 1097.
[4] See Christie's, London, July 12, 1995, lot 135.
[5] Timothy Schroder, *The National Trust Book of English Domestic Silver 1500–1900*, 1988, illus. p.184.
[6] G.E. Cokayne, ed., *The Complete Peerage*.

KETTLE, STAND AND LAMP

69

Silver (sterling standard), fruitwood
Maker's mark of Thomas Mason (Grimwade, no. 2832)
Hallmarks: London, 1722–3

Of loaf-form, on plain ring foot, stepped at the shoulder and with panelled swan-neck spout headed by a stylized bird head and issuing from a stepped octagonal socket, the overhead multi-scroll swing handle with turned wood inset; the removable domed cover with wood baluster finial; the circular stand on three panelled multi-scroll feet terminating in octagonal pads, with two hinged oval scroll handles and central frame supporting a circular lamp, the removable cover with hinged cap; the side engraved with a crest

Heraldry
The crest is that of Cope.

Because of its expense, tea was spooned sparingly into small teapots, usually of Chinese porcelain, and boiling water repeatedly poured over it. As a result, the kettle in which the water was heated is usually quite large. Nevertheless the monumental size of this example is exceptional. Because of their functional nature, kettles of this date tend to be of heavy-gauge metal and with little ornamentation. The earliest appears to be one of 1683 in Norwich Castle Museum which is an early version of this "cottage loaf" form probably based on Chinese ceramics. By the early eighteenth century kettles were often given their own tripod stand which stood on the floor next to the tea table but only a handful of these have escaped the melting pot.

The distinctive crest of a dragon's head issuing from a fleur-de-lys is first recorded for a Stephen Cope who was Serjeant of the Poultry to Henry VIII. There were several branches of his descendants living in the eighteenth century, including one in America, making precise identification with an individual impossible. A possible candidate, however, is Sir John Cope, 6th Bt, of Bramshill Park, who succeeded his father in 1721.

Marks
Struck under base and on lamp with hallmarks (leopard's head, lion passant, date letter) and with maker's mark, the cover flange struck with lion passant, leopard's head and maker's mark, the stand frame with lion passant, leopard's head, date letter, the interior of lamp cover with lion passant

Provenance
Benjamin Sonenberg, New York, sale, Sotheby's, New York, June, 1979, lot 594
Anonymous sale, Christie's, London, May 23, 1990, lot 207

Height: 15½ in (39.4 cm)
Width: 11 in (28 cm)
Depth: 10 in (25.4 cm)
Gross weight: 101 oz 15 dwt (3165 g)

**Detail from *The Gough
Family, 1741*
by Willem Verelst
(*fl.* 1734–c. 1756).**
Private collection

CREAM JUG

≈

70

Silver, gilt
Maker's mark of Paul de Lamerie (Hare, no. 4)
Hallmarks: none
c. 1735

Of oval bombé form raised on four scroll feet, with wavy rim, the sides and top of the lip engraved with scrolling panels of diaperwork and rocaille, *the top of the leaf-capped multi-scroll handle issuing from an applied shell, the front applied with a winged mask headed by* rocaille, *one side engraved with a crest*

The base with scratched ?inventory number 62

Heraldry
The crest, that of a stag trippant, pertains to a number of families.

A slightly more elaborate version of the same shape forms part of the Boissier tea equipage of 1735–6, also struck with Lamerie's maker's mark, at Temple Newsam House, Leeds. Writing of the Boissier cream jug, Anthony Wells-Cole commented: "The magnificent little cream-jug is certainly the most successful individual piece in the equipage … it stands full-bodied on substantial-looking feet and not, as once, teetering in precarious equilibrium on the back of a coiled snake."[1]

Marks
Maker's mark struck four times on base (thrice indistinctly), one foot also struck with French twentieth-century import control mark

Provenance
Anonymous sale, Christie's, London, March 26, 1975, lot 188
Hilmar Reksten, Bergen, Norway
The Reksten Collection, sale, Christie's, London, May 22, 1991. lot 61

Note
[1] "Two Rococo Masterpieces", *Leeds Art Calendar*, no. 79 (1976), pp. 13–18.

Height: 4 in (10.2 cm)
Width: 5 in (12.7 cm)
Depth: 2¾ in (7 cm)
Weight: 5 oz (156 g)

CREAM JUG

~

71

Silver, gilt
Marks: none
c. 1735

Of oval bombé *form, raised on three splayed*
dolphin feet with wavy tails, the sides cast and
chased with spiral panels of overlapping waves and
applied with random grape leaves, applied under the
lip with a naked bust-length female, the handle
formed as a snake-entwined scroll issuing from
rocaille and headed by a male turbaned head

Cream jug, silver,
c. 1735.
Christie's, London

An identical cream jug is in the Huntington
Library, San Marino, Calfornia,[1] while three
variants, all unmarked, are also known: one with
more pronounced shell feet in the Minneapolis
Institute of Arts,[2] another identical, ungilt[3] and
another without the mask under the lip in the
Gilbert Collection.[4] The problem of authorship of
these jugs has long puzzled silver scholars.
Traditionally, they have been attributed to Paul de
Lamerie's workshop, largely because the same
motifs appear on work with Lamerie's mark, such
as the bands of overlapping waves found also on a
coffee pot of 1731–2 in the Clark Art Institute,
Williamstown, Massachusetts.[5] Similar waves also
appear on work from the Kandler workshop, such
as a kettle on a stand of 1728–9 and 1731–2, made
for the 9th Duke of Norfolk. Nicholas Sprimont
(see p. 51) has also been put forward as a
candidate, largely on account of an unsigned
drawing in the Victoria and Albert Museum of a
salt cellar with similar dolphin supports, which
has been attributed in recent years to Sprimont.
This attribution appears to have been based on a
drawing of a tureen for a member of the Coke
family, signed "N. Sprimont", also in the Victoria

Height: 4¾ in (12.1 cm)
Width: 4⅜ in (11 cm)
Depth: 3 in (7.6 cm)
Weight: 11 oz 10 dwt (360g)

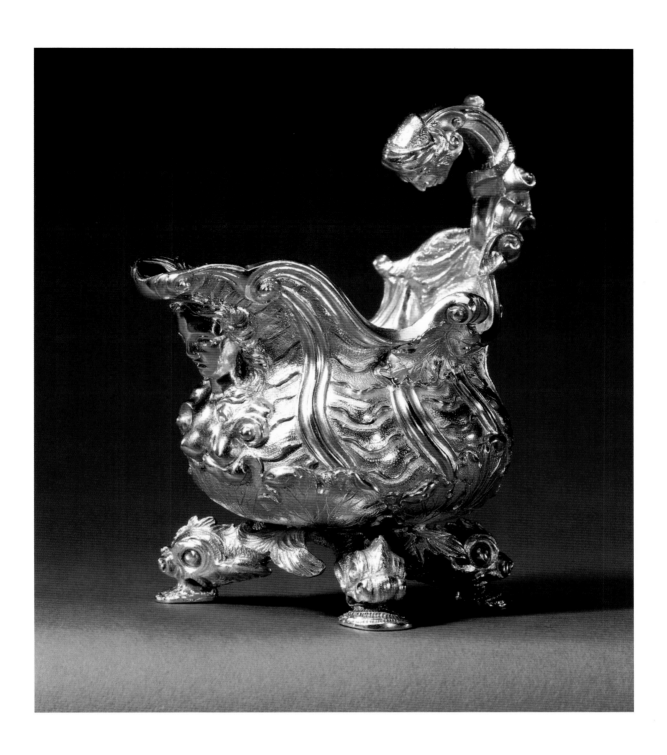

Design for a salt cellar, pen and wash, attributed to Nicholas Sprimont. Victoria and Albert Museum, London

Salt cellar, silver, before 1739, maker's mark of Paul Crespin. Christie's, London

and Albert Museum, but there are few similarities between the two objects depicted. The drawing of the salt has little affinity with the elaborate marine-inspired salts bearing Sprimont's mark in the Royal Collection, or his sauceboats which are supported on dolphins in the same collection. Splayed dolphin supports are a common feature on silver of the period, like the extravagant cup and cover of 1750 with Thomas Gilpin's maker's mark, exhibited in Toronto in 1958[6] and a tiered epergne of 1753 from Thomas Heming's workshop.[7] Arthur Grimwade has drawn attention to similarities between the work of Sprimont and Paul Crespin, his neighbour in Compton Street,[8] and has suggested that Sprimont, evidently in London some time before registering his own maker's mark in 1743, had Crespin submit work from his workshop to the assay office at Goldsmiths' Hall. The Crespin connection is strengthened by a salt cellar with similar dolphin supports, bearing Crespin's pre-1739 maker's mark.[9] The marks of these three men appear often on identical wares, however, and any attempt to differentiate work bearing

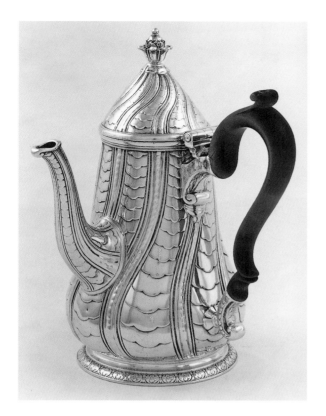

Coffee pot, silver, London,
1731–2, maker's mark of
Paul de Lamerie.
Sterling and Francine Clark
Art Institute, Williamstown,
Massachusetts

Kettle on stand, silver,
London, 1728–9 and
1731–2, maker's mark
of Charles Kandler.
Christie's, London

their marks by style or quality is fruitless. The
work of the group needs to be studied as a whole
and cream jugs such as these are probably the
result of the pooling of skills and resources
among the Lamerie group.

Provenance
Anonymous sale, Sotheby's, London, May 15,
1957, lot 157 (possibly)
The late Villiers David, sale, Christie's, London,
November 27, 1985, lot 121

Notes
[1] Robert Wark, *British Silver in the Huntington Collection*, 1978,
p. 63, fig. 151.
[2] Gerald Ward, ed., *English and American Silver in the Collection of
the Minneapolis Institute of Arts*, 1989, no. 46.
[3] The Reksten Collection, Christie's, London, May 22, 1991,
lot 79.
[4] Timothy Schroder, *The Gilbert Collection of Gold and Silver*,
1988, no. 54.
[5] Inv. no. 11.
[6] *Seven Centuries of English Domestic Silver*, exh. cat., Royal
Ontario Museum, no. G.34.
[7] Michael Clayton, *The Collector's Dictionary of the Silver and Gold
of Great Britain and North America*, 1985 edn, illus. p. 175,
fig. 266.
[8] "Crespin or Sprimont: An Unsolved Problem of Rococo Silver",
Apollo, August, 1969, p. 43.
[9] Christie's, London, November 25, 1987, lot 206.

COFFEE POT

~

72

Silver (sterling standard), fruitwood
Maker's mark of Paul Crespin (Grimwade, no. 2143a)
Hallmarks: London, 1736–7

Of tapering cylindrical form on spreading foot, chased above and below with bands of foliate scrolls and rocaille *enclosing diaperwork, with bird-head scroll spout chased with bull rushes on a matted ground issuing from scrolls and similar chasing, with wood scroll handle, the sockets formed of cast naturalistic scrolls, the hinged domed cover with similar chasing and baluster finial, engraved on one side with an oval* rocaille *and foliate scroll cartouche enclosing a crest*

Engraved under base with scratch weight 30=5

Heraldry
The crest is unidentified and may be a later replacement.

This coffee pot incorporates many common decorative features of the 1730s, such as the bird's head spout and flat-chased borders, both of which are based on rococo decoration. The asymmetrical shape of the chased borders, together with the *rocaille* motifs, give the pot a rococo flavour that is otherwise lacking. The form is still symmetrical and somewhat ponderous. Similar coffee pots were produced in most of the major workshops of London but rarely of such quality as those bearing Crespin's, Lamerie's, or George Wickes's, mark (see no. 75).

Marks
Struck under base with hallmarks (leopard's head, lion passant, date letter) and with maker's mark; the cover struck with lion passant

Provenance
Spink & Son Ltd, London

Height: 8¼ in (21 cm)
Width: 8 in (20.2 cm)
Depth: 4⅜ in (11 cm)
Gross weight: 30 oz 14 dwt (957 g)

JUG

73

Silver (sterling standard), ivory
Maker's mark of Christian Hillan
Hallmarks: London, 1738–9

Of baluster form on spreading domed foot, chased and applied with cherubs, shells, winged dragons, rocaille and scalework, the curved spout cast and applied with a shell-capped mask, the hinged domed cover with conforming decoration and baluster finial; with ivory scroll handle

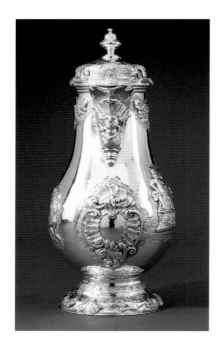

Work bearing Christian Hillan's mark, usually of small scale, is characterized by somewhat naive rococo chasing, much of it based on contemporary German prints. As his name suggests, he was probably an immigrant, of either German or Scandinavian origin. Until 1742 he occupied premises in Compton Street, Soho and it is likely that he did work for, or supplied silver to, the Lamerie group. The best work bearing his mark is a group of imaginative cream jugs and it is tempting to think that some of the jugs of this type, either marked or unmarked, that can be associated with the Lamerie group may have been done in his workshop.

Marks
Struck under base with hallmarks (leopard's head, lion passant, date letter) and with maker's mark

Provenance
Presumably John, 2nd Lord King and Baron of Ockham (1704–40) (see no. 12)
By descent to the Executry of the late Manon, Countess of Lovelace, sale, Christie's, London, May 12, 1993, lot 147

Height: 9¾ in (24.8 cm)
Width 8¼ in ((21 cm)
Depth: 4¾ in (12.1 cm)
Gross weight: 31 oz (964 g)

TEA CADDIES AND SUGAR BOX

74

Silver (sterling standard)
Maker's mark of Lewis Pantin I (Grimwade, no. 1962)
Hallmarks: London, 1739–40
Case: Silver, mahogany
Marks: none

The bombé bodies, cast and chased with foliage and fluted straps with shells, flowerheads and batswing, the sides with panels of trelliswork and shells, each on splayed feet, the caddies with sliding covers with reclining putto finials, the sugar box with similar cover with a dragon's head finial, engraved with a later crest; the rectangular bombé kingwood case with cross-banding and ebony inlay, applied at the corners with silver draped female and blackamoor figures, the front with scroll lockplate and thumbpiece, the cover with scroll handle and mounts

Engraved under bases with scratch weights:
24:19:12, 21:10 and 21:16:12

Heraldry
The engraved crest, and the finials formed as a crest, are unidentified.

These boxes and their case show English rococo silver at its most refined. In particular the mounts on the case are not only modelled with assurance but are technically brilliant. The set must have presented an elegant diversion when produced at the tea table; the box, with its strong horizontal lines, yields three boxes formed of continuous scrolls. Their vigorous movement is only put to rest when they are placed back in their case. Because of their small size and weight, the silver mounts on cases like this are seldom hallmarked. It is probable that, like the wooden case itself, they were produced by specialist outworkers and supplied to Pantin. Indeed, similar mounts appear on a case containing three caddies of 1738–9 from the Lamerie workshop.[1]

The use of heraldic crests as finials became increasingly common during the eighteenth century. The same crest appears on the tureen (no. 54) but, as it pertains to a number of families, identification is impossible. The bodies are engraved with a different crest which was probably added in the nineteenth century.

Marks
Struck under base with hallmarks (leopard's head, lion passant , date letter) and with maker's mark; the covers with lion passant and maker's mark

Provenance
Anonymous sale, Sotheby's, London, June 8, 1995, lot 149

Note
[1] *Silver by Paul de Lamerie in America*, exh. cat., Museum of Fine Arts, Houston, 1956, no. 39.

Height of pair: 5 in (12.5 cm)
Height of sugar box: 5½ in (14 cm)
Weight: 67 oz 15 dwt (14 g)
Height of case: 11 in (28 cm)
Width: 14⅞ in (37.9 cm)

Detail of case

COFFEE POT

75

Silver (sterling standard), fruitwood
Maker's mark of George Wickes (Grimwade, no. 927)
Hallmarks: London, 1740–1

Of tapering cylindrical form with tucked-in base, on spreading plain foot, the body chased with borders of foliate scrolls, with foliate scroll and rocaille spout and wood scroll handle, the hinged domed cover with similar decoration and bud-form finial

Heraldry
The coat-of-arms on the left, or husband's, side, of three boars' heads, pertains to a number of Welsh families; the arms on the right appear to be those of Brook or Lant.

George Wickes was one of the most successful retailers of silver and jewellery of the time. Thanks to the fortunate survival of a large part of his business records (see p. 47), we can glean a great deal about the silver he sold his clients. Without a definite identification, however, of the coat-of-arms engraved on this coffee pot, it is impossible to say who the original client was.

Nevertheless we know from his "Gentlemen's Ledgers" for 1741 that the price he was charging for coffee pots varied greatly depending on their elaborateness and size: Henry Penton was charged £14 1s 6d for one on March 26, 1741 weighing just over thirty ounces, while Governor Clinton, on October 27 of the same year, paid £22 9s 8d for a much larger one weighing over fifty-eight ounces. In this last case, the "fashioning" charge per ounce was much less. In both cases, an extra charge was made for "2 handles" (presumably one spare) and for engraving armorials.[1]

Marks
Struck under base with hallmarks (leopard's head, lion passant, date letter) and with maker's mark

Note
[1] Victoria and Albert Museum, Archive of Art and Design, VAM 2, GL2.

Height: 9 in (22.9 cm)
Width: 8¼ in (21 cm)
Depth: 4½ in (11.5 cm)
Gross weight: 32 oz (995 g)

TEAPOT

76

Silver (sterling standard), ivory
Maker's mark of Paul Crespin (Grimwade, no. 2149)
Hallmarks: London, 1740–1

The fluted ovoid body on shaped spreading foot cast and chased with scrolls, rocaille and scalework, applied at the shoulder with swags of seashells, with scroll spout cast with scrolls and rocaille and headed by a serpent mask, and leaf-capped silver handle with ivory insulators, the hinged cover within an engraved border of scalework and shells and applied with shells and with shell-form finial, engraved on each side, probably in the nineteenth century, with a crest and ducal coronet

Heraldry
The crest and coronet are those of the Dukes of Hamilton.

This teapot, with its fluted body and shell enrichments, is an unusual example of rococo motifs applied to a teapot. While cream jugs and kettles are frequently encountered in the rococo style, teapots are rare and it would seem that by this period the porcelain teapot had all but replaced silver on the tea table. Fish-scale and garlands of seashells, derived from the ornamental *Morceaux de fantasie* published in Paris during the 1730s, first appeared in England in works such as Edward Hoppus's *Gentleman's and Builder's Repository*, published in 1737.

Marks
Struck under the base with hallmarks (leopard's head, lion passant, date letter) and with maker's mark

Provenance
A Gentleman, sale, Christie's, London, March 3, 1993, lot 247

Bibliography
Arthur Grimwade, *Rococo Silver 1727–1765,* 1974, p. 49, illus. pl. 58B

Height: 4¾ in (12.1 cm)
Width: 5 in (12.7 cm)
Depth: 4¼ in (10.7 cm)
Gross weight: 21 oz (653 g)

Detail of cover

SALVER OR STAND FOR A KETTLE

77

Silver (sterling standard)
Maker's mark of Paul de Lamerie (Hare, no. 5)
Hallmarks: London, 1742–3

Of shaped circular form raised on three lion mask and paw feet enclosed by foliage, the rim cast and chased with reeded scrolls and garlands of flowers with rocaille at intervals, the field chased with a broad band of reeded scrolls and rocaille and applied with a profusion of exotic foliage, the centre engraved with a coat-of-arms within an asymmetrical foliate scroll and rocaille cartouche

The reverse with scratch weight 36=8

Heraldry

The arms are those of Franks impaling those of Evans, as borne by David Franks (1720–94) of Philadelphia, who married Margaret Evans in 1743.

Prosperous Americans were enthusiastic consumers of English silverware during the eighteenth century and elegant silver for the tea ceremony was a mark of gentility to which the wives of middle-class merchants, lawyers and plantation owners aspired. This salver formed part of a group of tea silver of which the kettle for this circular salver/stand, the slop bowl, sugar basket, cake basket and possibly cream jug can be traced. The equipage was ordered by, or given to, David Franks of Philadelphia possibly at the time of his marriage to Margaret Evans, daughter of the Collector of Customs for Philadelphia, in 1743 and added to in the two years following. The Franks silver is one of three groups of London-made tea wares with a Philadelphia provenance[1] and the only known group of silver from Lamerie's workshop made for an American patron.

David Franks was the youngest son of Jacob Franks, a merchant. He arrived in Philadelphia in 1740 and started as a general trader with his brother Moses, making a fortune in land speculation and the fur trade. He held lucrative posts as army victualler and contractor to the British forces during the French and Indian Wars. As a prominent Philadelphian (he was one of 84 in the city to maintain his own coach and horses) he signed the Non-Importation Agreement of 1765.[2] His fortunes were reversed, however, with the outbreak of the War of Independence, during

Height: 1½ in (4 cm)
Diameter: 11 in (28 cm)
Weight: 35 oz 16 dwt (1114 g)

Detail of foot

The salver (or stand)
reunited with the kettle

The kettle, silver,
London, 1744–5.
Metropolitan Museum of
Art, Irwin Untermyer
Collection

The salver of 1742–3 was
adapted, c. 1744–5, to
become the stand for the
kettle.
Photograph: Christie's,
New York

which, branded as a Tory, he was imprisoned. He was exchanged with other prisoners in 1780 and taken to New York, whence he sailed for England. A broken man, he settled in Isleworth in Middlesex, close to his brother Moses. It seems, though, that David Franks managed to recover some of his assets and possessions and shipped them to England, where, after his death in 1794, his silver was dispersed among his relations.[3]

David Franks's niece, Isabella, who married Sir William Cooper, Bt, appears to have received three pieces of the tea equipage: a kettle, a cake basket and a smaller basket which was probably intended for sugar. These were sold by her descendant, Dame Isabella Cooper, in 1913.[4] A bowl of 1744–5, probably used as the slop bowl, is also known.[5] A cream jug formed as a shell on an entwined snake foot, of 1742–3, which may also have been part of the Franks equipage but does not appear to have had arms engraved on it, is known only from a catalogue description. It was sold by another collateral descendant of Franks, Sir Thomas Thornhill, in 1914.[6] A pair of tea caddies of 1742–3 from Lamerie's workshop, engraved with the arms borne by David's brother, Naphtali Franks (1715–96), is also known and it may be that these too formed part of the group and passed, after David's death, to Naphtali, who had his brother's arms replaced with his own.

This salver was evidently altered to act as the stand for the kettle in the equipage when the latter was purchased, along with the other components, in 1744–5. The high relief border of insects and plants amid foliage which encloses the coat-of-arms was probably added at this date to accommodate the kettle; the decoration is interrupted in three places to provide platforms for the feet of the kettle lampstand.[7] The restless movement and sculptural quality of this applied decoration are typical of the mid-1740s. This middle period of English rococo silver is quite different in feeling from the rococo of the late

1730s. The baroque decorative motifs one finds on the basket from Lamerie's workshop of 1739–40 (no. 39) have been almost totally replaced with purely vegetal and animal naturalism. All that remains of the classical symbolism of the Mountrath basket are the subdued lions which form the feet of the salver, but here they are no longer symbolic of might subdued by love; their purpose is purely decorative. The intention is to delight the eye with the intricate realism of the decoration, not for it to be "read" for its classical allusions.

Marks
Struck on reverse with hallmarks (leopard's head, lion passant, date letter) and with maker's mark. The reverse with Brooklyn Museum painted loan number *L60.2.8*

Provenance
David Franks (1720–94)

Subsequent provenance unknown until Mrs. John E. Rovensky (formerly Mrs. Morton F. Plant), sale, Parke-Bernet Galleries, New York, January 19, 1957, lot 910
Donald S. Morrison, New Jersey, sale, Sotheby's, New York, December 13, 1984, lot 142

Exhibited
Baltimore, Maryland, The Baltimore Museum of Art, *Age of Elegance: The Rococo and its Effect*, no. 383
Princeton, New Jersey, Princeton University Art Museum, *English Silver*, 1966, no. 47
Brooklyn, New York, The Brooklyn Museum, 1960–84

Bibliography
W.D. John and J. Simcox, *English Decorated Trays 1550–1850*, n.d., illus. p. 27
Auction Magazine, December, 1971, illus. p. 35
Jerry Bowles, "Legacy of a Collection", *Silver Collector*, October, 1985, illus. p. 32

Sugar or sweetmeat basket, silver, London, 1742–3, maker's mark of Paul de Lamerie.
Christie's, London

David Franks and his sister, Phila,
c. 1735–40.
American Jewish Historical
Society, Waltham, Massachusetts,
Capt. N. Taylor Phillips
Collection

Notes

[1] The earliest was purchased from Benjamin Pyne, Peter Archambo and John Farnell between 1720 and 1724 by James Logan (1674–1751), secretary to William Penn; the second was ordered by Edward Lloyd of Wye Plantation in Maryland through his agent Mathias Gale in London in 1763, and subsequently passed by marriage to the Cadwalader family; components of both groups are in the Philadelphia Museum of Art.

[2] *Dictionary of Anglo-Jewish Biography*, p. 23.

[3] For a full account of Franks's life, see J. McNab, "Lamerie Silver for the Franks Family", *Metropolitan Museum of Art Bulletin*, N.S., XXVI, December, 1967.

[4] Christie's, London, February 25, 1913: lot 34, the kettle of 1744–3; lot 35, the cake basket of 1744–5 (both are now in the Metropolitan Museum of Art, New York) and lot 36, the sugar basket of 1742–3 (subsequently sold by Christie's, London, November 22, 1995, lot 122).

[5] Sold, like this salver, from the collection of the late Mrs. John E. Rovensky, Parke-Bernet, New York, January 25, 1957, lot 542, now in the Metropolitan Museum of Art, Irwin Untermyer Collection.

[6] Christie's, London, July 17, 1894, lot 132; this connection was first discovered by Jessie McNab, Assistant Curator of Decorative Arts at the Metropolitan Museum of Art.

[7] I am grateful to Jessie McNab and the Metropolitan Museum of Art for allowing the kettle to be photographed with its stand.

Pair of tea caddies, silver,
London, 1742–3, maker's
mark of Paul de Lamerie.
Engraved with the arms of
Franks impaling those of
Franks, they were owned
by David Frank's brother,
Naphtali (1715–96).
Sotheby's, London

BOX

78

Silver (sterling standard), the interior and inner cover gilt
Maker's mark of Paul de Lamerie (Hare, no. 5)
Hallmarks: London, 1744–5

Of deep rectangular form with incurved corners, raised on four short scroll and flowerhead feet, the sides of double-walled construction, elaborately chased with Chinoiserie foliage and scrolls on a matted ground enclosing shaped panels of exotic foliage and pagodas, all on a matted ground, the corners applied with foliate trails, the hinged slightly domed cover with similar decoration with rocaille at intervals, surmounted by a cast berry finial, the interior with a gilt shaped rectangular lid, also double-walled, flat-chased with a continuous pattern of foliage, scrolls, diaperwork and rocaille on a matted ground, with cast berry finial

The function of this box is a mystery. Tea caddies were often produced in pairs with an accompanying larger box for sugar, like the set of 1751–2 (no. 81), but the extremely large size of this example makes it unlikely that it was for sugar. The other unusual feature is the double-walled construction, and the curious loose inner cover. The smooth surface of the inner walls allows this cover to move up and down, keeping the contents reasonably airtight. It may be that the original function was for holding tobacco.

For a discussion of Chinoiserie decoration on tea caddies, see nos. 79 and 81.

Marks
Struck under base with hallmarks (leopard's head, lion passant, date letter) and with maker's mark

Provenance
Anonymous sale, Nicolay, Paris, March 26, 1984, lot 40

Height: 6¼ in (16 cm)
Width: 5 in (12.7 cm)
Depth: 4 in (10 cm)
Weight: 43 oz (1339 g)

PAIR OF TEA CADDIES

79

Silver (sterling standard)
Maker's mark of Peter Archambo I (Grimwade, no. 2128)
Hallmarks: London, 1745–6

Of rectangular bombé form, the sides elaborately chased with Chinoiserie figures, pagodas, ruins, and birds amid foliate scrolls and rocaille, all on a matted ground, each long side with an asymmetrical lozenge enclosing an engraved coat-of-arms, the hinged covers with conforming decoration and with cast swirling foliage finials

Heraldry
The arms are those of a lady of the Brabazon family quarterly with those of Widdrington and Honeywood.

Inscription
Engraved under the bases: "In Memory of Mrs. D. Barclay".

Unlike the Chinoiserie decoration popular during the 1680s, which was applied to a host of articles like tankards, monteiths and wall sconces as well as toilet services, the second wave of Chinoiserie, which appeared in the 1740s, is more feminine in nature and appears for the most part on small domestic articles associated with the serving of tea and coffee. Its whimsy was well suited to the tea table and tea caddies like this pair must have made delightful conversation pieces.

The Chinoiserie of the 1740s can be divided into two distinct styles. The crowded scenes chased on each side of these caddies, with exotic figures amid rococo scrolls forming an almost continuous pattern, relies for subject matter on the decorative panels Christophe Huet painted for Chantilly in the 1730s, which ultimately derive from the grotesque panels of Berain of half a century earlier.[1] Here, however, they have been given the curves and movement of the rococo. More static is the feeling of the panels on a set of three caddies of 1747–8, maker's mark of Peter Taylor, in the Museum of Fine Arts, Boston,[2] but the lack of any depth to the decoration on both these sets is quite

Height: 5 in (12.7 cm)
Width: 3 in (7.5 cm)
Depth: 4 in (10.2 cm)
Weight: 33 oz 18 dwt (1056 g)

Pair of tea caddies and a
sugar box, silver, London,
1747–8, maker's mark of
Peter Taylor.
Museum of Fine Arts,
Boston

different from the bolder modelling one finds on
most Chinoiserie tea caddies of this period, such
as the set of caddies from Lamerie's workshop
(no. 81), which appear to be more loosely based
on printed design sources.

Tea caddies like this usually flanked a larger
example, intended for sugar, and were contained
in a wood or shagreen-covered box (see nos. 74
and 81). Their inverted baluster form, of square
section, is reminiscent of Chinese porcelain.

Marks
Struck under bases with hallmarks (leopard's
head, lion passant, date letter) and with maker's
mark; interiors of the covers struck with lion
passant and maker's mark

Provenance
The late Mrs. William Salomon, sale, American
Art Association, New York, January 4–7, 1928,
lot 311
The Phillip H. & A.S.W. Rosenbach Foundation,
sale, Sotheby's, London, June 20, 1974, lot 83
Anonymous sale, Sotheby's, Amsterdam,
December 3, 1991, lot 237

Bibliography
Vanessa Brett, *The Sotheby's Directory of Silver*,
1986, illus. p. 191, fig. 800

Notes
[1] Oliver Impey, *Chinoiserie*, 1976, p. 82.
[2] Jessie and Sigmund Katz Collection.

Pair of Caddies and Sugar Bowl

80

Silver (sterling standard)
Maker's mark of James Shruder (Grimwade, no. 1683)
Hallmarks: London, 1748–9
Case: Shagreen, wood, silver
Marks: none

The caddies of deep straight-sided oblong form with undulating outline, each raised on four rocaille *scroll feet, the canted corners chased with overlapping* rocaille, *each side applied with an elaborate foliate scroll and* rocaille *asymmetrical cartouche engraved on one side with a coat-of-arms and on the other with a crest, with festoons of shells and sea foam above, the short sides with bullrushes, the slip-on covers enclosed by borders of fluting, with* rocaille *finials*

The sugar bowl of circular form on spreading foot cast and chased with foliate scrolls, rocaille *and marine motifs, applied with a similar cartouche front and back and similarly engraved, the domed cover applied with similar ornament within a tied reed border, with foliate finial*

The plain oblong case on four scroll feet, with shaped escutcheon plate and scroll handle, the base plate engraved, in the nineteenth century, with the initial L and earl's coronet

Heraldry
The arms are those of King with a martlet for difference denoting a fourth son, as borne by Thomas King, 5th Lord King and Baron of

Ockham (1712–79) (see no. 91). The initial and coronet on the case are those of the Earls of Lovelace.

Work from the Lamerie group during the late 1740s is characterized by its sculptural qualities. The bold modelling of the cartouches applied to the caddies and sugar bowl are based on designs for rococo asymmetrical cartouches published by Pierre-Edme Babel, Jacques de la Joue and others in Paris in the 1730s. Some of these were adapted and published in London by Augustin Heckel, a German gold chaser working in England. He is mentioned by Vertue in 1732 and again in 1748 as one of the best chasers in London and it is reasonable to suppose that he would have known, and possibly worked with, his fellow countryman Shruder and other members of the Lamerie group. The Lamerie group were significant suppliers of silver to the King family during the 1730s and 1740s (see nos. 12 and 73).

Apart from this applied decoration, however, there is nothing rococo about the tea caddies or the sugar bowl, as the shape of these pieces, and a

Caddies:
Height: 5¾ in (14.7 cm)
***Sugar bowl**:*
Diameter: 5¼ in (13.6 cm)
Weight: 64 oz (1990 g)

Detail of cover of sugar bowl

Design for a cartouche by
Jacques de la Joue, engraved
by Gabriel Huquier and
published in Paris c. 1734.
Victoria and Albert Museum,
London

Title page from *A New
Book of Shields, usefull for
all sorts of Artificers,
Invented & Drawn by
A. Heckell.*
Victoria and Albert
Museum, London

similar sugar bowl with Shruder's mark in the
Metropolitan Museum of Art, New York, is no
different from examples of thirty years before.
Like many tea caddy sets which have been kept in
their fitted cases, this set has a crispness that one
seldom encounters in other types of silver of
the period.

Marks
Struck under bases with hallmarks (leopard's
head, lion passant, date letter) and with maker's
mark; the covers struck with lion passant and
maker's mark

Provenance
Thomas, 5th Lord King and Baron of Ockham
(1712–79)
Then by descent to the Earl and Countess of
Lovelace, sale, Sotheby's, London, June 8, 1995,
lot 111

PAIR OF TEA CADDIES AND SUGAR BOX

81

Caddies and sugar box:
Silver (sterling standard)
Maker's mark of Paul de Lamerie (Hare, no. 5)
Hallmarks: London, 1751–2

Height of sugar box: 5 ½ in (14 cm)
Width: 3 ⅞ in (9.8 cm)
Depth: 2 ⅛ in (5.2 cm)
Height of caddies: 5 ½ in (14 cm)
Width: 3 ⅞ in (9.8 cm)
Depth: 2 ½ in (6.7 cm)
Total weight: 43 oz (1337 g)

Case:
Walnut, pine, shagreen and silver
Marks: none
Mid-eighteenth century
Height: 7½ in (19 cm)
Width: 10½ in (27 cm)
Depth: 5 in (12.6 cm)

Each deep rectangular with incurved corners, the sides chased with cartouches of Chinese figures picking tea in rural landscapes, and shells, foliage and lion masks within scrolls, the hinged covers cast and chased with shell and foliate finial, engraved on each short side with a crest within the Order of the Garter, and another crest and earl's coronet, and under the bases with an inscription, the shagreen-covered wood case of rectangular form, the cover applied with a silver plaque engraved with an inscription

Heraldry
The crests are those of Cornwallis, as borne by Charles, 2nd Earl Cornwallis and later 1st Marquess Cornwallis, KG (1738–1805) and of Elliot, as borne by Henry, 5th Earl of St Germans (1835–1911).

Inscription
The engraving under the base reads: "Given by Florence Lady Braybrooke to Henry Earl of St. Germans 1908". The plaque on the case is engraved "Tea Caddies which belonged to the 1st. Marquess Cornwallis".

In contrast to the flat Chinoiserie panels which decorate the sides of the tea caddies from Archambo's workshop (no. 79), the decoration on these caddies is moulded in high relief. This last wave of Chinoiserie, which reached the height of popularity in the 1740s, is a curious mixture of exotic scenes and vegetation, based on popular engravings like Bernard Picart's *Cérémonies*, published in Amsterdam in the 1720s, and auricular elements like the moulding which frames the cartouches. Tea caddies of this form were produced by members of the Lamerie group and others, including Thomas Heming, Edward Vonham,[1] and Emick Romer as late as 1761–2.[2] The present set is among the latest bearing Lamerie's maker's mark and was presumably assayed between May 29, 1751, when the date letter changed, and his death on August 1. In his will Lamerie directed that all work in hand at the time of his death was to be finished by his journeymen and sent for assay, but we do not know whose maker's mark would have been stamped on these objects. It is probable that

Detail of chasing

Phillips Garden was one of the purchasers of Lamerie's tools and patterns after his death and, interestingly, a set of identical caddies with Garden's mark of 1752–3 is known.[3]

Charles, 1st Marquess Cornwallis, is best known today for his surrender of the British forces to the Americans at Yorktown on October 19, 1781, thus ending the War of Independence. In spite of this defeat, however, Cornwallis was appointed shortly afterwards Governor General of India, where he forced the surrender of Tipoo Sultan. His share of the spoils was £47,244, which, as a magnanimous gesture, he refused to accept and had it divided among his soldiers. On his return he served as Lord Lieutenant of Ireland and in later life was instrumental in the negotiations between England and France which resulted in the Treaty of Amiens in 1802. In 1805 he travelled again to India, where he died at Ghazipore on October 5 of that year.

Marks
Struck under bases with hallmarks (leopard's head, lion passant, date letter) and with maker's mark

Provenance
Charles, 1st Marquess Cornwallis (1738–1805)
Charles, 2nd and last Marquess Cornwallis (1774–1823)
Jane, his daughter, who married Richard, 3rd Lord Braybrooke (1783–1858)
Then by descent to Florence, wife of Charles, 5th Lord Braybrooke (1823–1902)
Given by her to Henry, 5th Earl of St Germans (1835–1911)
Then by descent to the Trustees of the Earl of St Germans' Heirlooms Settlement, sale, Christie's, London, November 25, 1992, lot 90

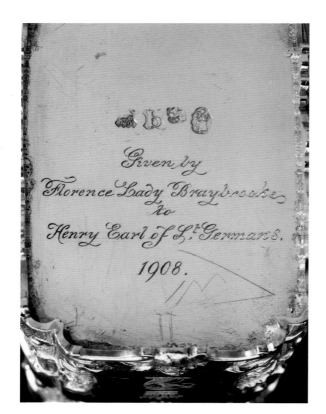

Detail of underside

Notes
[1] A pair of 1753–54, maker's mark of Heming, sold Sotheby's, New York, October 19, 1995, lot 446; a set of three of 1759–60, maker's mark of Frederick Vonham, sold Christie's, New York, April 18, 1995, lot 371.
[2] A pair is in the Fundacão Eva Rappaport, São Paulo.
[3] Christie's, London, July 10, 1992, lot 45.

Charles, 1st Marquess Cornwallis
by Thomas Gainsborough (1727–88).
National Portrait Gallery, London

JUG

82

Silver (sterling standard), fruitwood
Maker's mark of Phillips Garden (Grimwade, no. 2179)
Hallmarks: London, 1752–3

Of tapering cylindrical form with tucked-in base on spreading foot chased with a band of dentilation, the hinged domed cover with similar outer band, the upper part of the body and the cover chased with chrysanthemum heads and scrolls on a fish-scale ground and applied with a spout cast in the form of coffee leaves and flowers, with bud-form finial, the wood scroll handle with rocaille sockets

Coffee pots of this form, but with a long spout, are quite common from the 1750s but this appears to be one of the few surviving coffee jugs of this large size. Similar spouts formed of coffee leaves appear on two smaller jugs from Lamerie's workshop, dating from 1749,[1] and on a drawing of a coffee jug, dating from c. 1750, in the Victoria and Albert Museum, London. It has been suggested that such short-spouted pots were used for Turkish coffee, which enjoyed a vogue at mid-century.[2] Garden was one of the Lamerie group, but, most significantly, many of Lamerie's decorative motifs appear on Garden's work after 1751, the year of Lamerie's death, suggesting that Garden may have been one of the purchasers of Lamerie's models after the latter's death in that year.

By the 1750s coffee pots were usually struck with hallmarks on the rim (presumably the wardens of the Goldsmiths' Company felt this made it more difficult for an unscrupulous silversmith to insert transposed marks into the base and so avoid paying duty). This pot, like many from Lamerie's workshop, has been struck by Garden with his

Height: 12½ in (31.5 cm)
Width: 8¼ in (21 cm)
Depth: 5 in (12.7 cm)
Gross weight: 46 oz (1430 g)

Detail of spout

mark under the base, probably in the hope that the wardens would follow suit and so avoid damaging the delicate chasing at the rim. The blows of the steel punches of the hallmarks would often disfigure a piece of silver, making it necessary for the silversmith to devote more labour to it on its return from Goldsmiths' Hall. Although on this jug the hallmarks on the rim are obviously struck over the chasing, it is evident from some eighteenth-century works that silverware was sometimes sent to the Hall for marking before the decoration was completed.

The condition of this jug is exceptional; one can still see the traces of the burnishing tool on the flat surfaces.

Marks
Struck on rim with hallmarks (leopard's head, lion passant, date letter), under the base with maker's mark, and on cover flange with lion passant and maker's mark

Provenance
C.J. Vander Ltd, London, c. 1962
Clay P. Bedford
George S. Heyer, Austin, Texas
Tessier Ltd., London

Exhibited
Victoria and Albert Museum, London, *International Art Treasures Exhibition*, 1962, no. 183, exhibited by C.J. Vander Ltd
University Art Museum, Austin, Texas, *One Hundred Years of English Silver, 1660–1760*, 1969, no. 85, lent by Clay P. Bedford

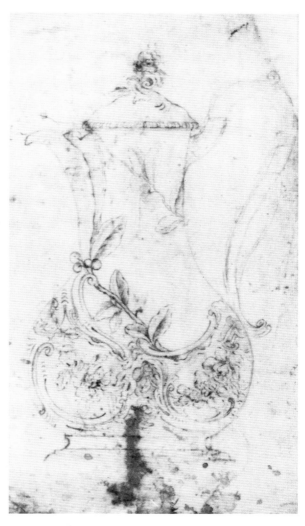

Design for a coffee jug, mid-eighteenth century.
Victoria and Albert Museum, London

Notes
[1] One is in the Sterling and Francine Clark Art Institute, Williamstown, Massachusetts, inv. no. 242; the other was sold Christie's, New York, October 27, 1992, lot 379.
[2] See *Paul de Lamerie, the Work of England's Master Silversmith*, exh. cat., Goldsmiths' Hall, London, 1990, p. 154.

SALVERS and WAITERS

A Dinner Party
by Marcellus Laroon
(1679–1772).
The Royal Collection © Her
Majesty Queen Elizabeth II

SALVER

83

Silver (Britannia standard)
Maker's mark of Augustine Courtauld (Grimwade, no. 385)
Hallmarks: London, 1714–5

Of octafoil form with moulded rim, raised on four shaped curving bracket feet, the centre engraved with an oval coat-of-arms within foliate scroll and bellflower mantling and surmounted by an esquire's helm and a crest

The reverse with scratch weight 45 onz. 6 dwtt and traces of a scratched inscription Jno. North July 6=95

Heraldry
The arms appear to be those of Gardener, Calais.

As Michael Clayton observed, "Of all shapes, the octafoil salver is one of the most satisfactory forms".[1] It enjoyed a brief vogue for about fifteen years.

Marks
The reverse struck with hallmarks (lion's head erased, Britannia, date letter) and with maker's mark

Provenance
Anonymous sale, Christie's, London, May 23, 1990, lot 210
S.J. Phillips Ltd, London

Note
[1]*The Collector's Dictionary of the Silver and Gold of Great Britain and North America*, 1985 edn, p. 319.

The Strode Family at tea
by William Hogarth
(1697–1764).
Tate Gallery, London/Art
Resource, New York

Height: 1⅛ in (2.9 cm)
Diameter: 13¾ in (35 cm)
Weight: 43 oz 18 dwt (1366 g)

SALVER AND TWO WAITERS

84

Silver (sterling standard)
Maker's mark of Edward Feline (Grimwade, no. 679)
Hallmarks: London, 1723–4

Each of square form with incurved corners and moulded rims, raised on four incurved bracket feet, engraved with a coat-of-arms within an elaborate square cartouche of foliate scrolls, pateræ, shells and masks against a horizontal ruled background

The two waiters with scratch weights 17 and 18

Heraldry
The arms are, quarterly, those of Howard, Brotherton, Warren and Fitzalan, with a mark of cadence for a fifth son, as borne by Philip Howard (1688/9–1749/50).

Phillip Howard was the fifth son of Thomas Howard of Worksop, Nottinghamshire, and nephew of Henry, 7th Duke of Norfolk. He married 7th January, 1723/4, Winifrede, daughter of Thomas Stonor, and it is possible that these salvers formed part of their wedding plate. Howard was obviously proud of his descent from the Dukes of Norfolk and had the quarterings showing his descent from the illustrious 2nd Duke, the victor of the Battle of Flodden in 1513, included on the shield. This seems to have left no room for his wife's arms, which are omitted.

Howard's wife died in 1730/1 and he subsequently married Harriot (some accounts say Henrietta), the widow of Peter Proli of Antwerp and daughter of Edward Blount. Howard died January 23, 1749/50 and was buried at the ancestral seat of Arundel Castle.

Marks
The reverses struck with hallmarks (leopard's head, lion passant, date letter) and with maker's mark

Provenance
Philip Howard (1688/9–1749/50)
Subsequent provenance unknown until Brand Inglis Ltd, London, 1978
Anonymous sale, Sotheby's, London, June 19, 1986, lot 77
E. & C.T. Koopman Ltd, London

Height: 1 in (2.6 cm)
Salver: 11⅞ in (30.3 cm) square
Waiters: 5⅛ in (13 cm) square
Weight:
salver 50 oz 2 dwt (1560 g)
waiters 19 oz 2 dwt (594 g) together

WAITER

85

Silver (Britannia standard)
Maker's mark of Paul de Lamerie (Hare, no. 3)
Hallmarks: London, 1725–6

Of square form with incurved corners, raised on four shaped and fluted scroll bracket feet, with moulded border enclosing a plain border with chased stylized leaves at the corners, the field engraved with a border of bellflowers and strapwork enclosing diaperwork and flowerheads with foliate scroll vacant cartouches at each corner; the centre with a circular band of pearls enclosing a coat-of-arms within foliate scroll and rusticated mantling

The reverse with traces of scratch
weight 11 oz-18 dwt

Heraldry
The arms are those of Mellish impaling those of da Costa, as borne by Henry Mellish who, in 1735, married Kitty Villareal (*née* da Costa).

Henry Mellish's marriage to Katherine, or Kitty, da Costa occurred just after a breach of promise suit had been brought against her by her cousin, Philip da Costa Mendez. The case became one of the *causes célèbres* of the eighteenth century. Kitty, a daughter of Joseph da Costa, a rich Portuguese merchant, had been previously married to Joseph da Costa-Villareal. Their daughter, Elizabeth, in 1747 married William Monckton, subsequently Viscount Galway, and so became the first Jewish woman to marry into the British aristocracy.

A fine oblong salver of 1726–7, engraved with the same arms, is in the Sterling and Francine Clark Art Institute, Williamstown, Massachusetts.[1] This descended in the Mellish family until the twentieth century but the early provenance of this waiter is unknown.

The use of a circular pearl cartouche and rustication as a backdrop to heraldic engraving was common in the 1720s and 1730s. When this waiter was sold at auction in 1982, the catalogue suggested that the engraving might be by William Hogarth. While the da Costa arms appear impaled by those of Suasso in a pull from a salver in the British Museum which has traditionally been attributed to Hogarth,[2] it is most likely that this engraving and the arms on this waiter come from the workshop of Ellis Gamble, to whom Hogarth

Height: 1¼ in (2.8 cm)
6 in (15.2 cm) square
Weight: 11 oz 16 dwt (368 g)

Detail of engraving on waiter

Salver, silver, London,
1726–7, maker's mark of
Paul de Lamerie.
Sterling and Francine Clark
Art Institute, Williamstown,
Massachusetts

was apprenticed in 1713. Evidence has in recent years been uncovered revealing a partnership between Gamble and Lamerie between 1723 and 1728 (see p. 49), with Lamerie evidently supplying finished silver which Gamble engraved and sold from his retail establishment at the Golden Angel in Cranborn Street.[3]

The use of rustication as a backdrop to heraldic engraving dates back to the work of the Gribelins, while similar circular cartouches are a common feature of the period, perhaps the most notable examples being the plate commissioned by the Goldsmiths' Company in 1740 which was engraved by Charles Gardner. On the present waiter there are traces that the present heraldic charges replace earlier engraving, perhaps accounting for the discrepancy in dates between its manufacture and the Mellish/da Costa marriage.

The outer border of the salver is typical of the Lamerie group during the 1720s and is based on the printed designs of Jean Berain, published earlier in the century.

Marks
The reverse struck with hallmarks (lion's head erased, Britannia, date letter) and with maker's mark

Provenance
Henry Mellish, c. 1735
Subsequent provenance unknown until the Hon. Mrs Stockdale, sale, Sotheby's, London, November 30, 1972, lot 136
Anonymous sale, Sotheby's, London, March 18, 1982, lot 133

Details from two plates of ornament by Jean Berain (1639–1711), published in Augsburg, early eighteenth century

Notes
[1] Inv. no. 407; sold by the executors of the late Colonel Henry Mellish, Sotheby's, London, April 30, 1936, lot 116.
[2] Charles Oman, *English Engraved Silver*, 1978, illus., p. 92.
[3] Robert B. Barker, "De Lamerie, Gamble and Hogarth", privately circulated paper, 1988.

SALVER

86

Silver (sterling standard)
Maker's mark of Thomas Farren (Grimwade, no. 2749)
Hallmarks: London, 1727–8

Of circular form raised on three fluted bracket feet each fixed by three rivets, the raised fluted border with scalloped rim, the field engraved with a band of panels of bellflowers and scrolls against rustication with scroll cartouches at intervals enclosing baskets of flowers alternating with male masks, the centre with a coat-of-arms within a rusticated and foliate scroll cartouche flanked by demi-putti holding garlands of bellflowers, with a ribbon motto below and surmounted by an earl's coronet

Heraldry

The arms are those of Knight impaling those of others, as borne by Robert Knight, son and heir of Robert Knight, Cashier to the South Sea Company, who was born in 1702.

Robert Knight's father fled to Paris when an inquiry was instituted into the affairs of the South Sea Company and was outlawed for high treason by parliament in 1729. The younger Knight was Whig MP for Great Grimsby 1734–47, for Castle Rising 1747–54, for Grimsby again 1762–8 and for Milborne Port from 1770 until his death. In 1745 he was created Baron Luxborough of Shannon in the Peerage of Ireland and subsequently in 1763 Viscount Barrells and Earl Catherlough. The addition of the earl's coronet on the present salver appears to date from the time of this creation; it is engraved over an erasure, possibly of a crest.

Knight married, as his first wife, in 1727, Henrietta, sister of the half blood of Henry, Viscount Bolingbroke. This salver evidently formed part of their wedding plate. She was, according to Horace Walpole, a "high-coloured, lusty, black woman, who was parted from her husband upon a gallantry she had with Parson Dalton ... She retired into the country and consoled herself, it is said, like Ariadne with Bacchus."[1] She died in 1756 and in the same year

Height: 2¼ in (5.4 cm)
Diameter: 16½ in (42.5 cm)
Weight: 60 oz 4 dwt (1872 g)

Knight married "Mary, Lady le Quesne, widow".
The identity of this lady is unclear. He died
without surviving heirs in 1772, when his titles
became extinct.

As the titles conferred on him were Irish ones,
Knight was able to retain his seat in the House of
Commons until his death. The way in which such
Irish honours were despised by some is well
shown in a letter of George Selwyn to Lord
Carlisle: "In Ireland ... that Riff Raff with titles
resembling our own desires to be confounded
with the nobility of this country, and very often
are so. It must be such a herald as myself to
distinguish between an Earl of Carlisle and an
Earl of Catherlough, the son of a transport."[2]

Thomas Farren operated one of the most
successful non-Huguenot workshops of the
period. He served as Subordinate Goldsmith to
the King between 1723 and 1742[3] and supplied
the basket (no. 7), to the Jewel House for the
Duke of Dorset on the latter's appointment as
Lord Steward of the Household. His mark also
appears on the candlesticks (no. 98), as well as on
a similar set he supplied to the Jewel House.

Marks
Struck on reverse with hallmarks (leopard's head,
lion passant, date letter) and with maker's mark

Provenance
Robert Knight (1702–72)
Subsequent provenance unknown until
J.P. Morgan, 12 Grosvenor Square, London and
Wall Hall, Hertfordshire, 1937[4]
Then by descent to Henry S. Morgan
The Estate of Mrs. Catherine A. Morgan, sale,
Christie's, New York, April 18, 1989, lot 570

Notes
[1] G.E. Cokayne, ed., *The Complete Peerage.*
[2] February 26, 1768.
[3] Major General H.W.D. Sitwell, "The Jewel House and the Royal
Goldsmiths", *Archaeological Journal*, CXVII, p. 154.
[4] The salver is included in an inventory of plate at both houses
drawn up by Crichton Bros. in 1937, now in the Pierpont Morgan
Library, New York.

SALVER

87

Silver
Maker's mark CK, mitre above and pellet below (see Grimwade, p. 36n),
probably for Charles Kandler
Hallmarks: none
c. 1730

Of square form with incurved corners and moulded borders, raised on four waisted feet with semi-circular pads flat-chased with bellflowers, the field engraved with a border of panels of diaperwork, bellflowers and scrolls with draped female and exotic masks at intervals, each corner with an eagle with head bowed and wings outstretched, the centre with a coat-of-arms within a fish-scale and foliate scroll cartouche flanked by eagles and surmounted by a shell

Heraldry
The arms are those of Beauchamp quartering others and impaling those of Jacomb.

While there is nothing unusual about the outline of this salver, or about the engraved cartouche in the centre, the engraved border is quite distinctive. The regularity of the flowers within a clearly defined border is quite German in feeling, as one would expect given Kandler's German origins (see p. 52), and unlike borders on salvers from the Lamerie/Gamble workshop (see no. 85). The eagles at the corners appear frequently enlivening cartouches enclosing coats-of-arms during the 1730s.[1]

The salver was never sent to Goldsmiths' Hall for assaying and hallmarking, thereby avoiding the tax payable on all silver. Kandler has struck his maker's mark on the piece, deliberately mis-striking three of the punches to give the appearance at first glance of a complete set of marks.

Charles Kandler entered two marks at Goldsmiths' Hall on August 29, 1727, one in partnership with James Murray. The maker's mark which appears on this salver, however, is apparently not registered at the Hall but there seems little doubt that it too was used by Kandler. It appears on a kettle[2] which, like this salver, is only struck with his maker's mark, suggesting that Kandler reserved this unregistered mark for his "duty dodgers".

Marks
Struck four times on reverse with maker's mark (thrice indistinctly)

Notes
[1] See Christie's, New York, April 17, 1996, lot 135 for a suite of salvers, 1735–6 and 1736–7, maker's mark of Robert Abercromby.
[2] Victoria and Albert Museum, London.

Height: 1½ in (3.9 cm)
11 in (28 cm) square
Weight: 37 oz 8 dwt (1164 g)

SALVER

88

Silver (sterling standard)
Maker's mark of Edward Cornock (Grimwade, no. 546)
Hallmarks: London, 1732–3

Of shaped circular form with "Bath" border, raised on four scroll feet, the centre engraved with a lozenge-of-arms within a cartouche of diaperwork enclosed by foliate scrolls flanked by two eagles, with a crest above and a bearded mask below

Heraldry
The arms are those of a lady of the Cheslin family of London with those of Flaxney of Oxfordshire on an escutcheon of pretence.

The undulating outline of the border of this salver, formed of double ogees, has traditionally been called a "Bath" border by dealers and collectors, a term probably originating in the nineteenth century. The engraved cartouche incorporates eagles, a popular motif (see no. 87) and foliate scrolls, both common features of the rococo in the following decade, but here handled in a totally symmetrical way, heightened by the diamond-shaped shield, denoting arms borne by a lady.

Marks
Struck on reverse with hallmarks (leopard's head, lion passant, date letter) and with maker's mark

Provenance
Anonymous sale, Christie's, London, June 24, 1942, lot 52
Thomas Lumley Ltd, London
Anonymous sale, Christie's, London, May 23, 1990, lot 196
S.J. Phillips Ltd, London

Bibliography
Arthur Grimwade, *Rococo Silver 1727–1760*, 1972, illus. pl. 18a

Height: 1⅛ in (2.7 cm)
Diameter: 17½ in (44.4 cm)
Weight: 80 oz 12 dwt (2509 g)

SALVER

89

Silver (sterling standard)
Maker's mark of Charles Kandler (Grimwade, no. 341)
Hallmarks: London, 1734–5

Of shaped circular form, the moulded rim applied with six female masks against shells with bound rosettes between, raised on three splayed scroll feet terminating in shells, the field flat-chased and engraved with a band of scrolls enclosing shells and diaperwork, all on a matted ground, the centre engraved with a crest and viscount's coronet, the reverse engraved, at a later date, with the initials EK

Heraldry
The crest is that of King.[1]

The engraved crest and coronet seem to have been added some years after the salver was made. There are two candidates, both viscounts, who had the initials EK. The first, Edward King, was the son of Sir Henry King, Bt, of county Roscommon, Ireland, born in 1726. He sat in Parliament from 1749 until 1764, when he was created Baron Kingston and so took his seat in the House of Lords. On November 15, 1766 he was created Viscount Kingston and, on August 25 of the following year, Earl of Kingston, making it likely that the crest and coronet were added during the brief period of his viscountcy. His

grandson, also Edward, could also have added the engraving. As heir to the 2nd Earl, he bore the courtesy title of viscount from his youth until his death, of typhus fever in a debtor's prison, in 1837 at the age of 37.

The boldly-modelled border on this salver is typical of Kandler's workshop, as is the engraved border, which should be compared with other works from the same workshop during the 1730s.[2]

Marks
Struck on reverse with hallmarks (leopard's head, lion passant, date letter) and with maker's mark

Provenance
Partridge Fine Arts PLC, London

Notes
[1] I am grateful to Timothy Schroder and Lucy Morton of Partridge Fine Art for this identification.
[2] See two pots and a pair of salvers discussed by Timothy Schroder in *The Gilbert Collection of Gold and Silver*, 1988, pp. 210–13; a cup and cover of 1736–7 in the Holburne of Menstrie Museum, Bath, illustrated in Alexis Butcher and Eric J.G. Smith, *A Catalogue of Silver at the Holburne Museum, Bath*, 1996, no. 38, and a sugar bowl and cover, Sotheby's, New York, April 23, 1993, lot 290.

Height: 1⅛ in (2.7 cm)
Width: 9⅜ in (23.4 cm)
Depth: 10 in (25.4 cm)
Weight: 21 oz (653 g)

SALVER

90

Silver (sterling standard)
Maker's mark of Lewis Pantin I (Grimwade, no. 1956)
Hallmarks: London, 1735–6

Of shaped square form with boldly moulded foliate scroll rim, on four splayed shell feet, the field engraved with a band of diaperwork enclosed by foliate scrolls and rocaille with baskets of flowers, the centre with a lozenge-of-arms within a foliate scroll and diaperwork cartouche with a wild mask and with a shell below

Heraldry
The arms, the impaled coat of a lady, are unidentified.

Lewis Pantin was presumably the son of Simon Pantin II and grandson of Simon I, maker of the pair of salvers (no. 4). There is no record of his apprenticeship or freedom of the Goldsmiths' Company but he entered a mark in 1734. Work bearing his mark is characterized by boldness of modelling giving an effect of high relief. On this salver the border is composed of tight scrolls which are totally different from the scrolls found on the borders of his contemporaries' work (see nos. 91 and 92). The contrast of these scrolls with the severely square outline of the salver creates a dramatic tension. A similar effect is shown on a pair of candlesticks of 1734–5 from his workshop made for Sir Watkin Williams-Wynn,[1] and on a

cup at Anglesey Abbey, Cambridgeshire. Pantin's equally distinctive chased borders on this salver can also be seen on a salver of 1733–4 he supplied to Wickes as part of an order for Frederick, Prince of Wales.[2]

Marks
The reverse struck with hallmarks (leopard's head, lion passant, date letter) and with maker's mark; also struck four times with a device (possibly a Catherine wheel) and maker's mark

Bibliography
W.D. John and J. Simcox, *English Decorated Trays 1550–1850*, n.d., illus. p. 54

Provenance
Henry Hardcastle Ltd., York, c. 1960
Anonymous sale, Christie's, London, July 8, 1987, lot 171
A.D.C. Heritage, London

Notes
[1] Sotheby's, London, May 23, 1985, lot 69.
[2] Corporation of Bath; A.G. Grimwade, *Rococo Silver 1727–1765*, 1974, illus. pl. 8.

Height: 1½ in (3.2 cm)
12½ in (31.6 cm) square
Weight: 54 oz (1690 g)

PAIR OF WAITERS

91

Silver (sterling standard)
Maker's mark of John White (Grimwade, no. 1735)
Hallmarks: London, 1735–6

Of shaped square form with moulded rims, raised on scroll feet terminating in oval pads, flat-chased with a border of rocaille and panels of trelliswork within interlaced scrolls, the centres engraved with a coat-of-arms within an asymmetrical foliate cartouche

The reverses with scratch weights 10=17 and 11=4

Heraldry
The arms are those of King with those of van Troye on an escutcheon of pretence, as borne by Thomas King (1712–79).[1] Thomas King succeeded to the Barony of King in 1767.

Small salvers like this, used for serving drinks, are usually called "waiters" although in eighteenth-century accounts a "waiter" often refers to a larger-size salver.[2] As on the punch bowl from White's workshop (no. 64), the quality of the engraving on these waiters is superb.

The King estates and title passed between the four sons of Lord Chancellor King (d. 1734), all of whom, with the exception of Thomas, 5th Lord King, whose arms appear on these waiters, died without issue. This Lord King, like his two

elder brothers, Peter and William, had never been expected to succeed to the family estates. He had been sent at an early age to work in a Dutch mercantile house and it was in Delft, in 1734, that he married Wilhelmina, the daughter of John Troye, a rich Brabant merchant. King's arms, without those of his wife, appear on the tea equipage, (no. 80).

Marks
The reverses struck with hallmarks (leopard's head, lion passant, date letter) and with maker's mark

Provenance
Thomas, 5th Lord King and Baron of Ockham (1712–79) (see no. 80)
Subsequent provenance unknown until anonymous sale, Sotheby's, New York, April 19, 1991, lot 282

Notes
[1] For the arms of Troye, see J.-B. Rietstap, *Armorial Général*, 1887, vol. II, p. 943.
[2] For example, Parker and Wakelin supplied Sir Robert Clayton with a gadrooned waiter 16 inches in diameter.

Height: 1 in (2.5 cm)
6 in (15 cm) square
Weight: 21 oz 2 dwt (657 g)

SALVER

92

Silver (sterling standard)
Maker's mark of Paul de Lamerie (Hare, no. 4)
Hallmarks: London, 1736–7

Of square form raised on four fluted bracket feet chased with palmettes against matting, the tied reed rim applied on each side with wild masks amid foliage and rocaille *and, at each corner, with* rocaille; *the field flat-chased and engraved with a border of scrolls, foliage, cascading water and* rocaille *enclosing asymmetrical cartouches at each corner, each cartouche and the reverse engraved with a crest and earl's coronet, the centre engraved with a similar cartouche enclosing another crest and baron's coronet*

Heraldry
The crest in the centre is that of a three-towered castle, in the corners that of a single tower with flag.

T he borders of expansive engraved rococo decoration are typical of work from Lamerie's workshop during the mid 1730s. Square and oblong salvers like this were called "tables"or "waiters" in contemporary accounts and were often supplied in sets. Earl Fitzwalter bought the following from Lamerie on May 5, 1738:[1]

To a large sqr. Table Wrought	
150 oz: at 5s 11d per oz:	£44. 7. 6
Fashion 3s 6d per oz:	26. 5. 0
Engraving a fine Border & Arms	10.10. 0

While over three times the weight, the salver must have been in similar style to this example.

The asymmetrical cartouche in the centre of this salver was intended for a coat-of-arms, and the way in which the crest and coronet sit somewhat awkwardly in it suggest that they replace the original engraving and were possibly added later in the eighteenth century.

Marks
The reverse struck with hallmarks (leopard's head, lion passant, date letter) and with maker's mark

Provenance
E. & C.T. Koopman & Son Ltd, London

Note
[1] Mildmay Papers, Essex Record Office, Chelmsford, D/DM/F13.

Height: 1⅞ in (5 cm)
13½ in (34.2 cm) square
Weight: 54 oz 12 dwt (1700 g)

FOUR WAITERS

93

Silver (sterling standard)
Maker's mark of Paul Crespin (Grimwade, no. 2143a)
Hallmarks: London, 1736–7

Of square form with incurved corners, each raised on four fluted bracket and scroll feet, the ovolo rims applied with female masks against rocaille and scrolls at each corner, the border flat-chased with foliate scrolls and rocaille, the field flat-chased with a band of foliage, scrolls and rocaille enclosing panels of diaperwork and flowers, the centres engraved with a coat-of-arms against drapery mantling

The reverses numbered 1 to 4 and with scratch weights 23-6 changed to 23-9, 23-16, 23-4 and 23-7 respectively

Heraldry

The arms are those of Watson quarterly with those of Monson, impaling those of Pelham, with a crescent mark of cadency for a second son, as borne by Lewis Watson, formerly Monson (1728–95).

Lewis Monson, the second son of John, 1st Lord Monson, assumed the name of Watson on the death, in 1745, of his cousin, Thomas, 3rd and last Earl of Rockingham, on inheriting the latter's estates in Kent and Northamptonshire. In 1752 he married Grace, third surviving daughter and co-heiress of Henry Pelham, the Prime Minister. As Watson was created Baron Sondes in 1760 and would have borne a coronet and supporters after this date, the engraving of the arms can be dated to 1752–60. The use of drapery mantling is typical of heraldic engraving of the 1750s.

Marks

The reverses struck with hallmarks (leopard's head, lion passant, date letter) and with maker's mark

Provenance

Lewis Watson, 1st Lord Sondes (1728–95)

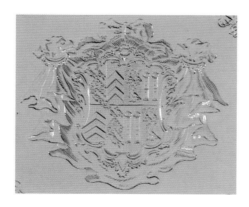

Height: 1⅝ in (4.2 cm)
7 ⅝ in (19.4 cm) square
Weight: 90 oz (2802 g)

PAIR OF WAITERS

94

Silver (sterling standard)
Maker's mark of Paul de Lamerie (Hare, no. 5)
Hallmarks: London, 1745–6

Of shaped square form, raised on four cast vine tendril feet, the rim elaborately cast with leafy vine tendrils with shells at the corners, the field flat chased with a border of trailing vines, shells and scroll enclosing engraved crest and earl's coronet, the undersides engraved with another crest and baron's coronet

Heraldry

The crest and earl's coronet are those borne by Charles Henry Coote, 7th Earl of Mountrath (1725–1801); the crests and coronets on the reverses are those of one of the Barons Monson and were probably added in the nineteenth or early twentieth centuries.

The 6th Earl of Mountrath, who had been a major customer of Lamerie (see no. 39), died in 1744 and was succeeded by his son. It is possible that these waiters were purchased by the 7th Earl at the time of his inheritance, but it may also be that they were part of an existing order of silver placed with Lamerie by the 6th Earl to augment his already considerable plate and were not delivered until after his death. This last explanation is given weight by the presence of another, larger, pair of salvers identical to these waiters, also with the date letter 1745–6, and engraved with the 6th Earl's armorials (see p. 203, n. 6). None of these additional pieces appears to have been owned by the 6th Earl's widow, however, as they do not seem to have been part of the silver she left to Caroline, Lady Milton, at the time of her death in 1768 and it seems more likely that they were owned and used by the 7th Earl. Unfortunately the provenance of both pairs of salvers in the nineteenth century is unknown, and there does not appear to be any connection between the Cootes and the Monson family.

It is clear, though, that the 7th Earl continued to

Height: 1½ in (3.8 cm)
Width: 6½ in (16.5 cm)
Depth: 6⅛ in (15.5 cm)
Weight: 26 oz (808 g)

Pair of salvers, silver, London, 1745–6, maker's mark of Paul de Lamerie, engraved with the arms of the 6th Earl of Mountrath; they evidently formed part of the same order of plate as the pair of waiters. It seems that the order was not completed and hallmarked until after the earl's death in 1744.
Sotheby's, New York

Pair of sauceboats, silver, London, 1749–50, maker's mark of Paul de Lamerie. These are also engraved with the crest of the 7th Earl and show that he like his father was a faithful customer of Lamerie's workshop.
Christie's, New York

patronize Lamerie's shop, for between 1748 and 1750 he purchased a pair of sauceboats and a ladle from him.[1] He showed little of his father's interest, however, in politics or society. He was unmarried, and for much of his life, lived "absolutely the life of a recluse".[2] The *Annual Register* for 1802 describes his eccentricities, particularly his fear of smallpox, which was so great "that he had relays at five houses between his seat in Norfolk and his house in Devonshire to prevent the chance of infection; and at these houses small establishments were kept, as he dared not sleep at an inn." With his death the earldom became extinct.

The design of these waiters continues the Bacchic theme of the Mountrath silver, but it is not unique among the output of the Lamerie workshop. A single example engraved with the arms of Ralph Congreve (see no. 30) is known,[3] and a pair was commissioned from Lamerie in 1747–8 by another Whig grandee, Admiral Anson.[4]

Marks
Struck on reverses with hallmarks (leopard's head, lion passant, date letter) and with maker's mark

Provenance
Charles Henry, 7th Earl of Mountrath
(1725–1801)
Subsequent provenance unknown until
A Lady, sale, Sotheby's, London, November 17, 1960, lot 154
Hilmar Reksten, Bergen, Norway
The Reksten Collection, sale, Christie's, London, May 22, 1991, lot 53

Bibliography
Susan Hare, ed., *Paul de Lamerie: the Work of England's Master Silversmith,* exh. cat., Goldsmiths' Hall, London, 1990, p. 133

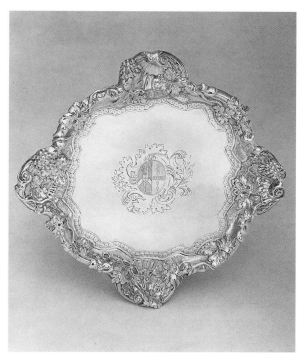

Waiter, silver, London, 1736–7, maker's mark of Paul de Lamerie. The Bacchic theme, with its grapevine border, was clearly a popular one for dining room plate.
Gilbert Collection

Notes
[1] Christie's, New York, April 28, 1992, lot 238.
[2] G.E. Cokayne, ed., *The Complete Peerage.*
[3] Gilbert Collection. On this example, the Congreve arms appear to have been added a few years later.
[4] In the Gans Collection, Virginia Museum of Fine Arts; see Joseph R. Bliss, *The Jerome and Rita Gans Collection of English Silver,* n.d., p. 72.

SILVER for
LIGHTING

Pamela by Philippe
Mercier, (1689/91–1760).
Private collection

Pair of Candlesticks

95

Silver (sterling standard)
Maker's mark EG, crowned anchor between, possibly for Edward Gibson
(Jackson, p. 147, line 22)
Hallmarks: London, 1693–4

The bases of square form with canted corners, cast and chased with gadrooning, rising to part-fluted baluster stems headed by lion masks, the wells engraved with a coat-of-arms within scroll mantling

Heraldry
The arms are those of Dormer.

Candlesticks made of cast sections rather than of sheet silver soldered together first appear in the 1680s, although bellied, or baluster, stems appear on French examples fifty years earlier. The designs of the French ornamentalist Jean Berain (1639–1711) include numerous variations of baluster, bellied and vase-shaped candlestick stems which provided the standard models for silversmiths until the middle of the eighteenth century. The use of bold gadrooning is a feature of French silver of the early seventeenth century and first appears on London-made silver in the 1680s. It is not clear, however, whether candlesticks like these examples were what are referred to as "French fashion" in contemporary records; for example, William III was supplied with "18 white candlesticks, 8 of them monument fashion, 4 of them square and 6 small ffrench fashioned".[1]

The casting of candlestick components was probably a specialized activity and it is possible that one workshop, perhaps operated by Huguenots, supplied such parts as bases, stem sections and sockets, to a number of different suppliers. This mark appears frequently on cast candlesticks of the period and has been attributed by Ian Pickford to Edward Gibson who was made a freeman of the Haberdashers' Company in 1690 and entered a mark as a largeworker in 1697. He is recorded as a plateworker with an address near Half Moon Alley, Bishopsgate Without between 1691 and 1713. If the attribution of this mark to Gibson is correct it may be that these candlesticks were supplied to Gibson as finished articles or as components by Huguenot "outworkers". Much of the surviving work bearing this maker's mark is technically advanced and in the "French" style, such as a silver-gilt porringer and cover of 1686–7, with broad bands of cast dentilation and elaborate cut-card work.[2]

Marks
Struck under the bases with hallmarks (leopard's head, lion passant, date letter) and with maker's mark; traces of lion passant on the sockets

Notes
[1] James Lomax, *Country House Lighting*, exh. cat., Temple Newsam, Leeds, 1992, p. 48.
[2] In the collection of the Duke of Hamilton, H.H. Mulliner, *The Decorative Arts in England 1660–1780*, 1923, fig. 93.

Height 5⅞ in (15 cm)
Diameter of bases 4⅜ in (11.1 cm)
Weight 25 oz 18 dwt (807 g)

PAIR OF CANDLESTICKS

96

Silver (Britannia standard)
Maker's mark of Philip Rollos I (Grimwade, no. 2383)
Hallmarks: London, 1702–3

On octagonal bases cast and chased with a band of
stylized water leaves on a matted ground, enclosing
circular central wells, rising to knopped tapering
triangular stems, the lower parts chased with
similar leaves on a matted ground and above with
panels of shells and bellflowers between applied
openwork scroll brackets, applied above with cherub
heads below a knop of radiating leaves and
spool-form sockets with conforming decoration
and mid-ribs

The octagonal bases and baluster stems of these candlesticks are typical of the period but the way in which they are embellished with applied bellflowers, leaves and openwork scrolls appears to have no parallel in English silver of the period.

Philip Rollos is recorded as a plateworker as early as 1675[1] but does not appear on the denization lists until 1691. He became free of the Goldsmiths' Company in 1697. He was one of the Subordinate Goldsmiths to William III and subsequently to Queen Anne. His work is characteristic of the French style and these candlesticks well illustrate Grimwade's observation that "his work lacks the refinement of detail shown by the Haraches and Willaume, while at the same time possessing a breadth of design and sense of scale which makes his larger pieces always imposing".[2]

Marks
Struck with hallmarks under base (lion's head erased, Britannia, date letter) and with maker's mark; lion's head erased struck on sockets

Provenance
Spink & Son Ltd, London

Bibliography
Octagon, vol. XXVI, Autumn, 1989, illus. p. 42

Exhibited
Christie's, London, *Art Treasures Exhibition*, 1932, no. 537

Notes
[1] Sir Ambrose Heal, *The London Goldsmiths, 1200–1800*, 1935, p. 234.
[2] *The London Goldsmiths, 1697–1830*, rev. edn, 1990, p. 646.

Height: 8⅛ in (20.5cm)
Width: 5⅛ in (13 cm)
Depth: 5⅛ in (13 cm)
Weight: 47 oz 4 dwt (1499 g)

PAIR OF CANDLESTICKS

97

Silver (Britannia standard)
Maker's mark of Thomas Merry I (Grimwade, no. 2017)
Hallmarks: London, 1712–13

On domed faceted octagonal bases rising to knopped and tapering octagonal stems and faceted octagonal campana-shaped sockets, the bases engraved with a circular coat-of-arms within a foliate scroll and bellflower cartouche, and on the other side with a crest

Heraldry
The arms are those of Chaloner impaling those of Foulis, as borne by William Chaloner of Gisborough (d. 1715). The crest, that of a heraldic antelope's head erased, however, is not the Chaloner crest and was probably added later in the eighteenth century.

Wiilliam Chaloner, the son of Sir Edward Chaloner, Kt, and his wife, Anne, daughter of Sir Richard Ingoldsby, married Honora, daughter of Sir John Foulis, Bt, on 15th August, 1682. They had fifteen children. William Chaloner died February 18, 1715 and his wife was buried on October 8 of the same year.

The use of geometric shapes like the octagon is typical of the early eighteenth century. These candlesticks rely for their effect on their bold outlines and the play of the light on their faceted surfaces, rather than on ornamentation.

Thomas Merry appears to have been a specialist supplier of candlesticks and snuffer stands. He was one of the signatories as a "working goldsmith" to the petition complaining of the competition of "necessitous strangers" of 1711.[1]

Marks
Struck under base with hallmarks (lion's head erased, Britannia, date letter) and with maker's mark; the sockets struck with Britannia

Provenance
William Chaloner (d. 1715)
Subsequent provenance unknown until
A Lady, sale, Christie's, London, December 14, 1988, lot 245

Bibliography
Christie's Review of the Season, 1989, illus. p. 310

Note
[1] Stanley T.B. Percival, "Thomas Merry, Citizen and Goldsmith of London", *The Connoisseur*, August, 1970, pp. 270–4.

Height: 7½ in (19 cm)
Width: 4 in (10.2 cm)
Depth: 4 in (10.2 cm)
Weight: 22 oz 18 dwt (712 g)

Pair of Candlesticks

98

Silver (sterling standard), gilt
Maker's mark of Thomas Farren (Grimwade, no. 2749)
Hallmarks: London, 1728–9

Each on domed shaped circular base chased with panels of diaperwork and interlaced strapwork and bellflowers on a matted ground, each side applied with alternating female and male masks, with central wells, rising to knopped baluster stems chased with panels of scrolls and flowers, strapwork and bellflowers, with octagonal shoulders with similar panels and applied with similar masks, with campana-shaped sockets with similar decoration

With two later removable nozzles, one part-marked for London, 1830, maker's mark of Robert Garrard I (Grimwade, no. 2320), of shaped circular form, flat-chased with scrolls

These candlesticks follow the typical baluster form found in Jean Berain's designs from the late seventeenth century and incorporate many of his design features such as panels of diaperwork and wild masks which were so popular on French silver during the Régence period. Their overall effect, however, is somewhat ponderous and decidedly un-French and the closest parallels are found in German silver. A set of similar candlesticks also with Farren's mark, engraved with the royal arms, is in the Spencer collection at Althorp, and may have formed part of Stephen Poyntz's official plate issued to him on his appointment as Commissioner to the Congress of Soissons.[1]

Marks
Struck under bases with hallmarks (leopard's head, lion passant, date letter) and with maker's mark

Provenance
S.J. Phillips Ltd, London

Note
[1] A.G. Grimwade, "Silver at Althorp - II", *The Connoisseur*, March, 1963, p. 3; he was issued with "Tenn p^r. of wrought Candlesticks and Snuffers & ffour large garandoles to put onto them; all weighing 807=10=0", Public Record Office, London, LC/9/44.

Height: 7¾ in (19.6 cm)
Width: 5¼ in (13 cm)
Depth: 5¼ in (13 cm)
Weight: 51 oz 18 dwt (1616 g)

PAIR OF CANDLESTICKS

99

Silver (Britannia standard)
Maker's mark of Paul de Lamerie (Hare, no. 3)
Hallmarks: London, 1729–30

On broad square bases with moulded edges, engraved with panels of diaperwork with rosettes, bellflowers and shells at intervals, with central wells, rising to knopped part-octagonal stems and spool-form sockets

Paul de Lamerie's workshop produced many candlesticks of this plain, functional form during the 1720s and 1730s. An unusual feature of this pair, however, is the broad base, presumably to give extra stability, and the border of fine engraving around the edges.

Marks
Struck under bases with hallmarks (lion's head erased, Britannia, date letter) and with maker's mark

Provenance
Miss M. Richardson, sale, Sotheby's, London, May 23/30, 1985, lot 62
Spink & Son Ltd, London

Bibliography
Octagon, vol. XXII, no. 3, October, 1985

Height: 6⅜ in (16 cm)
Width: 4¾ in (12 cm)
Depth: 4¾ in (12 cm)
Weight: 34 oz 2 dwt (1062 g)

PAIR OF CANDLESTICKS

100

Silver (sterling standard)
Maker's mark of Charles Kandler (Grimwade, no. 341)
Hallmarks: London, 1730–1

Each on square pedestal base with incurved corners, chased with a border of ovolo enclosing panels of strapwork, bellflowers and rosettes on a matted ground, with central wells, rising to knopped and octagonal baluster stems chased with rosettes, palmettes, bellflowers and overlapping waves, all on a matted ground, the shoulders formed of four massive scrolls with bifurcated tops, applied with female masks and applied with festoons between, supporting part-octagonal campana-shaped sockets with conforming chased decoration, the wells engraved with a coat-of-arms within a foliate scroll cartouche

Heraldry
The arms are those of Meynell quarterly with those of Littleton and Poyntz and impaling those of Alleyne, as borne by Littleton Poyntz Meynell (d. 1751).

Littleton Poyntz Meynell, the son of Godfrey Meynell of Bradley, Derbyshire, who had served as High Sheriff of Derbyshire in 1681, married Judith Alleyne, an heiress of Barbados in 1720, who bore him several sons. The second, Hugo, who is traditionally credited with the development of fox hunting in England, was MP for Lichfield and High Sheriff of Derbyshire in 1758.

Meynell was evidently a significant customer of Kandler, as his arms appear also on a pair of soup tureens of about 1735 with Kandler's mark.[1] A tray, or plateau for a centrepiece, of 1726–7, with the maker's mark of Francis Nelme, is in the Gilbert Collection.[2]

Like the salver of the same period from Kandler's shop (no. 89), the style of these candlesticks is quite striking and unlike work from other workshops of the period. The form follows Berain's outline designs for candlesticks (see no. 98) but the open canopies formed of scroll brackets are unique in English silver of the period, although openwork brackets appear on

Height: 8⅝ in (21.8 cm)
Width: 5¼ in (13.4 cm)
Depth: 5¼ in (13.4 cm)
Weight: 57 oz (1774 g)

Set of four candlesticks,
silver-gilt, London,
1795–6, maker's mark of
Robert Sharp.
Christie's, London

French ormolu candlesticks of the Régence
period. A pair of identical examples of 1728–9 are
recorded with the maker's mark of Charles
Hatfield, which may be a mis-reading of Kandler's
mark.[3] Interestingly, the form was copied in
candlesticks supplied by Robert Sharp to the
Prince Regent as part of his decorative work at
Carlton House in 1795–6 and to Lord Bute.[4]
Subsequent copies were made by Garrard's in the
nineteenth century.[5]

The Hon. Elizabeth Cairns Hindley
Anonymous sale, Sotheby's, London, October 14,
1954, lot 149
Anonymous sale, Sotheby's, London, June 20,
1988, lot 153

Marks
Struck under bases with hallmarks (leopard's
head, lion passant, date letter) and with
maker's mark

Provenance
Littleton Poyntz Meynell (d. 1751)
Subsequent provenance unknown until Lord
Hillingdon, c. 1900

Notes
[1] Sotheby's, New York, June 16, 1982, lot 77.
[2] Timothy Schroder, *The Gilbert Collection of Gold and Silver*,
1988, no. 44.
[3] Vanessa Brett, *The Sotheby's Directory of Silver*, 1986, p. 197.
[4] A pair sold Christie's, New York, April 18, 1991, lot 349; and
another set of four supplied to John, 1st Marquess of Bute,
1795–6, sold from the Bute Collection, Christie's, London, July,
1996, lot 101.
[5] For example a set of four of 1846–7, Christie's, New York,
October 18, 1989, lot 26 and another four, 1874–5, Christie's,
Geneva, November 17, 1980, lot 13.

PAIR OF CANDLESTICKS

101

Silver
Maker's mark of John White (Grimwade, no. 1735)
Hallmarks: none
c. 1737

On square bases with incurved corners, with vase-shaped baluster stems and vase-shaped sockets, all cast and chased with fronds, shells and flaming torches on a scalework ground, with panels of matting, scalework and laurel leaves, the stems with panels of quilting, with removable spool-form nozzles with circular drip-pans, with similar chased decoration, the bases and nozzles engraved with a crest and baron's coronet

Heraldry
The crest is that of King, probably as borne by John, 2nd Lord King and Baron of Ockham (1706–40).

These candlesticks are virtually identical to a number of examples from Paul de Lamerie's workshop and show the interchangeability of designs among members of the Lamerie group of the 1730s and 1740s. For example, a pair of identical candlesticks with four-light branches, struck with Lamerie's maker's mark and engraved with the crest of Sir Robert Walpole, is in the

Gilbert Collection, while another set with Lamerie's mark, of 1732–3, was sold from the Marcos Collection, Christie's, New York, January 28, 1990, lot 134. Similar stems appear on a pair of silver-gilt examples with Lamerie's mark of 1736, now in the Al-Tajir Collection, London. Of the Walpole candelabra, Timothy Schroder remarks that "… typical of Lamerie are the arched shoulders and panels of scalework on the stems, the applied trophies on the bases, and the shaped band of matting around the centre of the bases and sockets. The first stirrings of the Rococo are seen here in the swirling fluting and foliage."1

The form of the candlesticks is based on designs by Jean Berain (1639–1711), who published plates of endless variations of candlesticks with vase and baluster-shaped stems. Although, as Timothy Schroder observed, certain rococo elements are typical of the mid-1730s. Like the cup of 1737–8 (no. 12), also supplied by White to the King family, these candlesticks are a Lamerie form and it may be that they are from Lamerie's workshop (see pp. 50–1).

Height 9½ in (24.1 cm)
Width: 4⅝ in (11.6 cm)
Depth: 4⅝ in (11.6 cm)
Weight: 50 oz (1555 g)

*Ornemens Inventez par
J. Berain / Et se vendent
Chez Joseph Friderich
Leopold. A: 1703.* Plate of
designs for candlesticks
showing engraving of
no. 101

It is most likely that these candlesticks were
supplied by White to Lord King about the time of
the cup and cover. White registered a new mark
in June, 1739, so they can be dated before this.
Their lack of official hallmarks signifies that no
duty was paid on them, suggesting that they were
a special commission rather than stock items
offered for sale in White's shop. An identical pair
of candlesticks, fully hallmarked for 1746–7 and
with Robert Tyrrill's mark, also belonged to the
King family and was sold in the same 1993 sale.[2]
Another pair of unmarked candlesticks of
identical form, originally part of the Dorset toilet
service, is illustrated on p. 415.

Marks
Struck twice under bases with maker's mark

Provenance
Probably John, 2nd Lord King and Baron of
Ockham (1706–40)
By descent to the Executry of the late Manon,
Countess of Lovelace, sale, Christie's, London,
May 12, 1993, lot 145

Notes
[1] *Paul de Lamerie, the Work of England's Master Silversmith*, exh.
cat., Goldsmiths' Hall, London, 1990, p. 97.
[2] For a discussion of the King family, see no. 91.

PAIR OF CANDELABRA

102

Silver (sterling standard)
Maker's mark of James Shruder (Grimwade, no. 1682)
Hallmarks: London, 1742–3

On shaped square bases naturalistically cast and chased with rocks and foliage, rising to plain waisted stems of square section supporting satyr terms garlanded with flowers and wearing baskets of flowers on their heads, each with two foliate scroll branches supporting everted acanthus wax pans and sockets; each centre applied c. 1835 with a further removable everted foliate socket

Numbered under bases 57 and 58, the flanges of the branches numbered 59 and 62

Arcadian figures of Bacchus make a striking theme for these candelabra in the "picturesque" style. The image of a bearded Bacchus term, garlanded with foliage, was a popular one from the sixteenth century onwards; it is found in the decorative work of the Fontainebleau School, and in engravings that circulated throughout Europe from the middle of the sixteenth century onwards. Hans Vredeman de Vries's plates of *Figures d'atlantes à bustes engaines*, of c. 1560–70, include bearded Bacchic demi-figures, and they feature prominently in the printed designs of Jean Berain and others at the end of the seventeenth century. Bacchic terms were a common motif in Nicolas Poussin's paintings, such as *Bacchanal before a Herm* and *The Kingdom of Flora*[1], and the series of stone terms made for the garden at Vaux-le-Vicomte, now at Versailles, were designed by him. Engravings of these by Thomassin enjoyed great popularity in the early eighteenth century. Female caryatids made popular supports for silver candlesticks and candelabra during the 1740s, using seventeenth century designs by Jean le Pautre and others for inspiration, but male terms are much rarer.

Height: 15¼ in (38.6 cm)
Width: 16 in (40.6 cm)
Depth: 5¾ in (14.5 cm)
Weight: 165 oz 14 dwt (5153 g)

Candelabrum, bronze,
mid-eighteenth century.
Christie's, London

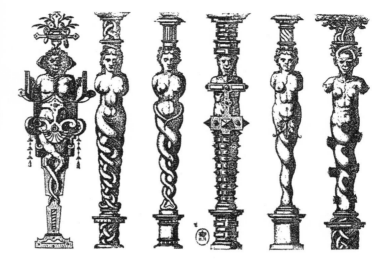

Engraved designs for
terms by Hans Vredeman
de Vries, Antwerp,
c. 1560–70

Several versions bear the mark of Paul de Lamerie, but these differ from the present examples as Bacchus is depicted with his arms raised, holding aloft a basket of grapes which becomes the candle socket.[2] The Shruder examples, with their truncated arms, follow the Poussin model more closely.

A bronze version dating from the middle of the eighteenth century is also known.[3] This was copied at the beginning of the nineteenth century, also in bronze, and evidently retailed by the silversmith William Frisbee (fl. 1782–1820), whose signature appears on the bases. These bronze versions may give us an idea of the original appearance of these silver examples,

where the third foliate branch has been replaced, probably during the nineteenth century, with a different candle socket.

Marks
Struck under bases with hallmarks (leopard's head, lion passant, date letter) and with maker's mark

Provenance
Anonymous sale, Christie's, London, May 4, 1893, lot 124
Henry Walters, Baltimore
Mrs. Henry Walters, sale, Parke-Bernet, New York, December 3, 1943, lot 894
Anonymous sale, Sotheby's, London, March 15,

Bacchanal before a Herm by
Nicolas Poussin (1594–1665).
National Gallery, London

1962, lot 148
A Gentleman, sale, Sotheby's, London, October
24, 1989, lot 491

Bibliography
Vanessa Brett, *The Sotheby's Directory of Silver*,
1986, p. 208, fig. 902

Notes
[1] The picture entered the Dresden royal collection in 1722 and it
is tempting to speculate if Shruder, whose origins are unknown,
may have come from there.
[2] A pair of 1747–8 with three-light branches is in the Sterling and
Francine Clark Art Institute, Williamstown, Massachusetts; a set
of four candlesticks of the same design, 1744–5, made for
Thomas, 5th Earl of Dumphries (d. 1768) was sold from the Bute
Collection, Christie's, London, July 3, 1996, lot 101.
[3] Christie's, London, July 4, 1986, lot 286.

**Set of four candlesticks,
silver-gilt, London,
1744–5, maker's mark of
Paul de Lamerie.**
Christie's, London

FOUR CANDLESTICKS

103

Silver (sterling standard)
Maker's mark of Phillips Garden (Grimwade, no. 2184)
Hallmarks: London, 1742–3

On shaped square bases cast and chased with exotic masks amid rocaille, foliage and fruit at the corners, with central circular wells bordered by applied ovolo, rising to knopped baluster stems and campana-shaped sockets all chased with foliage and rocaille, with ovolo rims and removable shaped square nozzles chased with scrolls and rocaille, the wells engraved with a coat-of-arms within a foliate scroll cartouche and, on two, with a crest and earl's coronet

Numbered under the bases 1 through 4 and with scratch weights 23-7, 26, 25-16½ and 24=10 respectively, each also pricked in the early twentieth century with the initials GDW (for George D. Widener)

Heraldry
The coat-of-arms is unidentified.

The usual shaped-square form of candlestick of the 1730s and 1740s, with a stem formed of knops and balusters, was frequently elaborated on by the Lamerie group and others, like Elizabeth Godfrey, by the addition of garlands of foliage, or vines, and Bacchic heads. The way the garlands drape the stems and the *rocaille* on the nozzles give the form a certain rococo movement, but the overall effect continues to be more baroque than rococo.

Marks
Struck under bases with hallmarks (leopard's head, lion passant, date letter) and with maker's mark

Provenance
George D. Widener, Philadelphia (d. 1912)
Then by descent to a Florida Collector, sale, Christie's, New York, April 29, 1986, lot 178
Spink & Son Ltd, London

Height: 8½ in (22 cm)
Width: 5 in (12.6 cm)
Depth: 5 in (12.6 cm)
Weight: 98 oz 2 dwt (3054 g)

CANDLE SNUFFERS AND TRAY

104

Silver (sterling standard)
Maker's mark of James Shruder (Grimwade, no. 1682)
Hallmarks: London, 1745–6

The snuffers of scissor form, the loop handles and oval box with chased ovolo borders, baluster prick and steel-edged blade, the side of the box engraved with a coat-of-arms and earl's coronet

The interior engraved with scratch weight 5 oz=11 dwt

The tray of shaped oblong form with waisted sides, raised on four scroll and shell feet, with applied ovolo rim and leaf-capped scroll handle, the centre engraved with a coat-of-arms and earl's coronet

The base engraved with scratch weight 12 oz=15 dwt

Heraldry
The arms are those of Booth as borne by George Booth, 2nd Earl of Warrington (1675–1758).

The Earl of Warrington appears to have been unaware of the rococo style. His silver purchases into the 1740s continue to be in the bold, plain style of the silver he purchased in the 1720s. On these snuffers and their stand, the only concession to the rococo appears to be the *rocaille* shell-form feet on the stand. The earl's life and silver purchases have been well documented.[1] An avid consumer of silver for much of his life, the earl is of great interest to us today, as the inventory he made, in his own hand, of his silver survives. From this we know not only exactly what he had, but how he used it, and we can differentiate – thanks to the weights recorded – between a "hand bason" and a "bason to wash my mouth", or between a "large green teapot" and a "large Bohea teapot". It is also fortunate that the earl's silver descended in his family until the early years of this century, when most of it was dispersed in sales. As a result, the Warrington plate is one of the best documented groups of eighteenth-century silver and provides us with an insight into the life of this otherwise shadowy figure.

Snuffers:
Length: 6 in (15.2 cm)
Weight: 5 oz 6 dwt (167 g)
Tray:
Length: 8 in (20.2 cm)
Weight: 12 oz (400 g)

George Booth, 2nd Earl of Warrington by Michael Dahl (1656–1743) (detail). Dunham Massey, Cheshire: National Trust Photographic Library/John Hammond

Unlike his contemporaries such as the Earl of Chesterfield and the Earl of Mountrath, Warrington was not a public figure; a contemporary wrote that "this gentleman makes no great figure in his country, Parliament or person". He spent his life attempting to recover his family's fortune, which had been lost by his father, who had died in 1693 leaving his son nothing but an earldom, prodigious debts and a pretentious pamphlet entitled "Advice to his Children". The new earl at once set about finding a rich heiress to marry and settle his debts. His search was the talk of society – a newspaper of

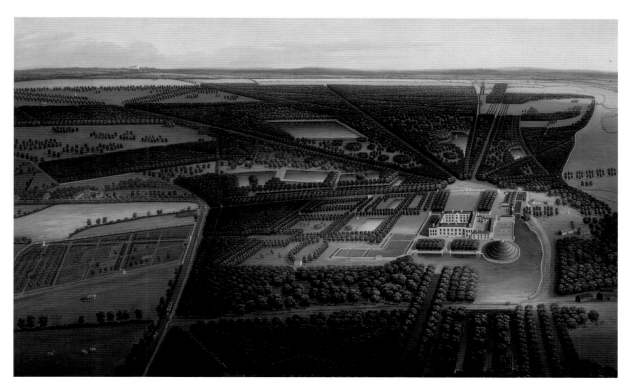

Dunham Massey from the North
by John Harris II
(*fl.* 1722–c.1759), early
eighteenth century.
Dunham Massey, Cheshire:
National Trust Photographic
Library/Angelo Hornak

1694 recorded that "a match is agreed upon, and will be speedily consummated, between the young Earl of Warrington and Madame Thomas, a great heiress of Wales, who has £3,000 or 4,000 per annum". The match never took place, nor did the one reported between him and a daughter of Lord Crewe; or the one purportedly between him and a "Madame Offley of Crewe Hall, with whom he is to have £20,000".[2]

The earl finally married Mary Oldbury, daughter of a London merchant, in 1702. She brought him a dowry of £40,000 but the marriage was not a success; in the oft-quoted remark: "some years after my lady had consigned up her whole fortune to pay my lord's debts, they quarrell'd & lived in the same house as absolute strangers to each other at bed and board".[3] His wife's dowry went a considerable way towards settling Warrington's debts, and he used whatever surplus cash he had in the years following either to plant trees on his estate at Dunham Massey in Cheshire or to buy silver. Both these activities he saw as laying down wealth for his descendants: of the trees, he wrote "you may think it strange that I do these things; but I have the inward satisfaction in my own breast; the benefit of posterity; and my survivors will receive more than double the profit, than by any other method I could possibly take for their interest".[4] This last remark is telling, for the earl obviously sought to provide his heirs with a substantial cushion of money and plate and to leave no debts as his father had done, for the earl must have been ever mindful of the times he saw his father "fall aweeping from the greatness of his debts".

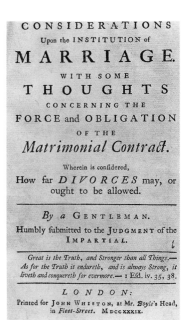

CONSIDERATIONS
Upon the INSTITUTION of
MARRIAGE.
WITH SOME
THOUGHTS
CONCERNING THE
FORCE and OBLIGATION
OF THE
Matrimonial Contract.

Wherein is confidered,

How far *DIVORCES* may, or
ought to be allowed.

By a GENTLEMAN.

Humbly fubmitted to the JUDGMENT of the
IMPARTIAL.

*Great is the Truth, and Stronger than all Things.—
As for the Truth it endureth, and is always Strong, it
liveth and conquereth for evermore.*— 1 Efd. iv. 35, 38.

LONDON:
Printed for JOHN WHISTON, at Mr. *Boyle's* Head,
in *Fleet-Street.* MDCCXXXIX.

The Earl's treatise on divorce, 1739.
The Van Pelt-Dietrich Library, University of Pennsylvania, Special Collections

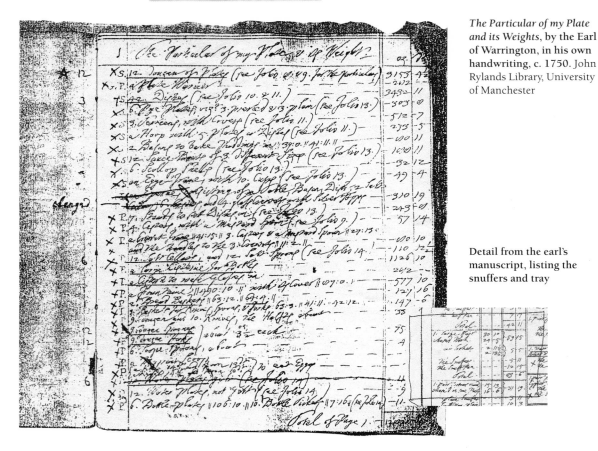

The Particular of my Plate and its Weights, by the Earl of Warrington, in his own handwriting, c. 1750. John Rylands Library, University of Manchester

Detail from the earl's manuscript, listing the snuffers and tray

Warrington's obsession with his financial security, his plate and his estate provide a stark contrast to the sadness of his private life; the rift with his wife was never healed and this led him to publish in 1739 a pamphlet on the advantages of divorce entitled *Considerations Upon the Institution of Marriage, with some Thoughts concerning the Force and Obligation of the Matrimonial Contract, Wherein is considered, How far Divorces may, or ought to be allowed. By a Gentleman. Humbly submitted to the Judgement of the Impartial.* The earl had an only daughter, Mary, who married the 4th Earl of Stamford in 1736. After Warrington's death in 1758, Dunham Massey passed to them and subsequently to their descendants, the Greys, who became Earls of Stamford.

Twelve pairs of candlesticks are listed in the earl's inventory, all of them accompanied by snuffers and their trays, as scissor-form snuffers were essential for trimming wicks until the invention of the "self-trimming" wick in the nineteenth century rendered them obsolete. This pair and tray are the heaviest listed under the heading "Candlesticks", and accompanied "1 Large Pair Chas'd Work" candlesticks which themselves weighed nearly sixty ounces.[5] The candlesticks, however, date from 1731–2 and bear the mark of Peter Archambo. They are in the French classical style (see no. 9) and bear little stylistic affinity to the snuffers and tray.[6]

Marks

The snuffers struck on interior of box and on blade with hallmarks (leopard's head, lion passant, date letter) and with maker's mark; the tray struck on reverse with hallmarks (leopard's head, lion passant, date letter) and with maker's mark

Provenance

George Booth, 2nd Earl of Warrington (1675–1758), bequeathed to his daughter Mary, Countess of Stamford (1703–72)
Then by descent to Catherine, Lady Grey and Sir John Foley-Grey, Bt, sale, Christie's,

Pair of candlesticks, silver, London, 1731–2, maker's mark of Peter Archambo. These candlesticks are listed with the snuffer and tray in the earl's manuscript inventory, although they are some fifteen years earlier in date.
Christie's, London

London, April 20, 1921, lot 6
Anonymous sale, Christie's, London, March 28, 1962, lot 138
The late Samuel Messer, sale, Christie's, London, May 13, 1992, lot 235

Notes
[1] J.F Hayward, "The Earl of Warrington's Silver", *Apollo*, July, 1978; Timothy Schroder, "George Booth and William Beckford, a Study in Patronage", *International Silver and Jewellery Fair Annual*, 1989.
[2] G.E. Cokayne, ed.*The Complete Peerage*.
[3] This comment appears written in the margin of P. Bliss's copy of *Royal and Noble Authors* in the British Museum.
[4] Quoted in Gervase Jackson-Stops *et al.*, *Dunham Massey*, 1981, p. 32.
[5] f. 17.
[6] The Tythrop Park Collection, sale, Christie's, London, April 27, 1995, lot 84.

PAIR OF CANDLESTICKS

105

Silver (sterling standard)
Maker's mark of Nicholas Sprimont (Grimwade, no. 2102)
Hallmarks: London, 1746–7

On stepped shaped square bases cast and chased at the corners with foliate scrolls, with central tied reed circular wells, rising to knopped baluster stems, the shoulders with flat corners chased with overlapping waves, alternating with incurved sides applied with trailing foliage, the spool-form sockets applied with foliage and reeding, with removable foliate nozzles

One engraved under the base with scratch weight 62 0 oz, the sockets and nozzles numbered with notches

Pair of candlesticks, silver, London, 1747–8, maker's mark of Paul de Lamerie.
Al-Tajir Collection

These candlesticks are larger and much more striking than the ones of 1742–3 (no. 103). The usual baluster stem of candlesticks of the period has been opened up and garlands of foliage inserted at the shoulder. The effect is striking and typical of the more ambitious works of the Lamerie group in the late 1740s. An identical pair of candlesticks is known with the mark of Lamerie, marked a year later in 1747–8, and it is a matter of speculation in whose workshop the various stages of production were carried out. A slightly watered-down version of 1750–1, is also known, with the mark of another member of the Lamerie group, William Cripps.

Marks
Struck under base with hallmarks (leopard's head, lion passant, date letter), and with maker's mark

Provenance
Anonymous sale, Sotheby's, London, May 3, 1990, lot 123

Height: 10½ in (26.7 cm)
Width: 5¼ in (13.3 cm)
Depth: 5¼ in (13.3 cm)
Weight: 60 oz 8 dwt (1878 g)

The Morning Levee by
William Hogarth
(1697–1764), from his
Marriage à la Mode.
National Gallery, London

SILVER for the BEDROOM and WRITING TABLE

EWER

106

Silver (sterling standard)
Maker's mark ?W in script in heart-shaped punch surmounted by a crown,
possibly for David Willaume I
Hallmarks: London, 1696–7

The helmet-shaped body on spreading circular foot cast and chased with a band of gadrooning with foliage at intervals, rising to a stem with part-fluted knop, the lower part of the body applied with vertical palmette straps under a moulded rib, applied at the shoulder with a band of bold dentilation and under the lip with a scroll and shell motif above chased auricular waves, the harp-shaped handle applied with trailing beading

The maker's mark which appears on this ewer appears to be the same as that illustrated in Jackson (p. 132, line 19), recorded on the back of a round brush and a pair of candlesticks of 1674, attributed to David Willaume. This is presumably the reason why Ambrose Heal records Willaume in London as early as this date, which is impossible as he would have been only sixteen. His denization is not recorded until 1687, and it seems that Jackson mis-read the date letter on the brush and candlesticks.

The identity of Willaume's pre-Britannia standard mark has always been open to conjecture; judging from the French style of this ewer and its assured handling, it seems reasonable to attribute it to a workshop of Willaume's stature. He is recorded as established at "The Windsor Castle" (his shop sign) in Charing Cross as early as 1686 but after 1697 he had moved to the fashionable neighbourhood of St James's.

Willaume was the son of Adam Willaume, a goldsmith of Metz, and, like Pierre Harache, he appears to have succeeded in leaving his native land with much of his wealth which enabled him

Height: 11¼ in (28.5 cm)
Width: 4¾ in (12.1 cm)
Weight: 48 oz 4 dwt (1500 g)

Marks
Struck on rim by handle with hallmarks (leopard's head, lion passant, date letter) and with maker's mark, lion passant struck on top of foot

Provenance
Anonymous sale, Christie's, London, June 28, 1933, lot 89
The Estate of Oscar Dusendschon, Geneva, sale, Sotheby's, London, November 17, 1960, lot 28
Hilmar Reksten, Bergen, Norway
The Reksten Collection, sale, Christie's, London, May 22, 1991, lot 142

Bibliography
Sidsel Helliesen, *Hilmar Rekstens Samlinger*, 1971, illus. p. 132
Arthur Grimwade, *Silver for Sale*, 1994, pl. 3 shows the ewer being sold in the 1933 sale (see below)

to establish a banking and silversmithing business which attracted an extensive noble clientele.

The helmet-shaped ewer is a French form which replaced the earlier "jug" shape with applied spout in the 1680s. It is often embellished with bold gadrooning or dentilation, as on this example, or strapwork. Frequently accompanied by a basin, larger examples were intended solely for display, the "basin" being by this time a flat dish providing nothing more than a suitable backdrop for elaborately engraved armorials, their function in the dining room rendered obsolete by the advent of the fork. Smaller versions, like the present example, however, often appear as components of toilet services and were evidently intended for use in the bedroom. There is a ewer of similar form, of 1701–2, maker's mark of John Porter, at Eton College.[1]

This ewer was evidently given to a church, sometime in the nineteenth century, and it was engraved under the lip with the sacred monogram. This, and later gilding, have recently been removed.

Note
[1] E.A. Jones, *The Plate of Eton College*, 1938, p. 14.

Sale of ewer as lot 89 at Christie's, London, June 28, 1933. Grimwade is seen to the right with his back to the camera.
Christie's, London

CASKET

107

Silver (Britannia standard)
Maker's mark of Louis Cuny (Grimwade, no. 422)
Hallmarks: London, 1704–5

Of rectangular form with moulded borders, raised on four bun feet, the hinged cover engraved with initials in a mirrored cypher within an oval enclosed by an elaborate architectural cartouche flanked by seated lions amid foliate scrolls and berried foliage enclosing panels of fish-scale and shell-work, the top entablature flanked by two putti, the bottom hung with bellflowers and a mask amid foliage

This casket probably formed part of a toilet service. Rectangular boxes of this size were intended for jewels or for arrowroot, which was mixed with alcohol to make a perfume. Daniel Marot's engraved designs include designs for "boîtes à racines". Toilet services were often given to a bride by her groom on their wedding day and, unlike other personal silverware, which was regarded as an asset and treated as such, they were often specifically mentioned among the bequests in a lady's will (see no. 110).

The levee, during which a lady of fashion received guests in her bedroom, was a French custom introduced to England at the end of the seventeenth century. Her dressing plate would be displayed on the dressing table, the looking glass and the table itself often covered in expensive fabric. Hogarth's picture *The Morning Levee* (pp. 400–1) shows such a service displayed.

Certain stylistic features in the engraved cartouche on this casket bear similarities to a body of engraving on plate which was first suggested as the work of "the Master of George Vertue" by Charles Oman.[1] Arthur Grimwade has subsequently made a convincing case that the identity of this engraver may be Blaise Gentot, born in Lyons in 1658, who was evidently well established in London by the end of the 1680s.[2] His signature appears on the well-known table top at Chatsworth engraved with the arms of the 1st Duke of Devonshire, which has been dated about 1700.[3] The use of bold architectural brackets and berried laurel sprays appear to be characteristic of Gentot's work and are well represented in the engraving on this casket, but perhaps the most striking comparison can be made between it and two dishes, the engraving on which has been attributed to Gentot by Grimwade. The first,

Height: 3¾ in (9.5 cm)
Width: 10⅜ in (26.4 cm)
Depth: 7¾ in (19.7 cm)
Weight: 77 oz 10 dwt (2410 g)

Page from Benjamin
Rhodes's *A New Book of
Cyphers*, early eighteenth
century

London in 1683, which can be seen flanking the
cypher on the Cuny casket.

The date of this casket, however, is several years
after Gentot went bankrupt and returned to
France (thought by Grimwade to have been about
1701), although doubtless as one who had "the
top reputation of any in Town", he left
journeymen and apprentices – the young George
Vertue among them – continuing to work in his
style. Engraving must be seen in terms of schools
rather than individual artists and while it is
certain that Gentot was responsible in large part
for the spread of this style of engraving in
London, it would doubtless have been copied
not only by his own journeymen, but also by
other workshops.

Intricate cyphers, often containing a mirrored
image of the initials, were extremely popular
during the end of the seventeenth and beginning
of the eighteenth centuries. Engravers could
rely on works like Benjamin Rhodes's *A New
Book of Cyphers*, which was probably the most
popular book of these designs of the early
eighteenth century.

Marks
Struck under base and cover with hallmarks
(lion's head erased, Britannia, date letter), and
with maker's mark

Provenance
T.A. Bird, Esq., Christie's, London, November 24,
1971, lot 70
S.J. Phillips Ltd, London

belonging to the Duke of Sutherland and now at
the Bowes Museum in Northumberland, is from
the workshop of Elie Pacot and bears Lille
hallmarks of about 1692, while the second, also
made in Lille, now belongs to the City of
Westminster. These dishes are engraved with
virtually identical elaborate cartouches which, in
addition to Gentot's typical berried foliage and
heavy plinths, incorporate distinctive swirls of
acanthus incorporating pateræ, probably deriving
from the designs of Jean Tijou, published in

Notes
[1] 1978, pp. 91–3.
[2] "The Master of George Vertue. His Identity and Oeuvre", *Apollo*
February 1988, pp. 83–9.
[3] *Treasures from Chatsworth, English Engraved Silver*, exh. cat.
Royal Academy, London, 1978.

TWO BOWLS

108

Silver (sterling standard)
Maker's mark of David Willaume II (Grimwade, no. 514)
Hallmarks: London, 1728–9

Each of fluted circular form on spreading circular foot, with scalloped rim; the first engraved in the centre with the Howe crest and a viscount's coronet; the second engraved on the exterior, c. 1825, with the Howe and Curzon crests and an earl's coronet

Heraldry
the first:
The crest is that borne by Emanuel Scrope, 2nd Viscount Howe. His third son was Richard, the 4th Viscount and celebrated Admiral. Richard's youngest daughter and co-heiress, Louisa Catherine, married John Denis, 1st Marquess of Sligo in 1787.
the second:
The crests are those borne by Richard William Penn Curzon who was created Earl Howe on July 15, 1821. He was Lord Chamberlain to Queen Adelaide, consort of William IV.

The function of these small bowls is unclear. The Earl of Warrington, in his manuscript inventory of his silver drawn up about 1752, lists a "basin to wash my mouth" (see no. 104) but the scalloped rim on the present examples would seem to preclude this function. Warrington also owned a set of six bowls of approximately the same size as these examples which Judith Bannister suggested may have been for potpourri or flowers.[1]

Marks
Struck under bases with hallmarks (leopard's head, lion passant, date letter) and with maker's mark

Provenance
the first:
By descent to Denis, 10th Marquess of Sligo, sale, Christie's, London, May 13, 1953, lot 180
the first and second:
Nathaniel Mayer, 3rd Lord Rothschild, GM, sale, Christie's, London, June 27, 1963, lot 41
A Lady, sale, Christie's, London, November 21, 1973, lot 81
President and Mrs. Ferdinand Marcos
The Republic of the Philippines through the Presidential Commission on Good Government, sale, Christie's, New York, January 30, 1988, lot 36

Note
[1] *The Treasure Houses of Britain*, exh. cat., National Gallery, Washington, D.C., 1985, no. 108.

Height: 3¾ in (9.5 cm)
Diameter: 5⅞ in (15 cm)
Weight:
the first 15 oz 6 dwt (476 g)
the second 14 oz 6 dwt (446 g)

INKSTAND

109

Silver (Britannia standard)
Maker's mark of Paul de Lamerie (Hare, no. 3)
Hallmarks: London, 1730–1

Of oblong form with incurved corners and moulded rim, raised on four scroll bracket feet, the border flat-chased and engraved with panels of strapwork and scrolls, the field with a border of diaperwork, paterœ and shells within interlaced strapwork, with one large and two smaller circular wells, the larger fitted with a removable bell with octagonal baluster handle with alternating plain and trellis panels, with octagonal finial, the body unscrewing from the handle and engraved with bands of trellis and rosettes, the two smaller each with a baluster pot decorated at the shoulder with conforming decoration, with removable covers, one pierced for pounce with crosses and foliate scrolls, the other for ink; the field, bell and pots engraved with a crest

Heraldry
The crest is that of Bugge of Harlow, Essex.

The engraved borders on this inkstand are somewhat more expansive than the engraving found on work from the Lamerie/Gamble workshop in the 1720s (see the waiter, no. 85) and it may be that after his split with the engraver and retailer Ellis Gamble in 1728, Lamerie employed new engravers (see p. 49).

Inkstands of this period are usually fitted with an inkpot and another pot, with pierced top, to sprinkle sand over a sheet of paper, essential before the invention of blotting paper.

Pots and bells which accompany inkstands at this period are often found without hallmarks, suggesting that the stands may have been sent to Goldsmiths' Hall for assay without either the fittings or the mounting rims applied, so avoiding a portion of the tax normally payable on wrought plate.

Marks
Struck under base with hallmarks (lion's head erased, Britannia, date letter) and with maker's mark

Provenance
The Property of a Nobleman, Phillips, London, June 2, 1989, lot 172

Height: 6½ in (16.5 cm)
Width: 8¾ in (22.2 cm)
Depth: 6¾ in (17.2 cm)
Weight: 25 oz 8 dwt (79 g)

TOILET SERVICE

110

Silver, gilt, cut glass, silk, walnut
Marks: none except for twentieth-century French control marks
c. 1750

Comprising:

A looking glass, the shaped frame chased with a border of rosettes on a matted ground, surmounted by a satyr's head amid *rocaille, the two feet formed as dolphins flanking a central winged cherub head, applied with a ribbon engraved with the initial D under a ducal coronet*
Height: 27 ¼ in (69 cm)

A ewer, of helmet-form, on circular foot chased with swirling leaves on a matted ground, the knop above chased with quatrefoils, the body finely chased with lobes and foliage and a scene of two figures beside a spring, with the bearded mask of a river god above, the border with further quatrefoils and shells, the rising handle formed as a dolphin, engraved with the same initial and coronet
Height: 9½ in (24.2 cm)

A basin, of deep circular form, repoussé and chased with swirling foliage and scrolls capped by shells on a matted ground, the interior border repoussé and chased with shells, scrolls, diaperwork and floral festoons on a similar ground, engraved with the same initial and coronet
Height: 4¼ in (10.8 cm)

A pair of glove trays, of oblong form, each on four scroll feet, the borders chased with scrolls, rocaille and female masks on a matted ground, engraved with the same initial and coronet
Width: 10 in (25.5 cm)

A pair of silver-gilt mounted cut-glass scent bottles, of square form with canted corners, the hinged covers chased with panels enclosing rosettes on alternating matted or trelliswork grounds, engraved with the same initial and coronet
Height: 6¾ in (17 cm)

A pair of bowls and covers, of circular form on spreading bases chased with a band of rosettes, the bodies chased with a broad band of alternating spiral scrolls and leaves on a matted ground; the removable covers with similar chased bands enclosing circular plaques each chased with a putto astride a sea monster, engraved with the same initial and coronet
Diameter: 4¾ in (12 cm)

A pair of oblong boxes and covers, with incurved corners, the sides and hinged covers chased with scènes galantes, all within borders of chased rosettes

Weight without scent bottles and
looking glass:
221 oz (6873 g)

on a matted ground, engraved with the same
initial and coronet
Width: 6¾ in (17 cm)

A pair of square boxes and covers, matching the
preceding, similarly engraved
Width: 5¼ in (13.5 cm)

An oblong pin cushion, matching the preceding,
similarly engraved
Width: 8 in (20 cm)

Initials
The initial and coronet are those of Elizabeth
Sackville, Duchess of Dorset (d. 1768).

Pair of candlesticks, silver-gilt, unmarked, c. 1740. These candlesticks were part of the Dorset service when sold in 1959. Christie's, London

Silver toilet services became less common towards the middle of the eighteenth century, due in part to the fact that the morning levee, during which a lady received people while attending to her toilette, declined in importance. Other materials, such as porcelain and enamel, also competed with silver for a place on the fashionable dressing table. The small number that survive from after 1740 are – with a few exceptions – clearly composite sets put together using various components from a silversmith's stock, and they often lack a cohesive design. The present set originally included a pair of unmarked candlesticks which are identical to examples produced in the workshops of Paul de Lamerie and others in the 1730s (see no. 101). They have little stylistic affinity with the boxes in this service. Similarly, the two glove trays in the service (and a pair of matching larger examples engraved with the armorials of the duke, which were also included in the service when sold in 1959), are quite different in decoration and manufacture. They are not double-walled like the rest of the pieces.[1]

The service poses a number of questions about its

origins. Stylistic elements, such as bands of *rocaille*, guilloche borders and use of dolphins, are typical of the late 1730s or 1740s, and the slender spiral plumes chased on the basin and other pieces are found on English silver of this period, but the proportions of the components and the general handling are not English. The double-walled construction, moreover, is not characteristic of London-made silver of the period, although it is a feature of a few other toilet services of the mid-century, such as Thomas Heming's service made for Princess Caroline, daughter of George III, in the Kunstindustrie Museum, Copenhagen.[2] Both this service and the Dorset service have nuts and bolts holding the chased plaques in place. The *Commedia dell'Arte* scenes chased on the sides and covers of the boxes are based on works by Watteau which were engraved and published by C.-N. Cochin in 1729. Eminently suitable for a toilet service, these scenes were sometimes used by German immigrant gold chasers working in London, like Augustin Heckel, for watch cases. They are a far cry from the scenes and imagery from Ovid's *Metamorphoses* which usually figure on earlier toilet services. The dolphins which appear as the

Detail of ewer handle

Title page from *Paisages Maritimes* by Stefano della Bella.
Museum Boymans van Beuningen, Rotterdam

("*Ferrières*"), two pomade cups, two cups, one covered and one uncovered, three brushes, a box for patches, two candlesticks, a basin to wash the hands, a ewer, the whole in silver-gilt weighing ninety-one *marcs*, four *onces*, seven *gros*, at sixty-six *livres* the *marc*, amounting to *livres* 6,046:10.

With charges for the materials and construction of the case, and miscellaneous extras, the total is 6,976:10 *livres* which is converted to English currency at the end of the bill "*sur le pied du change*" at £250 14s.

It is possible that this bill refers to the Dorset service, although only one pair of *gantiers*, or

feet of the mirror and the handle of the ewer, symbolic of nobility as well as of Venus, the goddess of love, recalling her birth from the sea, are very similar to those that appear in the designs of Meissonnier, which were engraved by Huquier and published in the 1730s.

A clue to the service's possible origins may lie in a receipt headed "Mémoire de la Toilette de Madame La Duchesse" in the Sackville Papers, which unfortunately is neither dated nor signed:[3]

> Firstly, Two square covered boxes, two glove trays, a mirror, a dressing weight, two powder boxes, a cup stand, two ?scent bottles

Title page of *Cinquième Livre d'Ornemens inventés par J.A. Meissonnier*

glove trays, is listed. The two pairs of trays, one of which is still part of the service, are clearly German in origin and unlike the rest of the service, and may have been added at a later date. The box for patches, or *boette à mouches* (so essential for the lady, or man, of fashion at the time) has evidently been converted subsequently to a pin cushion, and the three brushes have been lost. A *ferrière* was a small bottle to hold orange flower water and the *ferrières* mentioned may refer to the pair of cut-glass and silver-gilt scent bottles which form part of the service, although similar small scent bottles were usually referred to as *flacons* in contemporary accounts.[4]

If this bill is indeed for the Dorset service, its origin and that of the service itself is still uncertain. It is unlikely that the bill is French, given the grammatical errors in it. The service itself does not appear to be French either, as few parallels to its decoration or construction can be found in contemporary French silver, and, given the strictness of the French hallmarking laws of the time, the absence of any hallmarks also make this extremely unlikely. The style and quality of the chased scenes is similar to Dutch gold work and a Low Country origin is possible.

Elizabeth, Duchess of Dorset, was the daughter and co-heiress of Lieutenant General Walter

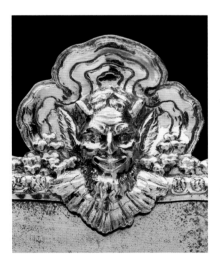

Detail of cresting of mirror

Detail of front of ewer

Philip Colyear, the brother of Lord Portmore. To her husband, the 1st Duke of Dorset, whom she married in 1708, she was "my dear, dear Colly" (see no. 7).[5] She, like her husband, was active at the courts of both George I and George II and she was Mistress of the Robes to Queen Caroline, wife of George II, when she was Princess of Wales and, after 1727, as Queen. It was traditionally thought in the Stopford-Sackville family, to whom the service descended, that the service had been given as a wedding present by the Duke of Dorset to his daughter, Caroline, on her marriage in 1742 to Joseph Damer, who was subsequently created Lord Milton. It is unlikely, though, that this is the case, as the service is engraved with the initial and coronet of the duchess. It is much more likely that this was the duchess's personal service, and the one bequeathed by her to her daughter in 1768. Her will, dated May 17 of that year, says:

> … I give and bequeath unto my Daughter the Right Honourable Lady Milton my Silver Gilt Toilet with everything belonging to the same,

Elizabeth, Duchess of Dorset
attributed to Hans Hysing
(1678–1753).
Private collection

Mémoire de la Toilette de Madame La Duchesse,
c. 1750. This appears to
be the bill of sale for the
toilet service.
Sackville Papers, West
Kent Archive Office,
Maidstone

my Diamond Ear Rings with Pearl Drops and
Pearl Necklace and my Ring with Queen
Caroline's Picture.[6]

Two years before, Caroline, Lady Milton had been
left the Mountrath plate by the Countess of

Mountrath (see no. 39) but unlike that silver,
which remained in her husband's family and
ultimately descended to the Earls of
Portarlington, she gave or bequeathed her toilet
service to her brother, Lord George Sackville, or
to his wife.

Provenance
Elizabeth, Duchess of Dorset (d. 1768)
Bequeathed by her in 1768 to her daughter,
Caroline, wife of Joseph Damer, afterwards Lord
Milton (d. 1775)
Probably bequeathed by her in 1775 to her
brother, Lord George Sackville, subsequently 1st
Viscount Sackville (1715–85)
By descent to William Bruce Stopford-Sackville,

Caroline Damer, Lady Milton
by Pompeo Batoni (1708–87).
She was bequeathed the toilet
service by her mother the
Duchess of Dorset in 1768.
Private collection

Drayton House, Northamptonshire
Thomas Lumley Ltd, London, 1959
Antenor Patiño
The Patiño Collection, sale, Christie's, New York,
October, 28, 1986, lot 12
Spink and Son Ltd, London

Bibliography
Octagon, vol. XXV, no. 2, Autumn, 1988, illus. p. 5

Exhibited
South Kensington Museum, London, 1862, *Loan
Exhibition of Old English Plate*, no. 5991: "The
silver-gilt toilet service of Lady Caroline Damer,
bequeathed to Charles, Duke of Dorset ... circa
1700", lent by W.B. Stopford, Esq.

Notes
[1] These are now in a private English collection; the candlesticks
were sold Christie's, London, November 10, 1993, lot 234; when
sold in 1986, the set also included a plummit (a weight for the
drapery on a dressing table), in similar style to the circular boxes.
[2] Arthur Grimwade, "Royal Toilet Services in Scandinavia",
Connoisseur, May, 1956.
[3] Sackville Papers, West Kent Archive Office, Maidstone,
U269 F43.
[4] For an explanation of the various components of an eighteenth-
century toilet service, see Peter C. Kaellgren, "French Influence
in a Toilet Service by David Willaume I" in *Versailles: French
Court Style and its Influence*, University of Toronto School of
Continuing Studies symposium, 1992, pp. 74–80.
[5] Vita Sackville-West, *Knole and the Sackvilles*, rev. edn,
1991, p. 151.
[6] Copy in the Sackville Papers, U269/ T84/14.

PAIR OF TOILET BOWLS AND COVERS

111

Silver (sterling standard)
Maker's mark of George Wickes (Grimwade, no. 927)
Hallmarks: London, 1741–2

Of square vase-form with fluted corners, the rim and
spreading feet cast and chased with gadrooned
borders, each with two leaf-capped scroll handles,
the fluted covers with reeded baluster finials

These bowls and covers probably formed part of a toilet service. By the 1740s such services had become less common than in the seventeenth century. Services often included a pair of two-handled cups and covers, which were probably the "cups Cover'd or open, to wash chaps" mentioned in the oft-quoted poem by John Evelyn, *Mundus Muliebris*, which described a fashionable lady's toilet service of the late seventeenth century. Ointments and pomades, for chapped skin or for cosmetic purposes, would have been kept in cups like these, or oatmeal, which was rubbed on the face to cleanse it.

Marks
Struck under bases with hallmarks (leopard's head, lion passant, date letter) and with maker's mark

Provenance
The Dormer Collection
Anonymous sale, Christie's, London, June 12, 1923, lot 66
Anonymous sale, Christie's, London, July 1, 1925, lot 137
Anonymous sale, Christie's, New York, October 27, 1992, lot 371

Height: 4½ in (11.5 cm)
Width: 6¾ in (17cm)
Depth: 4⅛ in (10.4 cm)
Weight: 31 oz (964 g)

Achievement   The full armorial display of coat-of-arms (q.v.), crest (q.v.), supporters (q.v.) and motto, often contained in elaborate mantling of a cartouche (q.v.).

Alloy   Base metal, usually copper, added to silver to yield a more hard-wearing medium to make silver articles.

Anthemion   A stylized flower (probably the honeysuckle) which first appears in Greek art.

Assay   The testing of silverware to ascertain the proportion of silver in the alloy (q.v.) used.

Auricular   Word given to describe sinuous molten curves (literally ear-shaped), made popular by the Van Vianen family of designers and silversmiths in the early seventeenth century.

Baluster   A bellied form popular from the end of the seventeenth century onwards for silver vessels like casters, coffee pots and candlestick stems.

Baron   The fifth degree of the peerage.

Baronet   A hereditary knight (q.v.), often abbreviated Bt, or Bart.

Baroque   A style incorporating classical motifs and dynamic surfaces creating a feeling of movement, and prevalent in European decorative arts of the seventeenth and early eighteenth centuries.

Britannia Standard   The name given to a standard of silver alloy (q.v.) introduced for silverware on March 27, 1697 and in effect until June 1, 1720. It is over 95% silver, some 2.5% more than sterling standard, which it replaced, and the result is a much softer alloy. With the reintroduction of sterling alloy in 1720, Britannia continued as an optional higher standard and was used by some silversmiths, like Paul de Lamerie and Augustine Courtauld, because of its malleability and brighter surface colour.

Burnishing   Process of rubbing the surface of silver to produce a bright, smooth finish; stone tools were often used.

Cadency, Mark of   Symbol applied to a coat-of-arms to denote a son of the bearer.

Cartouche   Derived from parchment scrolls, it is a tablet-form motif, usually oval, containing a coat-of-arms or monogram and enclosed by an elaborate frame.

Casting   Technique by which molten metal is poured into a mould. Lost wax casting involves a wax model which is encased in clay or plaster and then burned out, leaving a mould. Sand casting was also frequently used for candlesticks and other components. Here a model is made in wood, lead or beeswax and pressed into a bed of sand. the molten silver is then poured into the impression.

Chasing   Process of embossing the surface of an object by placing it against a bed of pitch and striking the front of it with punches of various shapes, resulting in a three-dimensional effect.

Chinoiserie   Designs or articles in the Oriental taste. The first phase enjoyed a brief vogue in the 1680s, and was confined to line decoration of the surface of silver articles. In the 1730s the taste revived and Chinoiserie decoration is found chased and cast on smaller wares, usually associated with tea and coffee. By the mid-century articles imitating Chinese objects like tea chests, are found.

Coat-of-arms   The process of identifying an individual with a decorated shield developed in the Middle Ages and by the seventeenth century, the right to bear a coat-of-arms was avidly sought as a symbol of gentility. The practice of engraving or applying arms on silverware as identification blossomed during the eighteenth century, and nowadays often makes the identification of the original owners possible. A coat-of-arms is sometimes erroneously referred to as a "crest" (q.v.).

Coronet   A circlet worn by a peer (q.v.), or peeress, to denote their rank.

Countess Wife of an earl.

Crest Heraldic badge originally worn on the helmet as identification when the visor was closed. It appears above a coat-of-arms as part of armorials and sometimes appears engraved on silver separately from the shield. A crest can pertain to a number of families, making precise identification difficult if it appears alone without a shield, initials or a coronet of rank.

Cut-card work A method of decorating with shapes cut from flat sheet which are soldered flat onto the surface of the vessel. It was introduced from France in the early 1670s and used by German and other immigrant craftsmen. Its popularity peaked at the end of the century and the demand for it by then was filled to a large extent by the Huguenot workforce, who were skilled in these French techniques.

Date letter An official, or hall-, mark, struck on silver to denote the year in which the object was assayed. Formed of a letter of the alphabet, it was changed in May each year.

Diaperwork Continuous pattern of crossing diagonals, creating a trellis effect.

Duke The highest rank of the peerage.

Earl The third degree of the peerage.

Edict of Nantes Henry IV's edict granting religious freedoms to the Huguenots, which was revoked by Louis XIV in 1685, causing a tremendous exodus of refugees from France.

Engraving Surface decoration done by using hand-held burins, or gravers, to incise a small line. Unlike chasing, which only moves the metal, engraving removes a small amount of the metal.

Escutcheon of pretence If a man marries an heiress (a daughter with no brothers), he can display her family's arms on a small shield (or escutcheon) superimposed on his own coat-of-arms, rather than impaling them (q.v.).

Flat chasing Same process as chasing but resulting in a single fine line of decoration with no relief effect.

Gadrooning Ornament consisting of convex slightly curved lobes which was very popular as an applied edge to silver objects from the early eighteenth century onwards. In contemporary accounts, it is often referred to as "knurling".

Gilding Gold-plating of silver, in which gold was melted in a crucible with mercury and the resulting paste was brushed over the surface of the silver. The mercury evaporated, leaving the gold, which was then burnished to a high polish. This process, which was extremely dangerous to the participants, was replaced by electro-gilding in the nineteenth century.

Goldsmiths' Company The trade guild of the gold- and silversmith of London, incorporated by a charter from King Edward III in 1327. It continues to oversee the regulation of the manufacturing trade and its assay office continues to test the alloy of new silverware.

Hallmarks Official stamps, or marks, struck on finished silverware by the wardens of the Goldsmiths' Company to signify that the silver was of the legal standard of alloy. Not to be confused with makers' marks, which are not official stamps, but registered with the goldsmiths' company by manufacturers or retailers, of silver.

Huguenot The name given to French Protestants in the sixteenth and seventeenth centuries, usually thought to derive from the Dutch *eedgenot* or the Swiss German *eidgenoss* meaning confederate, assimilated with the name of a Genevan burgomaster, Besançon Hugues.

Impalement A man can "impale" his own coat-of-arms with those of his wife's family, by dividing the shield down the centre and displaying his own on the left and his wife's on the right.

Journeyman A craftsman, who having completed his apprenticeship, was employed by a silversmith (the word comes from the French *journée* meaning a day's duration: a journeyman was hired and paid by the day). Journeymen were distinct from silversmiths who had registered a maker's mark at Goldsmiths' Hall and were in business on their own account.

Knight A member of an order of chivalry. Knighthood confers the title of Sir.

Largeworker In the early eighteenth century, makers' mark were recorded in two books at Goldsmiths' Hall, one for "largeworkers" , i.e., makers of full-scale articles and one for "smallworkers", i.e., makers of small items and components like the mounts of boxes.

Leopard's head Stamp, i.e., hallmark, denoting silver made in London, used from the Middle Ages to the present day, with the exception of the period 1697–1720 when it was replaced with the lion's head erased (q.v.).

Lion's head erased Stamp, i.e., hallmark, to denote silver assayed in London between 1697 and 1720. "Erased", a heraldic term, refers to the way in which the head is cut off with a jagged line.

Lion passant Stamp, i.e., hallmark, used to denote sterling standard silver, depicting a lion with his right (*dexter*) foreleg raised as if walking.

Lozenge Coat-of-arms depicted in a diamond-shaped shield, denoting arms borne by a spinster or widow or a peeress in her own right.

Marquess The second degree of the peerage.

Order of Bath An order of chivalry whose members could display their coat-of-arms enclosed by the symbol of the order, a garter inscribed with the motto "Tria juncta in uno".

Order of the Garter An order of chivalry instituted by King Edward II. It is the premier order in Great Britain and the oldest in Europe. Members of the order can enclose their own coat-of-arms with the symbol of the order, a garter inscribed with the motto "Honi soit qui mal y pense".

Ounce, see p. 66.

Peer A nobleman bearing one of the titles of rank.

Peeress A noblewomen, wife of a nobleman.

Pennyweight Fraction of a troy ounce, see p. 66.

Plate The term given to silverware (probably derived from the Spanish word for silver, *plata*). in recent times, it has sometimes been used to refer to silver-plated articles.

Raising Highly-skilled process by which a piece of flat sheet silver is hammered over iron or wooden stakes to form the body of a vessel. Periodic "annealing", in which the metal is heated to a dull red colour and then plunged in cold water, thereby relieving the stresses that have built up in the crystalline structure of the metal, is necessary to prevent the metal from splitting.

Rocaille Decoration of stylized shells introduced with the rococo style.

Rococo A nineteenth-century word used to describe the asymmetrical curves and naturalism of the 1730s and 1740s, the final flowering of the baroque. The main ingredient of rococo is *rocaille* (q.v.), broken or foliate scrolls, and naturalistically depicted flowers, leaves and fauna.

Sacred Monogram Device consisting of the letters IHS which was originally an abbreviation of the Greek form of the word Jesus, often found on ecclesiastical silver.

Scratch weight The weight of an object expressed in ounces and pennyweights, see page 66, engraved or scratched under the base of an object by the silversmith or valuer for inventory purposes.

Shagreen Skin of shark or ray used for covering boxes.

Smallworker, *see* Largeworker.

Sterling Silver alloy (q.v.) used as the legal standard since the Middle Ages, except for a brief period between 1697 and 1720 when the higher, Britannia, standard was used. In 12 troy ounces of metal, 11$\frac{1}{10}$ ounces are pure silver. This is the equivalent of 92.5% pure silver in the alloy.

Supporters The heraldic beasts or human figures which flank a coat-of-arms in a full armorial achievement (q.v.).

Tinctures The colours of the components of a coat-of-arms. As colour cannot be depicted in engraving, a system of hatching different backgrounds, each one denoting a colour, evolved in the seventeenth century.

Viscount The fourth degree of the peerage.

The following list is extremely brief and includes only general books on the subjects concerned and some catalogues of collections which are still widely available. Primary and secondary sources cited in the text are listed in the endnotes.

SILVER

Ellenor M. Alcorn, *English Silver in the Museum of Fine Arts, Boston*, vol I: *Silver before 1697*, 1993

Claud Blair, ed., *The History of Silver*, 1987

Michael Clayton, *The Collector's Dictionary of the Silver and Gold of Great Britain and North America*, rev. edn, 1985

Philippa Glanville, *Silver in England*, 1987

Arthur Grimwade, *Rococo Silver 1727–1765*, 1974

Alain Gruber, *Silverware*, 1982

J.F. Hayward, *Huguenot Silver 1688–1727*, 1959

James Lomax, *British Silver at Temple Newsam and Lotherton Hall*, 1992

Harold Newman, *An Illustrated Dictionary of Silverware*, 1987

Charles Oman, *Caroline Silver 1660–1688*, 1970

Charles Oman, *English Engraved Silver 1150–1900*, 1978

Timothy Schroder, *The Gilbert Collection of Gold and Silver*, 1988

Timothy Schroder, *The National Trust Book of English Domestic Silver 1500–1900*, 1988

Gerald Taylor, *Silver*, 1956

HUGUENOTS

Berard Cottret, *The Huguenots in England, immigration and settlement c. 1550–1700*, 1991

Robin D. Gwynn, *Huguenot Heritage: the history and contribution of the Huguenots in Britain*, 1985

The Quiet Conquest: the Huguenots in Britain, exh. cat., Museum of London, 1985

DINING AND DRINKING

Sarah Bradford, *The Story of Port*, rev. edn, 1983

Colin Clair, *Kitchen and Table*, 1964

J.C. Drummond and Anne Wilbraham, *The Englishman's Food: Five Centuries of English Diet*, rev. edn, 1957

Stephen Mennell, *All Manners of Food: Eating and Taste in England and France from the Middle Ages to the Present*, 1985

Sarah Paston-Williams, *The Art of Dining*, 1993

STYLES AND DESIGNS

Courts and Colonies: The William and Mary Style in Holland, England and America, exh. cat., Cooper-Hewitt Museum, New York, 1988

Alain Gruber, ed., *L'Art décoratif en Europe: Classique et Baroque*, 1992

Rococo: Art and Design in Hogarth's England, exh. cat., Victoria and Albert Museum, London, 1984

HISTORY AND SOCIAL TRENDS

Linda Colley, *Britons: Forging the Nation, 1710–1837*, 1992

Peter Earle, *The Making of the English Middle Class: Business, Society and Family Life in London 1660–1730*, 1989

Mark Girouard, *Life in the English Country House*, 1978

Michael Reed, *The Georgian Triumph, 1700–1830*, 1983